Brain Desire

Sex, Drugs, & Rock 'n' Roll
in the Brain

Bruce H. Hinrichs

Printed in the United States of America
1st printing

ISBN: 978-0-9790129-4-5
0-9790129-4-5

Ellipse Publishing Company
225 Groveland Avenue
Minneapolis, Minnesota 55403

*"My own brain is to me the most unaccountable of machinery –
always buzzing, humming, soaring, roaring, diving, and then
buried in mud. And why? What's this passion for?"*

– Virginia Woolf

*"She's got it. Yeah, baby, she's got it.
Well, I'm your Venus, I'm your fire,
At your desire."*

– From *Venus* by Shocking Blue, 1969,
written by Robbie van Leeuwen

"Rock 'n' Roll is here to stay, it will never die. It was meant to be that way, though I don't know why. I don't care what people say, rock 'n' roll is here to stay."
– Rock 'n' Roll is Here to Stay by Danny and The Juniors

Table of Contents

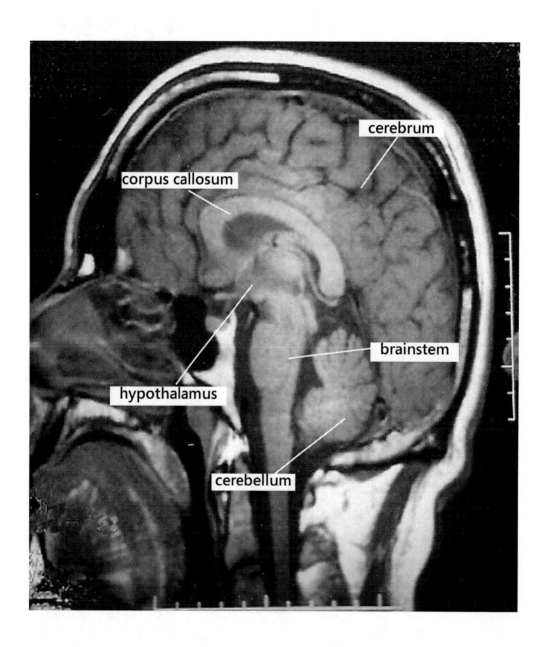

"Just let me hear some of that rock'n'roll music, Any old way you choose it.
It's got a backbeat, you can't lose it, Any old time you use it.
It's gotta be rock-roll music, If you wanna dance with me."
— Rock 'n' Roll Music by Chuck Berry

1

Brain Matters

*T*homas Edison quipped, "The chief function of the body is to carry the brain around." And, from humorist Ambrose Bierce: "The **brain** is an apparatus with which we think we think, and the **mind** is a mysterious form of matter secreted by the brain; it's chief activity consists of the endeavor to ascertain its own nature, the futility of the attempt being due to the fact that it has nothing but itself to know itself with."

Pretty humorous, huh? Now, here's a fascinating and mind-bending idea: You are able to read and understand these words because you have a brain in your head. Did you ever wonder how the scarecrow in *The Wizard of Oz* knew he didn't have a brain? If he didn't have a brain, how did he know he didn't have a brain? With no brain, how could he know anything? Or walk around? Or talk? Oh, and of course, your brain not only understands these words, but creates your emotional reactions to them, too. Did you smile, groan, smirk, or shrug when you read the above? Your brain did that!

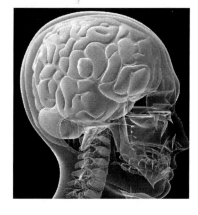

You can read and understand these words because your brain is not a brand-new brain, but an experienced brain, a seasoned brain, that has been shaped and molded by evolution, your heredity, and your personal experiences in life. Your brain has learned and remembered, it has absorbed language and developed cognitive abilities, and now it acts like a computer taking in information and processing it. However, your brain is not like any other computer with which you may be familiar. Your brain uses biological functions to process information, as when you read and understand this sentence. And, your brain uses biological processes to create a reaction of amusement, curiosity, puzzlement, boredom, or whatever emotion or feeling you have, too. How does it do that?

For one thing, your brain is made of living cells that create networks that are capable of sensing, remembering, and processing incoming information such as the light reflected from the ink on this page. But brains, of course, do much more than read. The activity of complex networks and systems of cells in your brain also gives you the motivation to read, the desire to eat, drink, sleep, and to crave so many other things, and also produces your consciousness, your awareness of the world, your sense of self, and also creates in your conscious mind any emotions that you might feel as you comprehend these ideas that you are now experiencing and thinking about. Cool, huh?

This book is about desire. It is about the biopsychology of desire; the psychological neuroscience of cravings and motivations. Sex, drugs, music, and emotions are all topics to be considered. But before getting into those endlessly engaging topics and even more, it is important to first learn a bit about brains. Brains, it turns out, are pretty darn complicated. It is wise to consider what physicist Emerson Pugh said: "If the human brain were so simple that we could understand it, we would be so simple that we couldn't."

Evolution

The very earliest animals on Earth, animals near the bottom of the evolutionary tree, such as worms, snails, and insects, have very simple brains that are, in essence, bundles of cells known as **ganglia**. For example, because it has ganglia throughout its body, a worm can perform many behaviors even with its brain removed. Insects' brains are miniscule, yet they can accomplish movement, sensing, mating, finding food, and other actions. So, it apparently does not take a humongous number of cells to control a variety of complicated behaviors.

A step up the **evolution** ladder gives us birds, reptiles, and fish, whose brains are small, but have some complex areas devoted to specific tasks. Smell and vision have separate modules in these brains, for instance. Though their brains are small, these animals have much more complex behaviors than worms or insects. Saying someone is a bird brain is not that much of an insult, really. We should probably use the term "worm brain" instead.

Mammals are another story, since they have evolved brains of various shapes and sizes. The largest brain is that of the blue whale, about four times the size of yours. However, size alone is not a perfect indicator of brain intelligence or computing ability. Whales don't do calculus. A bird's brain is much smaller than that of

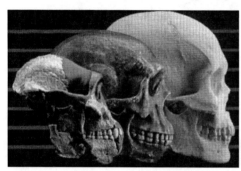

a whale, but they are both complex and efficient in their own way. We might say that in general the larger the brain, the more intelligent the animal; but the ratio of brain to body is important, too, as well as how the brain is organized and which regions have evolved the most.

Non-human animals at the highest levels of intelligence, such as chimpanzees and dolphins, have wrinkled brains just like us compared to the smooth brains of less intelligent animals. A baby's brain is smooth until about six months of development when the characteristic wrinkles begin to appear in the **cerebrum**. A chimpanzee brain has lots of wrinkles, nearly similar to a human, but the front part of the brain is not as well evolved as in the human brain. Apparently, increase in the **frontal lobe** (front region) is the most recent change in the evolution of the human brain. The species of chimpanzees and humans were separated in evolutionary development many, many millions of years ago, reminding us that evolution is typically a very slow process.

Human brains evolved over a very long period of time, millions of years. **Hominids** of four million years ago had brains about one-fourth the size of present humans. **Homo erectus**, who lived nearly two million years ago, had bodies about the same size as present humans, yet their brains were half as large. One of the most noticeable changes in human brain evolution is the massive size of the cerebrum, particularly in the front, relative to the lower brain areas, such as the brainstem.

Developing Brains

Comedian Groucho Marx: "I've got the brain of a four-year-old. I'll bet he was glad to be rid of it."

An adult human brain weighs about three pounds and contains about a hundred billion **neurons** (the brain cells that communicate). During the prenatal period, the brain develops more neurons than needed – in fact the brain must develop neurons at a rate of about fifty thousand per second for most of the nine months in the womb. This large number of neurons is decreased (**pruned**) just before and after birth. Experience will determine which synapses become strong and which ones disappear. The baby will learn some things and not others (think about learning a specific language, for example – some synapses are strengthened and some vanish). By adolescence, the teenage brain has fewer neurons and synapses, but they are better organized into networks. Still, the teen brain has a ways to go to reach maturity.

Researchers in **developmental neuroscience** have found that neural networks are created at an astonishingly high rate during infancy and childhood. There are periods, however, early in life when such networks are being formed the fastest and most efficiently, so called **critical periods** or **sensitive periods**. Brains are most **plastic** (capable of change and re-organization) in the first years of life. For example, the brain's visual cells organize by about four months of age. If they are not stimulated by that time, the baby will have impaired vision. Research found that if cats' eyes were covered at birth so that vision was blocked, the cats later would not develop normal vision (Trachtenberg, 2000). Also, cats raised in an environment in which they see only horizontal lines will not develop the brain cells that allow for perception of vertical lines (Held & Hein, 1963). A more recent study has added more precision to our understanding: Michael Crair and others (1998) found that the basic structure of the cat's visual cortex was innate, but experience was required for development of specific features of the cortical maps and for selectivity of neurons. So, a little bit of both heredity and experience helps organize the brain for perception.

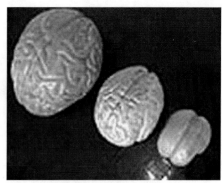
Adult, newborn, and premature brains.

Another example is **language**. The critical period for language appears to be approximately up to six years old. A child who does not hear and imitate language by then will likely have language difficulties forever more. The parts of the brain that organize for understanding and expressing language are particularly sensitive to auditory and visual input during early childhood. If we try to learn a language later in life, the task is much more difficult. A language accent developed early in life is hard to change later.

The point is that brains are not completely assembled and finished at the time of birth. Brains develop, and development is a process; we are not born with a fully formed brain. In addition, once the neural networks are established, they are still subject to possible changes. That is, brains are plastic, not static. They change with development and with experience. This ability to change, **plasticity**, is more pronounced in babies and children than later in life. However, research shows that even adult brains quickly reorganize with certain experiences. A musician who plays violin everyday will have larger brain regions (those for touch and movement of the hands) than before. If a person is blindfolded, then his or her brain will start to reorganize the normal visual processing region. Blind people, for example, use the visual part of the brain for perceiving touch. So, you see, brains change with experience, sometimes quite remarkably. A brain is not static; it is a dynamic organ.

Teenage Brains

As you might guess, the teen-age brain is not the same as the mature, adult brain. The brain's gray matter, the outer **cortex** of the **cerebrum** (the top, wrinkly part; the thinking part), continues to build up until about age 11 or 12, but then connections begin to thin out – a **pruning** process ensues. So, just as with infants, in **adolescence** pruning is part of the brain's organizing process. However, different brain regions mature at different times, and girls' and boys' brains show some differences in development, too; for example, girls' brains develop faster starting right after birth, with a proportionately larger frontal lobe, while boys' brains are larger on average, but show more frequent disorders such as **autism** and **attention deficit/hyperactivity disorder (ADHD)**.

In the case of **teenagers**, the **frontal lobe** is advancing, but the neural networks that give one the ability to plan, organize, and make careful decisions are not finished and have a long way to go. This is when the brain is vulnerable to chemical assault, and, unfortunately, it is when teens begin experimenting with drugs and alcohol. Research confirms that teens who binge drink alcohol do worse on tests of cognitive ability, such as memory, spatial perception, and paying attention. Unfortunately, **decision-making** ability is still immature in the teen brain.

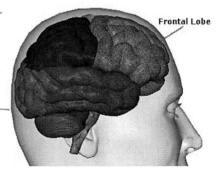
Frontal Lobe

In the **adolescent** years, the **frontal lobe** has not yet finished forming its connections with the lower, emotional brain. Therefore, the teenage brain is wired with a tendency to react emotionally and to not be especially proficient at controlling emotions using the thinking frontal lobe. This is because the neural networks that bind thinking in the frontal lobe with emotions in the lower brain are not fully formed. For instance, when researchers showed teenagers a photo of a person exhibiting fear, the teenagers reacted emotionally to the photo, but could not rationally identify why they did so. Also, they were poor at identifying the emotion that was being expressed in the photo. Adults, on the other hand, identified it every time (Yurgelun-Todd, 2007).

The teen brain is a work in progress. Many cognitive abilities are not mature yet for the adolescent, and it will take years for them to reach their peaks. Along with this development of the frontal lobe will come the realization that the world is more complicated than the teenager realized. Oscar Wilde once commented, "I am not young enough to know everything." During young adulthood – the college years and somewhat beyond – a person will likely develop much calmer and less erratic emotions, more complex reasoning, less risk-taking, and better coordination of both body movement and thinking. But, then too soon comes middle age, and a whole new set of issues.

The Aging Brain

An old joke: "As you get older three things happen. The first is your memory goes. I can't remember the other two."

The **middle-age** brain makes more errors, and also experiences the tip-of-the-tongue phenomenon more often, and, too, finds it more difficult to multi-task than did the young adult brain. Damage to brain cells also begins to accumulate in middle age, and this damage progresses even more rapidly in old age. Therefore, brain weight and volume decrease with age in older adulthood; for instance, at age 90 a brain will weigh about 5% to 10% less than it did at age 20. The grooves or wrinkles on the brain (**sulci**) widen with aging, and the bumps (**gyri**) on the surface get smaller. Structural changes in the temporal lobe in an area important for word recognition leave some older people with hearing loss. A common complaint of many in middle and old adulthood is difficulty recognizing words in a loud setting.

But, there is good news, too. In middle and older adulthood, brains show a number of somewhat surprising advancements over younger brains. Brains aren't getting any bigger as we move toward old age, but middle age and older brains can be getting better at complex reasoning, seeing the big picture, thinking holistically, recognizing patterns, making judgments, finding unique solutions to problems, and creating deeper understandings. We could say that cognitive expertise, in many respects, reaches a peak in middle adulthood.

Certainly, as people reach middle age and beyond, many begin to be concerned about losing their brain abilities such as memory, finding their way around, recognizing objects, and making judgments. There is a fear that brain cells will be lost and never recovered. But, research in this area offers some happy surprises: As long as people are healthy and free of brain disease they will maintain most of their brain cells for as long as they live. Also, brains continue to develop, change, and adapt well into old age.

Unfortunately, too many people as they approach and enter old age will suffer from a brain **dementia**, such as **Alzheimer's disease**. And, not only disease can slow a brain, but middle-aged brains will decline, too, if they are not challenged. Research demonstrates that there are many experiences that will help the middle-aged brain develop and fulfill its potentials. These include aerobic exercise, a proper diet (fruits, vegetables, antioxidants, low salt and little red meat), adequate sleep, low body fat, and experiencing mental challenges. There is a lot that can be done in middle and older adulthood to improve brain functioning.

Brain Imaging

The weight of an average human brain is about 3lbs, equal to a large bag of sugar, about the size of a cantaloupe, and wrinkled like a walnut. If you touched a brain it would feel like a soft avocado and look pink because of the blood flowing through it.

Today the most fascinating and helpful technologies for studying a living brain in action are brain imaging techniques. These tools allow researchers to look at both the structure and various aspects of the functioning of a brain in a living person without invasion. Here are brief descriptions and explanations of some of the many brain imaging techniques that are now being used:

1. The Electroencephalogram (EEG)

Brains consist of cells that create electrical energy, and hence brains give rise to electrical signals that combine to form what are called **brain waves**. These electrical patterns vary in intensity and frequency, qualities of electrical energy that can be measured by sensitive electrodes either placed directly on a person's scalp or embedded in an EEG cap that fits tightly on a person's head. The EEG can record abnormalities in a person's brain waves, such as those associated with epilepsy, can show brain wave patterns associated with various psychological states, such as sleep, and can represent changes in brain activity when learning, remembering, being surprised, or having various experiences.

 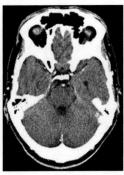 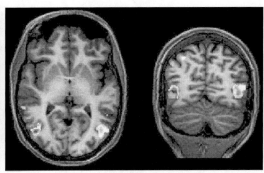 

From left to right: EEG cap, CAT scan, two fMRI images, and TMS.

2. Computerized Axial Tomography (CAT scan or CT)

In this technique, X-rays are taken of a series of parallel planes of the brain and the results are sent to a computer that then assembles a picture of the brain based on the X-ray data. A CAT scan shows only brain structures, not brain activity, so is not useful for localizing brain functions. The CAT scan can detect tumors, strokes, or other structural abnormalities, and can show the size of brain areas.

3. Positron Emission Tomography (PET scan)

In this procedure, a subject is injected with a small dose of a radioactive isotope that is used by active brain cells. This activity is detected and computed into an image of the brain. The PET scan shows brain functioning, not brain structures, or anatomy. That is, we get an image of where something is happening in the brain, not a picture of brain parts. A variation of the PET scan that is less expensive is single-photon emission computed tomography (**SPECT**). When using the PET scan, a typical procedure is to have a participant engage in a mental activity and then compare that brain image to one obtained when the person was not engaged in the activity. Below are PET scans taken while a person was seeing, listening to, and pronouncing/generating words. In the first case, activity is in the occipital lobe; second in the temporal lobe; and third more in the frontal lobe.

Seeing words passively   Listening to words   Pronouncing Generating words

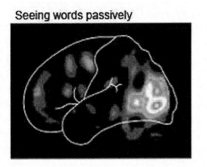 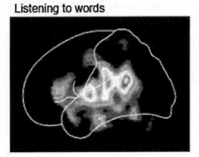 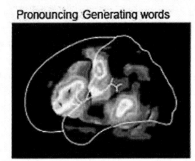

4. Magnetic Resonance Imaging (MRI)

In this procedure, a person's head is surrounded by electromagnets that align the magnetic fields of atoms in the brain. Signals from the brain are detected and then used by a computer to create an image of the brain. MRI shows anatomical features with great clarity, providing much better resolution than does the CAT scan.

5. Functional Magnetic Resonance Imaging (fMRI)

In 1990, scientists discovered that MRI could be used to detect magnetic fluctuations that occur in the blood. By 1991, researchers showed that this procedure would work in the cells of the human brain, which receive oxygen via the blood vessels. Thus, a new use of MRI was born that was called functional MRI and commonly abbreviated fMRI. While MRI shows only brain anatomy (structure), fMRI shows brain functioning. This technique even allows for the creation of high resolution 3D maps of the brain.

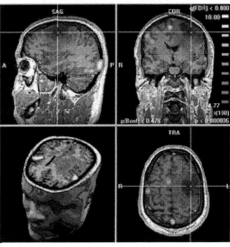

fMRI images.

6. Transcranial Magnetic Stimulation (TMS)

TMS is a safe, non-invasive procedure that uses powerful pulsing magnets positioned near a person's head to stimulate brain cells and help scientists determine the functions of brain areas. TMS is more a therapeutic procedure than a brain imaging technique, and is used to treat migraine headaches, strokes, hallucinations, and even depression.

Brain Bits

From Dr. Seuss: "I like nonsense, it wakes up the brain cells."

Brains are composed of **neurons**, brain cells that use electrical and chemical signals in order to send and receive information. The neurons in the brain form vast connections – **neural networks** – that process, analyze, and store information. The formation of neural networks is influenced by many factors, most importantly including our evolutionary history that gradually molded the anatomy and physiology of the human brain, our individual genetics, the DNA sequences that direct and guide numerous biological processes in our brains, and our personal experiences in the world that determine which brain connections (**synapses**) will become strong, which ones will be weak, which will form, and which will be eliminated.

Another category of brain cells called **glia** influence neurons and do housekeeping functions in the brain. Therefore, the glia contribute to neural processing. Psychological disorders and functions can be affected by the activity or dysfunction of **glial cells**.

The **neural networks** are spread out in the brain in various modules or regions devoted to certain functions; that is, certain areas of the brain have specific jobs. These different brain regions connect with one another to form systems that function collectively as a biological basis for body processes and psychological states. The collection of networks, modules, and systems makes up our brain anatomy and physiology. Now, how does it all work?

Neural Communication

"He who laughs last, thinks slowest."

Your brain generates 25 watts of power while you're awake - enough to illuminate a light bulb.

From Harper's Index: Estimated amount of glucose used by an adult human brain each day, expressed in M&Ms: 250.

Neurons are brain cells that have branches called **dendrites** growing out of their cell bodies (**somas**). The dendrites receive messages from other neurons and from physical energy received via the senses by using

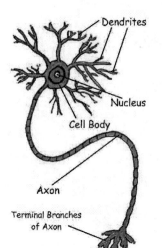

chemical reactions. A long branch growing out of the neuron's **soma** is called an **axon** and it carries the signal to another location. At the end of the axon are branches called **terminals** that will release a chemical when a signal comes down from the axon, thus sending the signal to another neuron or to a muscle.

A neuron has two methods of communication: electrical and chemical. The electrical signal is created by the movement of electrically charged particles (**ions**) in and out of the neuron. The inside of a neuron is more negatively charged than the outside. When the neuron is stimulated, positively charged ions enter the cell and a change in electrical energy is created. The *electrical* signal starts in the dendrites or cell body and travels down the axon to the terminals. The *chemical* process occurs at the dendrites when a message is received, and also at the terminals when a message is sent. The place where this happens (and the chemical process itself) is known as a **synapse**. There is a tiny gap between the sending neuron (**presynaptic**) and receiving neuron (**postsynaptic**); the two neurons do not touch.

Neurons have chemicals called **receptors** on their dendrites that respond to other chemicals, such as those released by another neuron, or those that come from outside the body and contact the cells in the eyes, ears, nose, skin, etc. The chemicals that are released by neurons that send a signal to another neuron or to a muscle are called **neurotransmitters**. The neurotransmitters match up with receptors much like a key fits into a lock. Each neurotransmitter has a number of

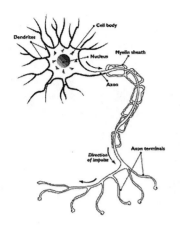
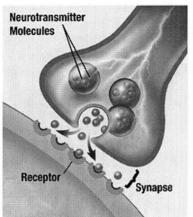
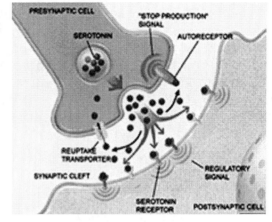

different receptors that respond to it. Psychoactive drugs have psychological effects because they influence this process. When a dendrite has a chemical reaction, when its receptors are stimulated, it can cause ions to enter the cell and then the electrical process occurs. A signal travels from one end of the neuron, the dendrites, down the axon, to the other end, the terminals, where neurotransmitter chemicals are released. When a signal travels the length of the neuron, we say the neuron has fired. Scientists call the process an **action potential**. It means an electrical signal has traveled the length of the neuron because positively charged ions have entered the cell making it more positively charged on the inside.

Mature neurons are covered with an insulating, fatty substance called **myelin** that is white in color. Neurons look gray. When we look at the surface of a brain we see gray matter. But the axons of those cells look white, because of the myelin. When we look at a mature spinal cord, or look at the interior of the brain, we see white matter. With a **myelinated** neuron, a signal can travel faster and is less likely to be accidentally fired by the firing of a nearby neuron. So, myelin is helpful; it allows cells to send signals faster and more efficiently. Unfortunately, there are a number of serious diseases that destroy myelin. **Multiple sclerosis** is the most common and well known of these. The result of such diseases is disruption of the neural processes, and thereby difficulty in body movement and cognitive processes.

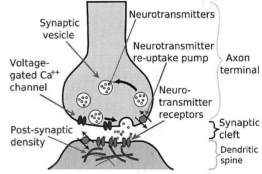

At the synapse, when a neurotransmitter chemical that is released by one neuron binds with a receptor chemical on a receiving neuron's dendrite (when the key fits into the lock), a chemical reaction takes place. This causes the **ion channels** of the receiving cell to either open or to close. The neurotransmitters that cause sodium ion channels to open are called **excitatory**, because they allow positively charged **sodium ions** to enter the neuron, causing **depolarization** (the electrical charges on the inside and outside of the cell are no longer polarized – no longer separated positive and negative charges because the inside is becoming more positively charged) and an action potential is created (the electrical signal travels down the axon to the terminals). Some other neurotransmitters are called **inhibitory**. They cause the cell to become less positively charged, thus making it more difficult to fire the neuron (they inhibit firing). It is necessary to have both types of neurotransmitters (excitatory and inhibitory), and to have them working in a proper balance. When we move an arm, for instance, we want some of our muscles to expand and some to contract. And, when we are awake, we need the brain to inhibit our dreaming. If all transmitters caused excitation, you would have an epileptic seizure every time you opened your eyes! We need both excitation and inhibition in proper balance.

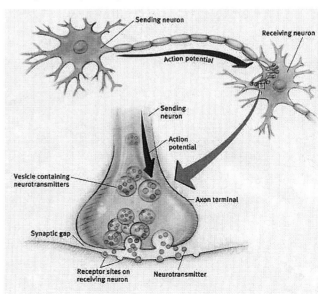

Neurons act like little batteries changing electrical charge from negative to positive over and over again, each time squirting out a chemical transmitter that influences the micro-structure, biochemistry, and electrical firing of other neurons. The brain has billions of neurons, each making thousands of connections (**synapses**) with other cells. In essence, then, the brain is a biological, computational organ that transmits information both by electrical and chemical processes. The result is a pattern of **neural networks**. As said by Kevin Kelly, "A brain is a society of very small, simple modules that cannot be said to be thinking, that are not smart in themselves. But when you have a network of them together, out of that arises a kind of smartness."

Chemical Clean-Up

After a neurotransmitter has been released by a neuron and is either in the synaptic gap or has been received by the receptors of another neuron, the chemicals must be cleaned up so that another message can come through. There are two ways that clean-up at the synapse occurs:

1. There are **enzymes** in the body that are housekeeping chemicals. Some of these enzymes have the job of recycling neurotransmitters; they attach to the neurotransmitter chemicals that have been released from the vesicles, and they recycle them. For example, one common enzyme that recycles transmitters is monoamine oxidase, commonly referred to as **MAO**. This enzyme is important for recycling the neurotransmitter **serotonin** and other neurotransmitters. Therefore, psychiatrists can use this fact to prescribe drugs that will influence the brain's enzymes. For example, some antidepressant medicines inhibit MAO and consequently leave more serotonin activity in the brain's synapses. Increasing serotonin activity often helps relieve depression.

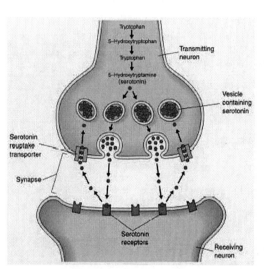

2. When a neurotransmitter is released by a neuron, some of the neurotransmitter molecules are carried back into the cell from which they came by molecules called **transporters**. That is, the presynaptic neuron, the sending neuron, squirts out a chemical and then some small amount of that chemical is brought back into the neuron. The squirt is followed by a suck! This process is called **reuptake**. Many drugs and medicines affect the transport of neurotransmitters back into the cell thus inhibiting the reuptake process. Cocaine, for example, is a drug that inhibits the reuptake of the neurotransmitter dopamine.

Some antidepressant medicines inhibit reuptake of serotonin, and sometimes inhibit reuptake of other neurotransmitters, too. The result is that less transmitter chemical gets pulled back into the presynaptic cell, leaving more transmitter chemical in the gap to signal the receiving receptors. These antidepressant medicines are **reuptake inhibitors**, and thus increase neurotransmitter activity in the brain.

The best known of these drugs is **Prozac**, one of a group of drugs known as **selective serotonin reuptake inhibitors (SSRIs)** because they work almost exclusively on the neurotransmitter serotonin. Others in this group include Paxil, Zoloft, and Celexa. The SSRIs work by decreasing the reuptake of serotonin, thereby allowing more serotonin to cross to the postsynaptic cell. Some other antidepressants are reuptake inhibitors for other neurotransmitters as well. These medicines include Wellbutrin, Cymbalta, Pristiq, and Effexor. For many people, these drugs improve mood, reduce anxiety, or help with obsessive-compulsive or addictive behaviors (cigarette smoking, for instance) by increasing the activity of various neurotransmitters in brain pathways.

Neurotransmitters

About 40% of the brain is **gray matter** consisting of brain cell bodies, the other about 60% is **white matter**, the axons connecting various regions. The brain has about 100 billion neurons. Neural transmissions travel at about 200 miles per hour through the brain and body.

Neurons pass signals to each other using chemicals called **neurotransmitters**. There are many different neurotransmitters; about a hundred have been identified. One of the most common neurotransmitters in the brain is **acetylcholine**. This chemical is used in many pathways of the brain and body, and therefore influences many behaviors and mental states. For example, muscle movements depend on acetylcholine, but so do memories and thoughts. Sensory functions, arousal, attention, reward, and sleep all depend to some extent on acetylcholine.

Another important neurotransmitter is **dopamine**. Dopamine is found in a number of brain pathways and therefore influences many psychological qualities, including mood, thinking, pleasure, and body movement. For instance, the reward or **pleasure pathway** in the brain uses dopamine. Psychoactive drugs influence this system.

In **Parkinson's disease**, the brain cannot make enough dopamine. One brain region that manufactures this chemical (**substantia nigra**) has been damaged. The damage can occur in a number of ways. Heredity is sometimes involved, and exposure to toxins, such as pesticides and herbicides, is often a

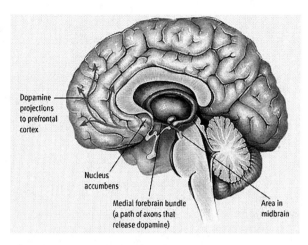

cause. The first symptoms of Parkinson's disease are tremors, uncontrollable shaking (particularly of the hands in the early stages), and other problems with muscle movements. Patients with Parkinson's disease can take a medicine, such as **L-dopa**, that is a precursor of dopamine and helps the brain produce more dopamine. This will work for a while, but eventually the brain will become so damaged that it cannot make dopamine even with the precursor chemical.

When L-dopa was first used in treating Parkinson's, it was discovered that patients who took too much of the medicine began to show symptoms similar to those of the severe psychotic disorder **schizophrenia**. Contrary to popular belief, schizophrenia is not the same as split personality, but, rather is a serious brain disorder that causes people to have hallucinations, delusions, and disordered thinking. Since Parkinson's disease patients exhibited these symptoms when they took excessive amounts of L-dopa, scientists theorized that schizophrenia was linked to excess dopamine. This view became known as the **dopamine hypothesis**. In fact, the **antipsychotic medicines** (also called **neuroleptics**) that help reduce the hallucinations and delusions experienced in schizophrenia are **dopamine blockers**. Reducing dopamine activity reduces psychotic symptoms.

Serotonin (also known as **5-HT**) is a very common neurotransmitter found in many different pathways in the brain. It's a bit like electricity in your house: it is used for lots of purposes. Both dopamine and serotonin are released by a small number of neurons in the brain, but they make thousands of connections; so, these two transmitters are involved in many functions. While serotonin is typically linked to **depression**, in fact the chemical plays various roles in mind and behavior. It is not a good idea to try to match neurotransmitters with certain psychological processes. Brains are complex biological organs whose properties and processes do not line up neatly with our English language concepts!

The chemicals used for communication in the brain are found in many different brain areas, and are found in the body proper, also. For example, serotonin is found in the gut where it regulates intestinal functions, in the blood as a vasoconstrictor, and also as a brain neurotransmitter is involved with mood, appetite, evaluating social situations, sleep, learning, and anxiety. There are many drugs and medicines, notably **antidepressants**, that can increase serotonin activity. Antidepressants are generally safe, however, there is some risk of a serious side effect known as **serotonin syndrome**, which can occur with the use of any substances that increase serotonin activity.

Glutamate is the most common excitatory chemical in the brain and is intimately involved in learning, memory, and cognitive processes. People suffering from schizophrenia and other psychological disorders often have impairments in their glutamate systems. The result is **cognitive impairment** of various kinds involving deficits in memory, thinking, decision-making, and so on. One of the glutamate receptors, known as **NMDA**, has been intensely studied because of its role in learning, memory, and **plasticity** at the synapse.

Another important neurotransmitter is **GABA**. Because GABA is an **inhibitory** chemical, it slows or inhibits the firing of neurons. When our GABA receptors are stimulated, we feel relaxed, calmed, and slowed down. The receptors for GABA in the brain respond to alcohol and to antianxiety drugs; therefore these substances inhibit the nervous system, that is, relax it and slow it down.

Finally, a common neurotransmitter is **norepinephrine**, which is also a hormone. Norepinephrine is involved with moods, mania, anxiety, stress, the fight or flight response, and regulation of heart rate and blood pressure. Many different brain regions use this important chemical as a neurotransmitter. Along with dopamine, norepinephrine plays a role in **attention deficit/hyperactivity disorder (ADHD)**. One class of antidepressant drugs (**SNRI**) inhibits the reuptake of this transmitter, and therefore is useful in treating a number of psychological disorders.

Cerebrum

From comedian Emo Philips: "I used to think that the brain was the most wonderful organ in my body. Then I realized who was telling me this."

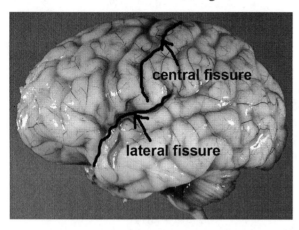

central fissure

lateral fissure

The large wrinkly part on the top of the human brain is called the **cerebrum**, and it is responsible for higher mental functions, language, purposeful body movement, memory, vision and other senses, and executive thinking. The outer surface of the cerebrum is called the **cortex**, which means bark, skin, or rind. The cortex is a thin layer of cells that wraps around, folding and bending, across the surface of the cerebrum. The cortex consists of columns of brain cells that represent a sophisticated circuitry for many psychological and physical functions. The cortex is considered the highest thinking part of the human brain.

The wrinkles on the cerebral cortex are called **fissures** or **sulci** (singular = **sulcus**), and the bumps that are formed by the wrinkles are called **gyri** (singular = **gyrus**). There is a major fissure that traverses down from top to bottom about in the middle of the cerebral cortex which is called the **central fissure**. If you are looking at the side of a human brain, the central fissure divides the brain roughly into a front half and a back half.

There is another major fissure that traverses sideways on the surface of the cerebrum from the front to about half way back. This is called the **lateral fissure**. If you look at a human brain from the side, the lateral fissure roughly divides the cerebrum into a top half and a bottom half.

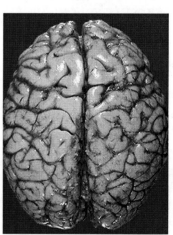

Next, think of viewing a human brain from the top – imagine looking down on the top of a brain. When doing so you will notice a large, deep groove going all the way from the front to the back of the cerebrum. This is called the **longitudinal fissure**. This groove divides the cerebrum into left and right sides known as **hemispheres**. So, the cerebrum has two hemispheres, left and right, and each hemisphere is divided into sections by deep groves, one moving roughly up and down (central fissure), and the other sideways from front to back (lateral fissure). Next, let's consider the hemispheres.

With only a few exceptions, the brain's left hemisphere is connected to the right side of the body and the right hemisphere is connected to the left side of the body. This connection is called **contralateral**, meaning "opposite sides." If a person has a stroke or any other damage in the left hemisphere, the resulting disability that the person will experience will be on the right side of the body. Similarly, damage in the right hemisphere will result in problems

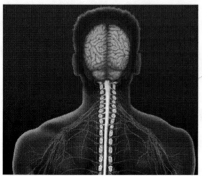

on the left side of the body. Also, if you touch something with your left hand, the signal is sent to the right hemisphere of your brain. And, too, if you want to move your right hand, the signal must originate in the left hemisphere of your cerebrum. The brain and body are wired left to right and right to left.

The **spinal cord** is a series of thin cables (**nerves**) traveling up and down the back protected by the vertebral column. The spinal cord carries signals to and from the brain and the body. These signals are transmitted only in one direction; they are not two-way highways. Some of the spinal cord nerves carry signals from the body to the brain, for example when you touch something with your hand. If these signals are damaged, or if the part of the brain that processes these signals is damaged, then you will experience **numbness**, a lack of feeling in

I don't get it?
one way, not 2 way but carries signals to & from?

your body. Other nerves in the spinal cord carry signals away from your brain to the muscles of your skeleton (so you can move). These signals travel from the brain down the spinal cord and then to muscles in various parts of the body. If these nerves are damaged, or if the part of the brain that originates these signals is damaged, then you will experience **paralysis**. Please note that numbness and paralysis are not at all the same thing – they are different conditions that are caused by damage to different systems of brain and nerves.

Connecting the Sides

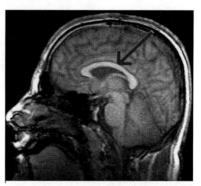

Deep down inside the cerebrum there is an area that connects the left and right hemispheres called the **corpus callosum**. This term literally means "hard body." If you had a brain in your hand and you pushed your fingers down between the two hemispheres – into the longitudinal fissure – you would eventually (after an inch or two) feel the corpus callosum. This is the brain part (the **tract**) that sends signals back and forth between the two hemispheres so that one hemisphere can "know" what the other "knows." That is, the corpus callosum is the communication tract between the left and right hemispheres.

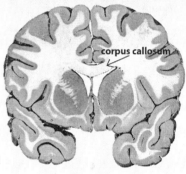

corpus callosum

Amazingly, there are some instances in which a person's corpus callosum is cut by surgeons. This is done in rare cases of severe **epilepsy** to save a person's life. Epilepsy is the condition in which a person has repetitive **seizures**, abnormal electrical firings of brain cells. Most people with epilepsy take medication to control their seizures. However, in the most severe cases the abnormal electrical activity can cross over the corpus callosum from one hemisphere to the other and the person could die. In these rare cases, a surgical operation is performed to cut the corpus callosum to reduce seizure activity and prevent the person's death.

The operation that is done could be called a corpus callosotomy, but it is more commonly called **split-brain surgery**. Surgeons sever the fibers that carry signals between the left and right hemispheres, the corpus callosum. The result is that the two hemispheres of the cerebrum then are separated and act independently of one another; the hemispheres are unable to receive signals from each other. The person who has had split-brain surgery, in effect, has two half cerebrums that cannot communicate with each other. Please note that nothing changes about the patient's personality, knowledge, memories, senses, or intelligence. The split brain patient is the same person after the surgery as before. However, the left and right hemispheres of the cerebrum cannot send signals to one another. The person has two half brains that are independent of one another. What must that feel like?

To One Side

The study of split-brain patients has confirmed that certain behaviors and psychological functions are processed more in one **hemisphere** than the other. In these cases, the behavior or function is said to be **lateralized** (meaning "to the side"). If we say that a particular function is lateralized, we mean that one hemisphere is better than the other at performing or processing that function.

For example, though a small percentage of people process language in their right hemispheres, and an even smaller percentage use both hemispheres for language, language is lateralized to the left in the vast majority of people (it's easy to remember: **L**anguage is in the **L**eft hemisphere). For most of us, in order to use grammar, syntax, semantics, sentence structure, and proper pronunciation, it is necessary to have a normally functioning left hemisphere.

While the left hemisphere is especially good at processing language, the right hemisphere specializes in spatial perception, or **visual-spatial** processes (being able to mentally picture things in space, such as a map of your surroundings, orienting in space, or locating objects in the environment). For instance, understanding what a word means is more a left hemisphere task, while understanding where a word is on the page is more a right hemisphere task. **R**ight is for o**R**ienting.

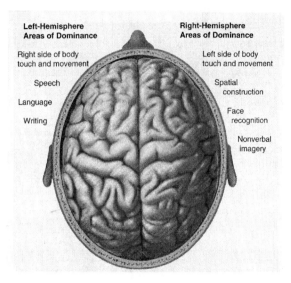

Warning: don't go too far in interpreting **lateralization.** The differences between the two hemispheres are mostly a matter of degree – that is, in some cases one hemisphere does something a little better than the other. A good example is the brain's processing of **music**. Textbooks for years have stated that music is a **right hemisphere** function. But one study used brain imaging to show that some music interpretation is computed in the area of the left hemisphere that processes grammar (Maess, 2001). In fact, an accomplished musician who reads music is more likely to use the left hemisphere when listening to a concert, while those of us who only listen to the melody are using our right hemispheres. So, perception of music, just as are most psychological functions, is complex and involves many components. Some of those are better processed by one hemisphere than the other.

Almost all psychological functions work by coordinating regions of the left and right hemispheres. It is rare that a function is completely centered in one hemisphere. It is better to think of the brain as a tightly organized bundle of interacting modules than to divide it into clearly distinct, separate regions with their own completely unconnected functions. After all, a brain is a communicating organ, and its various complex regions are highly interconnected.

Split Brain Results

Now, some curious findings from studies of people who have had their corpus callosums cut! First, suppose we blindfold a **split-brain patient** and then place an object, say a pencil, into her *left* hand. Her left hand touches the pencil and sends a signal about the pencil to her spinal cord where the signal ascends upward to her *right* cerebral hemisphere, to the part of the brain that processes the feeling of the pencil. We might say that her right hemisphere "knows" about the pencil; it feels it and remembers it. The right hemisphere, however, cannot send a message over to the left hemisphere because the corpus callosum has been severed. So the *left* hemisphere "knows" nothing about the pencil; it cannot receive any information about it, not from the left hand and not from the right hemisphere. If we then take the pencil from her left hand and place it on a table with a number of other objects and ask her to find it with her right hand (which is guided by the left hemisphere, which did not feel the pencil), she cannot identify the pencil as the object she was just holding; that is, more correctly, her

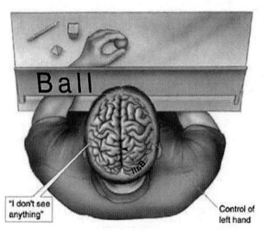

left hemisphere cannot identify the pencil. However, if she uses her left hand to find the pencil, she can do it easily because the left hand receives signals from the right hemisphere, which felt the pencil.

We might ask if the split-brain patient *knows* about the pencil or if she can *feel* the pencil. The answer is an astounding one: Her right hemisphere can feel the pencil and so it knows about the pencil, but her left hemisphere does not. She now has a right mind and a left mind; she is two people in a certain funny way. Her brain cannot share information from one cerebral hemisphere to the other, so what one hemisphere knows is separate from what the other hemisphere knows.

Next we put a pencil in her left hand and *ask* the split-brain patient to tell us what she is holding. Remember, the signal from the left hand travels to the right hemisphere, which does not control language. The left hemisphere controls language, so it will do the speaking, but it does not know about the pencil – the left hemisphere cannot receive information from the right hemisphere or from the left hand. Therefore, the left hemisphere will honestly say, "I do not know." The split-brain patient says she does not know what she is holding in her left hand! Her left hemisphere is speaking and telling the truth; it really doesn't know. But, you might wonder, does she know? Well, again, there are two minds here. Although her left hemisphere does not know about the pencil,

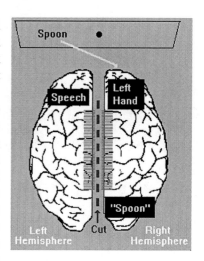

her right hemisphere does. How can we be sure? We can ask her to find the pencil among a group of objects using her left hand. She can do that. Also, we could ask her to draw a picture of the object using her left hand. She can do that. Any task that asks the question of the right hemisphere will give the right answer. Her right hemisphere knows, but her left hemisphere does not.

By the way, in the examples above the patient is being asked aloud to respond. That means she is using her hearing, her **auditory** sense, to receive the question. How is **hearing** wired in the brain? When we ask a question or give directions to the patient, both hemispheres receive the auditory message. Each ear is connected to both brain hemispheres. The left ear connects to both left and right sides of the cerebrum, and so does the right ear. However, a bit more of the message from an ear goes to the opposite hemisphere (contralateral) than to the same-side hemisphere (ipsilateral). For example, the right ear sends signals to both left and right hemispheres, but a bit more to the left hemisphere than to the right. And, similarly, the left ear is connected more to the right hemisphere than to the left.

Split Vision

The way the eyes are wired to the brain is very interesting. Each eye sends signals to both the left and right hemispheres. The cells of the eyes that respond to light are in the very back inside of the eyes in a layer known as the **retina**. The cells on the left side of the retina (in both eyes) respond to objects in the right **visual field**, and are then wired to the left hemisphere. So, the left hemisphere receives information from both eyes, but only from the left side of each eye, which is seeing objects in the right field of vision. The cells on the right side of the retina see objects on the left and then send the signal to the right hemisphere.

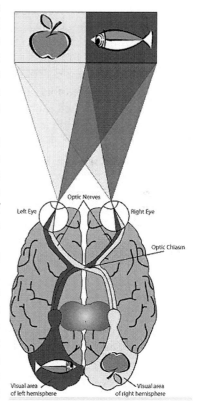

Cells in the retina send signals via the **optic nerve**, one coming out the back of each eye, and the two optic nerves meet at a place in the brain called the optic chiasm. At that point, half the cells from each eye go to the left hemisphere and half to the right hemisphere. So, both eyes send signals to the left hemisphere about objects that are seen on the right. Similarly, retinal cells on the right side of each eye receive light from objects in the left visual field and are wired the to the right hemisphere of the brain.

The result is that objects on the *left* are visually processed in the *right* hemisphere, and objects in the right visual field are seen in the left hemisphere. If an object is in your left field of vision, then the light coming from it will strike the cells on the right side of the retinas in the back of each eye. Thus, an object in your left visual field stimulates cells on the right side of the retina. And, those cells on the right side of each retina are connected to the right hemisphere. An object on the left will be seen in the right hemisphere. Likewise, an object in the right visual field will stimulate cells on the left side of each eye, cells that are wired to the left hemisphere. So, the left hemisphere sees things on the right while the right hemisphere sees things on the left.

Okay, now suppose a split-brain patient sits in front of a screen and is shown pictures projected on the left and on the right sides of the screen. Pictures on the right will be processed by her left hemisphere, while pictures on the left will be processed by her right hemisphere. Unlike in us, her corpus callosum has been cut, so the hemispheres cannot share information with each other. If we put a picture of a ball on the left side of the screen and a picture of a dog on the right side of the screen, her brain will see the ball in the right hemisphere and the dog in the left hemisphere. If we then give her a group of pictures and ask her to point to the object she saw using her left hand, she will point to a picture of a ball (left hand is controlled by right hemisphere, which sees things on the left). However, if we ask her to tell us what she saw, she will say "dog" since the left hemisphere controls speaking and it sees things on the right. Her left hand points at a ball, but she says "dog."

If we place an object in the patient's right field of vision, then it is seen by the left hemisphere and the person can say what it is. However, she will not be able to identify it with her left hand, since that hand is controlled by the right hemisphere. On the other hand (pun intended), if we put an object in the left visual field of the patient, then her right hemisphere will see it. In that case, she will not be able to talk about it, but she will be able to identify it with her left hand. When we see objects in our left field of vision, the visual signal is processed in the right hemisphere; objects in our right field of vision are processed in the left hemisphere. Of course for most of us, the information can pass via the corpus callosum to the opposite hemisphere for further processing. The split-brain patient cannot share information between hemispheres.

The Interpreter

In a well-known case study, a split-brain patient was shown a snowy scene on the left (seen by her right hemisphere) and a chicken claw on the right (seen by her left hemisphere). Then the patient was asked to point to pictures that corresponded with what she had seen. Her left hand (controlled by the right hemisphere) pointed to a shovel, and her right hand (controlled by the left hemisphere) pointed to a chicken. When asked why she was pointing to these things (remember, the left hemisphere does the speaking), she said she was pointing to the chicken because she saw a chicken claw, and she was pointing to the shovel because you use a shovel to clean out a chicken shed! The left hemisphere saw the chicken and did not know why the left hand (controlled by the right hemisphere that saw the snowy scene on the left) was pointing at a shovel. So, the left hemisphere interpreted the behavior by reaching a conclusion that seemed reasonable and plausible.

What this shows us is that humans give explanations. Apparently, we like to have reasons for what we do. The process is called **confabulation**. Perhaps it is learned, or perhaps it is a part of our evolutionary development, this tendency, this disposition to explain our behavior, to confabulate. Whatever the cause, we do it automatically, without being aware that we are doing it. The split-brain patient believes her explanation; she is not telling a lie.

Our left hemispheres apparently have a tendency to interpret or explain behaviors. Apparently we all do it; well, that is, our left hemispheres, the language hemispheres, do it. We make up good-sounding reasons for why we do things. The left hemisphere seems to be designed to be in charge of interpreting behavior – confabulating reasons to explain behavior.

Whole vs. Parts

The major findings of split-brain research can be summarized as follows: The **left hemisphere** is usually better at language, logic, analysis, and noticing details. The **right hemisphere** excels at **holistic** perception, patterns, orienting, spatial tasks, and emotions. If we give a split-brain patient a jigsaw puzzle to solve, her right hand (controlled by the left hemisphere) is terrible at it, but her left hand (right hemisphere) solves it right away. A verbal problem, on the other hand, would be solved much easier by the left hemisphere than by the right. A person who has a stroke or suffers damage by any cause to the left hemisphere will have difficulty with language, analyzing, and logical reasoning. Damage to the right hemisphere leads to problems in spatial perception, emotional reactions, and making sense of data holistically.

Right hemispheres are better at recognizing whole patterns; left hemispheres are better at perceiving and analyzing details. If we show a split-brain patient a face made of vegetables, the patient's left hemisphere will perceive the vegetables, while the right hemisphere will perceive the face. Left hemispheres analyze the parts, while right hemispheres put together a total whole, a **gestalt**. Also, right hemispheres are a bit better at visualizing spatial areas, like maps, or mentally rotating objects in the mind, while left hemispheres normally excel at language and verbal skills.

While research has shown that a number of psychological functions are lateralized (better done by one hemisphere than the other), it is important to remember that both hemispheres are involved in nearly all mental processing, particularly complex cognitive functions, and that they work together in coordinating our mental world. Be careful when you read or hear statements about the left and right hemispheres that oversimplify this concept. The hemispheres work together pretty much all the time; it's just that one hemisphere is a bit better than the other at some tasks.

Lobes

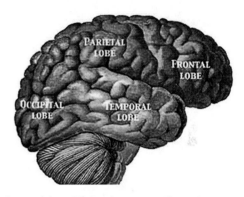

Scientists divide the brain's cerebrum into anatomical regions known as **lobes**. Each hemisphere has four lobes. Major fissures in the cerebrum's surface serve as partial boundaries for designating the four lobes. If we look at a cerebrum from the side we see a deep fissure extending down from the top about in the middle of the cerebrum. This is called the **central fissure**. In front of it is the **frontal lobe**, and behind it is the **parietal lobe**. We will also see a deep fissure that extends from the front toward the back known as the **lateral fissure**. Above it is the frontal lobe and below it is the **temporal lobe**. In the lower back beneath the parietal lobe is the **occipital lobe** which has the complicated job of visual processing. Each hemisphere is divided, then, into these four lobes.

The occipital lobe, in the lower back portion of the cerebrum, is all about **vision**. Vision is so complicated that is takes up a great deal of brain volume, more so than any other single function. The occipital lobe divides into various types of cells that process different elements about vision and then connect with other brain areas.

The parietal lobe, in the back upper portion of the cerebrum, receives information coming from the body and interprets touch, pain, and **body sensations**. This lobe also receives visual information and computes depth, location, and other visual factors involving **orientation** of the body in the surrounding environment.

The temporal lobe is on the side of the cerebrum. This lobe has many complicated functions. **Auditory processing** occurs here, and so does understanding of words and sentences. The inner portions of the temporal lobe are intimately involved with learning and memory. Damage to these areas, as occurs in alcoholism, Alzheimer's disease, and sometimes through stroke, will result in a variety of problems with understanding language, making new memories, and retrieving memories that are stored in the cerebral cortex.

The frontal lobe is the most recent evolutionary advance in the human brain. Its functions are often termed "**executive**." Higher thinking, holding things in memory (working memory), and modulating or controlling emotions are some of its jobs. The frontal lobe is the higher thinking part of the cerebrum.

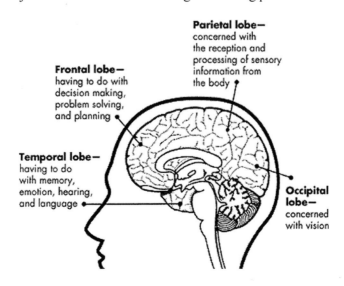

Frontal lobe— having to do with decision making, problem solving, and planning

Parietal lobe— concerned with the reception and processing of sensory information from the body

Temporal lobe— having to do with memory, emotion, hearing, and language

Occipital lobe— concerned with vision

Localization of Function

"If at first you don't succeed, sky diving might not be for you."

To some extent, the brain is divided into modules that perform specific functions for tasks. This is not the case for all psychological functions, nor is the brain organized according to English language concepts; for sometimes it's difficult to say exactly what the specialty is for a certain brain region. But in some cases, for some psychological functions, the brain does have separate (though interacting) modules. This idea that certain mental states and behaviors are controlled by a specific location in the brain is called **localization of function**. Here are some examples:

1. Vision is processed by cells in the occipital lobe. These cells are organized in layers that are labeled V1, V2, V3, and so on. The pathway of visual processing begins with the V1 cells on the surface of the cortex in the back of the brain and then flows forward in the brain, eventually dividing into two pathways.

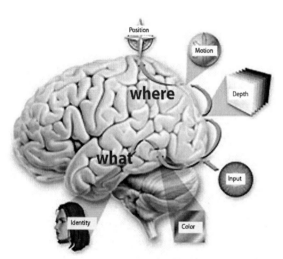

One visual pathway processes and remembers visual information about what was seen. This pathway flows into the temporal lobe and is simply called the **what pathway**. The other system of cells carries neural information forward and upward into the parietal lobe and processes and remembers where something was seen. This is called, as you might guess, the **where pathway**. The temporal lobe processes information about what is seen, while the parietal lobe computes where it was seen.

Damage in the occipital lobe, naturally, will adversely affect the processing of vision; that is, will lead to some sort of blindness or visual impairment. The particular visual problems that arise from damage in the occipital lobe depend on where the damage occurs. The cells of this area are very specific in their jobs. If the V1 cells (on the surface of the cerebral cortex, at the lower, back of the cerebrum) are damaged, a person will report an inability to see anything in an area of the visual field that is the same shape as the damage in the occipital lobe on the opposite side of the damage. Damage in the left occipital lobe in the shape of a star will result in a blind spot in the right visual field in the shape of a star.

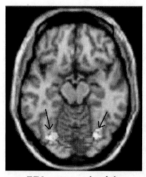

FFA on each side

Here's another interesting example: Damage to one area of the visual processing pathway will impair the ability to recognize familiar faces, a condition called **prosopagnosia**. In these cases, people do not recognize even very familiar people by sight; they need other stimuli, such as hearing the person's voice. This condition is caused by damage to a particular region of the brain (on the side, just behind the ear) known as the **fusiform face area** (**FFA**), a part of the what pathway. There's one FFA in each hemisphere, though the right side is better at face recognition. The FFA is a specialized area that allows quick recognition and memory of faces, and also is activated when a person becomes an expert at identifying objects visually. For instance, experienced bird watchers use their FFAs to quickly identify birds. Also, near the face area is a brain region that becomes active when a person is visually recognizing bodies. And, objects are recognized in another nearby area.

2. Hearing is perceived in two areas located in the lateral fissures of the temporal lobes of each hemisphere. Each area is known as a primary **auditory cortex**. The primary auditory cortex is located deep within the fold, or sulcus, just at the top of the temporal lobe on the side of the head. Damage to one of these brain areas, the primary auditory areas, would result in loss of some hearing in both ears because each ear sends some signals to the left and right hemispheres. The neural signals from an ear are mostly contralateral, but partially ipsilateral. That is, messages from an ear go mostly to the opposite hemisphere, but somewhat to the same-side hemisphere.

3. Body Movement is controlled by a gyrus, or bump, at the top of the cortex, at the very rear of the frontal lobe just in front of the central fissure, extending from the top down, nearly vertically. This area is known as the **primary motor cortex**, the **motor strip**, or simply the **motor area** (the term "motor" comes from the Latin and means "movement" or "motion"). The cells in this part of the brain send electrical signals to the skeletal muscles, initiating movement of the body. If you want to move your arm, leg, or any part of your body, the cells in this region must be activated. Signals from the primary motor area are sent to lower brain areas where other brain systems add to the neural signals that are sent to the muscles so that movements will be smooth and coordinated.

The **primary motor area** is arranged upside down. Cells at the top of the motor strip send signals to the feet, while the cells at the bottom of the motor strip control movements of the mouth and tongue. Damage to any section of the motor strip will cause difficulties in movement (**paralysis**) in the corresponding part of the body that the motor area controls. For instance, a person damaged at the top of the motor cortex in the left hemisphere will have paralysis of the right foot. Damage to the middle of the right motor strip will cause paralysis in the left arm.

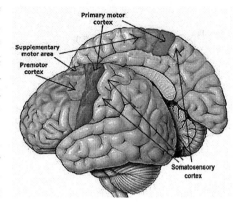

Other areas of the frontal lobe contribute to planning and organizing body movements. These areas are known as the **pre-motor area** and **supplementary motor area**. Body movements also need to coordinate with one another and muscle movements must be smooth, not jerky. Lower brain areas help with these coordinating functions, specifically the **cerebellum** and **basal ganglia** which are described below.

4. Body Sensation is processed by the cells in a brain gyrus (bump) just behind the central fissure in the parietal lobe. This brain bump is called the **primary somatosensory cortex, strip**, or **area**. It is located just behind the motor area – the motor area in front, and the touch area behind the central fissure. This place in the brain receives incoming signals from the body via the **spinal cord** and supports the perception of touch, temperature, body position, and pain; although, these perceptions are influenced by activation in other brain areas, too. Just as with the motor cortex, the somatosensory cortex is organized upside down. A person injured at the top of this strip in the right hemisphere would have **numbness**, a lack of feeling, in the left foot.

A person whose arm has been amputated, for example, will still feel touch and pain in his or her arm. This experience is called **phantom limb**. The feeling persists even though the limb is not there. A missing arm will itch and hurt. Phantom limb demonstrates that the sense of feeling is not in our limbs, but in our brains! We feel with our brains, not with our body proper. The feeling of a phantom limb is created in the somatosensory area of the cortex. Apparently this brain area is receiving signals from other brain areas about the missing limb. Some research has found that the signals are coming from the frontal lobe (Dingfelder, 2007) and not from nerves in the body. A **mirror box** can help people relieve phantom limb pain.

5. Language in most people is processed in the **left hemisphere**. Most right-handed people have a slightly larger left hemisphere where language abilities are concentrated. Left-handers sometimes process language in the right hemisphere, or in both sides of the brain, but about half of lefties also have their language areas in the left hemisphere. By language, we mean using grammar. Using a grammatical language is a complicated computational problem that requires a large number of brain networks. Amazingly, children all over the world learn language very easily and rapidly no matter the language community in which they are raised. This is because human brains are anatomically evolved to accomplish this wonderful feat. Language is an **instinct**. This does not mean it is inborn; rather, it means that the proficiency to learn language has evolved genetically within the species.

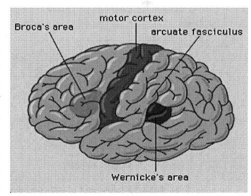

It has been said that language is the means by which we get an idea from one brain to another without surgery! Two brain regions are critically involved with language. An area in the left frontal lobe called **Broca's area** is important for pronunciation and grammar. If a person has damage in this region, say from a **stroke** (an accident in the blood vessels that deprives brain cells of oxygen, typically caused by a blood clot), the person is said to have **Broca's aphasia** or **expressive aphasia**. The term "aphasia" is used to designate any brain problem in the use or understanding of language. In Broca's aphasia, a person will have difficulty pronouncing words and producing correct grammar. Such people may sound intellectually impaired because of their slurred speech or improper grammar, but it is important to note that Broca's aphasia does not interfere with intelligence or the understanding of language. Understanding language is the main job of a different brain area.

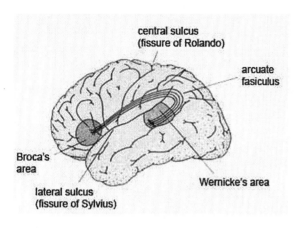

central sulcus
(fissure of Rolando)

arcuate
fasiculus

Broca's
area

Wernicke's area

lateral sulcus
(fissure of Sylvius)

The region of the brain involved in understanding language is called **Wernicke's area** and is located in the back of the temporal lobe. This brain region is involved in processing the meaning of words and sentences, whether read or heard. People with damage in this area are said to have **Wernicke's aphasia** or **receptive aphasia**. Such patients have difficulty understanding language. They may speak in ways that do not make sense, or they may create sentences that are very empty, using "like," "you know," and "whatever" to conceal their lack of understanding.

So, **Broca's area** is primarily an area for the **expression** or production of language. We use it to create speech, sign language, or when writing a sentence. **Wernicke's area** is predominantly a **receiving** or comprehension area for language, used when listening to language or when reading a sentence. When we want to speak, our brains must coordinate the two language areas. The meaning of what is to be said is pulled together in Wernicke's area and then a signal is sent to Broca's area, which is the sub-computer for grammar and pronunciation. From there the signal goes to the speaking apparatus in the mouth and throat.

The two language areas are connected below the surface of the cerebrum by a band of cells known as the **arcuate fasciculus**. Via this white bundle, Broca's and Wernicke's areas can communicate and cooperate with each other. Patients with damage to the arcuate fasciculus experience what is called **conduction aphasia**; they have difficulty making an association between the understanding of language and the expression of language. It's a bit like listening to a political press conference – questions are asked and understood, but answers are given that are not related to the questions! There is a lack of communication between reception and expression. Researchers have found higher rates of conduction aphasia in people with schizophrenia and people who smoke marijuana (Ashtari, 2005).

𝓟lasticity

Although the brain regions mentioned above are specialized for certain functions, it is important to remember that brains are dynamic, living organs that are complex, interconnected, and changeable. The sensory systems are in communication with each other and act like instruments in an orchestra – they react to each other and create a symphony through teamwork. Each instrument (brain region) is modulated by other regions. Also, brains can reorganize with experience. This is called **plasticity**.

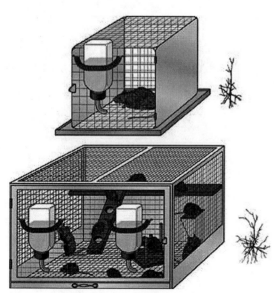

Rats raised in an enriched environment had neurons that were better developed.

One of the most common myths about brains is that they are static and unchanging. People are always asking whether some psychological condition is inborn, as if we are stuck with whatever we have at birth. What is inborn is what a baby has at birth. Isn't it obvious that we change? Not only do psychological qualities change over time, but, of course, the source of those traits, the brain, also changes with experience. None of our traits or conditions is inborn; they all develop.

When rats are raised in a complex, enriched environment, their neurons grow more **dendrites** and create more **synapses** (Greenough, 1975). In blind individuals who read Braille, the area of the brain that represents the index finger grows in size at the expense of the brain areas devoted to the other fingers (Pascual-Leone, 1993). People who experience damage to one area of the brain often experience compensation as nearby brain areas take over the damaged functions. Even when one hemisphere is damaged, the brain can reorganize so that the other hemisphere assumes tasks such as language and cognition, if the reorganization occurs early enough in life (Guerreiro, 1995).

Brains are not static, they are dynamic – they change with experience. For example, when people practiced five-finger piano exercises for only five days, researchers found that the area of the brain controlling the fingers was enhanced (Greenfield, 2001). Research by Michael Merzenich (1998) is among the most commonly cited regarding brain plasticity. Merzenich showed that areas of the brain will increase in size with experience. For example, if a monkey is trained to repeatedly touch something with an index finger, the area of the monkey's brain that feels touch in that finger will increase in anatomical size. The number of brain cells used for feeling the index finger will increase.

Similarly, brains reorganize in order to process incoming sensory data. When blind people listen to sounds, the cells in their visual cortex become active. Deaf people show activity in the auditory (hearing) area of the brain when they look at moving dots on a computer screen (Finney, 2001). Apparently the brain recruits cells from other areas in order to help organize incoming information.

Studies of brain plasticity remind us of **critical periods**, times when biological processes are more responsive to the environment. For example, a baby's brain has the capacity to change, respond, and remodel itself much more than an adult's brain. Of course, brains develop over time; the brain of an embryo, or even a newborn, is different from the brain of an adult. And, brain development depends not only on genetics, but on experience in the world. Cells in the eye and in the visual pathway depend on seeing (a newborn blocked from light will not develop normal vision), auditory cells depend on hearing sounds (in fact, noise can interfere with normal auditory cell development; Chang, 2003), learning a language depends on hearing it spoken, and so on.

Subcortical Areas

Deep inside the brain are a number of interesting areas that together are called **subcortical** because they lie below the **cerebral cortex**. These lower brain areas evolved earlier than the cerebral cortex, and therefore are more intimately involved with the activities necessary for day-to-day survival, such as basic emotions, motivations, hunger, sex, sensing the environment, the formation of memories, shifting attention to important stimuli, and maintaining body functions. Here is a list and brief description of some of the most important of these subcortical areas:

1. About in the middle of the brain is the **thalamus**, a relay center for the senses, and the center of the **limbic system**, a group of brain regions that work together. Sensory processing begins with signals coming into the brain from the eyes, the ears, the tongue, the skin, and from different parts of the body. The thalamus is an organizing area where sensory signals are sorted and distributed to other parts of the brain. The smell receptors in the nose send electrical signals to a brain area just at the bottom of the frontal lobe known as the **olfactory bulb** before being routed to the thalamus. The olfactory bulb represents a large proportion of the brain in some lower animals, but is a relatively small part of the human brain. The thalamus not only sends signals to various cortical areas for processing, it also receives signals back from the cortex. Some experts believe that this two-way, back-and-forth communication is essential for creating consciousness.

The limbic system is a center of emotion, motivation, and quick response without thinking. When in a dangerous situation, the limbic system reacts before the cerebral cortex can analyze the situation more thoroughly. Hence, we act without thinking in a **fight or flight** response.

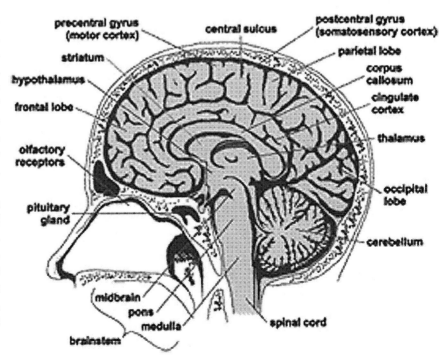

2. The brain area located just below the thalamus is the "below the thalamus," or the **hypothalamus**. This area acts as a regulator or control center for a number of motivations such as fight or flight, metabolism, body temperature, hunger, thirst and sex. Sometimes the hypothalamus is compared to a thermostat in that it measures bodily functions and then sends signals to the brain in response to those functions. The hypothalamus, for example, measures the amount of sugar in the blood (glucose), and when it is low sends out signals to initiate eating. Other parts of the hypothalamus coordinate signals to tell us when to start and stop eating. Thirst and body temperature work much the same way; in this sense the hypothalamus helps maintain balance, or equilibrium in our body drives and needs, which is known as **homeostasis**. Damage to certain areas of the hypothalamus, therefore, results in problems with motivations such as hunger, thirst, body cellular functions, and sex. The hypothalamus has been shown to be involved in many other motivations, such as anger, fear, and pain. An old joke says that the hypothalamus controls the four Fs: fighting, feeding, fleeing, and sex.

3. The **pleasure pathway** is the term given to an extended stream of neurons that reach from the brainstem through the limbic system, the amygdala, the **septum**, and into the frontal lobe of the cerebrum. The brain areas in this circuit are related to reward and addiction and when stimulated result in feelings of pleasure and well-being. This stream of cells is sometimes called the **reward pathway**, or **mesolimbic pathway**. Signals in the pleasure pathway are transmitted by the neurotransmitter dopamine and influence the release of brain chemicals called **endogenous opioids** (endogenous = "comes from within;" opioid = "similar to opium"). The result of activity in this brain circuit is a feeling of relaxation and euphoria.

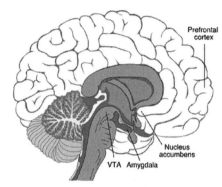

An area of the brainstem called the **ventral tegmental area (VTA)** is one brain region where dopamine is produced. This is one brain hotspot for pleasure and reward. Another region where the frontal lobe curls underneath and meets the limbic system, an area known as the **nucleus accumbens**, is commonly thought to be a central brain area for drug addictions and learned pleasures. Rats with electrodes in any of these areas, such as the septum, hypothalamus, VTA, or nucleus accumbens, will push a bar all day long to receive electrical stimulation of the brain cells along this stream. Rats will stimulate their pleasure centers repeatedly, sometimes thousands of times an hour, in preference to food and water, and females will abandon their pups to get such stimulation.

Near the pleasure pathway is the **punishment circuit** with pathways through the thalamus, hypothalamus, amygdala, hippocampus, and other areas. Rats that are given electrical stimulation in these brain areas will do anything to avoid further stimulation. This network is a major trigger for the **fight or flight response**, the body's automatic reaction to a dangerous situation in which the nervous system prepares for action, and some psychologists feel that the punishment circuit is not strictly a neural stream for feeling suffering, but rather is a control pathway for escaping or dealing with an unpleasant situation.

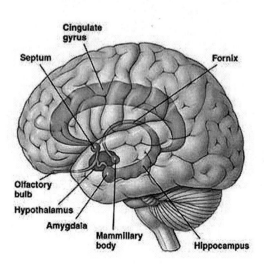

Feelings of pleasure and pain also include activation of brain areas in the **cortex**, including the **prefrontal** area and the **cingulate cortex** or **cingulate gyrus**, a region of the cerebrum below the surface that curls from front to back at the top of the limbic system. A feeling of physical pain is associated with activation in a number of these brain regions particularly including sections of the cingulate cortex.

Interestingly, when we experience **social pain** – being rejected or insulted, for example, or feeling envy or grief – the same brain circuits are activated. The same is true of **pleasure**: When we experience social pleasures, such as the pride we feel when giving to charity, the same brain areas that are stimulated by food, sex, or drugs, are activated. So, brains apparently have evolved to produce feelings of pleasure and pain to social situations in the same brain pathways as to physical pleasure or pain. When a people are depressed or ostracized and say they feel hurt, the brain will back up their claim! Fascinating, huh?

4. The **pituitary gland** is part of the **endocrine system**, which consists of many glands located throughout the body. Glands are body organs that secrete chemicals called **hormones** into the bloodstream, which then influence the functioning of various body parts and organs. Mood, behavior, and emotions are affected by hormones. The endocrine system is not part of the nervous system, but the two systems do work together cooperatively. Many of the glands throughout the body are stimulated by hormones that are released by the pituitary gland in the brain. Therefore, the pituitary has been called the master gland.

The pituitary receives its signals from the brain, principally from the hypothalamus. The pituitary is located just below the hypothalamus, a prime location for the neural connections necessary for signaling the pituitary gland to release hormones. For instance, when people are frightened, the brain signals the hypothalamus, which signals the pituitary, which releases hormones that travel through the bloodstream and influence other glands, such as the adrenal glands, which release adrenalin and other hormones that prepare the body to deal with a dangerous situation. Therefore, the endocrine system is important as a contributor to behavior.

5. The **hippocampus** (Greek for "seahorse," so called because of its curvy shape) bends around in the inside of the temporal lobe and is critically involved in learning and memory. The hippocampus is an important area for creating new memories, for recalling memories, for making new brain cells (**neurogenesis**), and for mapping our environment (spatial memory and navigation).

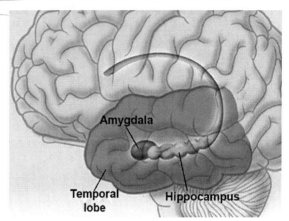

It has been found that taxi drivers in London have large hippocampi, apparently enlarged as maps of the city were stored in the drivers' brains (Maguire, 2000). Lower animals have hippocampal neurons called **place cells** that fire when the animal is in specific location of the environment (O'Keefe, 1978).

Even adult brains make new cells. This process is called **neurogenesis**. New cells are made every day in certain brain regions such as the hippocampus, and some of the new cells will survive and migrate to other brain areas where they join neural networks. Canadian author Doug Coupland joked, "Your brain forms roughly 10,000 new cells every day, but unless they hook up to preexisting cells with strong memories, they die. Serves them right."

The hippocampi, one on each side of the brain on the inside of the temporal lobe, are part of the **limbic system**, which controls and regulates emotion, motivation, quick reactions to stimuli, memory, and new learning. New cells are created there, too, cells that migrate out to other areas of the brain, such as the frontal lobe, to help program learning and memory into brain circuits. Long-term stress reduces the size of the hippocampus and slows learning (Kitayama, 2005). Stress can help an organism adapt in the short-run, but extended stress in the long-run can cause significant damage (Sapolsky, 1997). If you are living a stressful life, please consider making some changes!

When we learn new information, the hippocampus temporarily stores the information, registers it, and then circulates it to other brain areas where memories are created in neural networks. It has been discovered in animals that during sleep the same neurons are firing in the same pattern as when the animal was learning, suggesting that the hippocampus is laying down long-term memories even while asleep (Wilson, 1994). This finding has been replicated repeatedly, and expanded to include humans (Peigneux, 2004).

When memories are retrieved, the hippocampus helps collect the information from the scattered neural networks in the cortex and other brain regions. Damage to the hippocampus – from alcohol, marijuana, stroke, diseases such as Alzheimer's, or injury – results in **anterograde amnesia**, in which a person has difficulty creating new memories. Movies such as *Memento* (2000), *50 First Dates* (2004), and *Winter Sleepers* (1997) center on characters with anterograde amnesia.

By the way, the old saying that people only use 10% of their brains is not correct. You are "using" all of your brain, unless cells are dead – you can't use those. Neurons keep firing positive and negative and squirting out chemicals their whole lives. Woodrow Wilson quipped, "I not only use all the brains that I have, but all I can borrow." And, Cliff Clavin on the TV show *Cheers* said, "Interesting little article here. It says that the average human being only uses 17% of his brain. Boy, you realize what that means? We don't use a full, uh... 64%."

However, brains don't tell us everything they know nor everything they are doing. That is, brains process a lot of information that never makes it to the conscious mind. It's a funny notion, but the vast majority of our

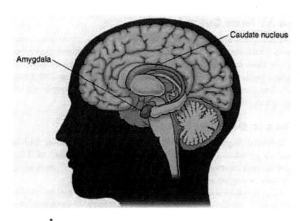

brain activity and cognition is unknown to us – is unconscious or non-conscious. Advice from Jack Handy: "For mad scientists who keep brains in jars, why not add a slice of lemon to each jar, for freshness?"

6. Near the end of the hippocampus is the **amygdala** (Greek for "almond"), which has an oval shape. There is one in each hemisphere. The amygdala is a center for emotions such as fear and anger, and even is important for recognizing facial expressions of emotions. For example, a woman whose amygdalae were both destroyed lost her ability to visually recognize what emotions were being expressed by people's faces, as well as her own ability to express emotions (Damasio, 1994). Researcher Joseph LeDoux (1996) has traced the formation of an emotional memory in the brains of rats and found that the network of cells involved is in the amygdala.

Signals coming into the brain go first to the limbic system via the thalamus (for a quick reaction without thinking), and then later are processed by the cerebral cortex (for a slower, thoughtful response). For example, if you see a snake in the grass in front of you, the visual information goes to the thalamus and then quickly to the amygdala and surrounding areas of the limbic system, which then alert the body – your heart beats faster, adrenalin flows, blood pressure goes up, and so on. But information about the snake also takes another pathway to the cerebral cortex where it is processed by thinking, memory, and judgment. This second avenue (via the cortex) takes longer than the limbic system route because it is more detailed and complex. So, we have two brain pathways for responding to emotionally charged situations: one quick – the limbic system – for immediate body response to danger, and one slower – the cortex – with more cognitive interpretation (Helmuth, 2003).

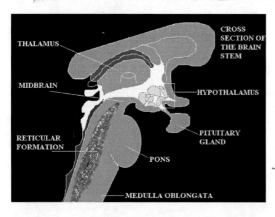

7. The **brainstem** is at the top of the spinal cord. It is the place where brain and spinal cord meet. The brainstem includes a number of nuclei (clusters of brain cells) each responsible for vital body functions necessary for survival and moment-to-moment functioning. For example, the **medulla** (full name = medulla oblongata) controls breathing, heartbeat, blood circulation, and muscle tone. The **pons** is a large bulging section of the brainstem that influences sleep, wakefulness, attention, and arousal.

Another important nucleus of cells in the brainstem is the **reticular formation**. These cells assist in keeping us awake and attentive to things in the environment. Because of its role in "activating" us, the system of nerves that extends up from the brainstem into other brain areas is often called the **reticular activating system** or **RAS**. It can be compared to the channel selector and volume control on a TV set. The RAS determines what we pay attention to and how intense our attention is.

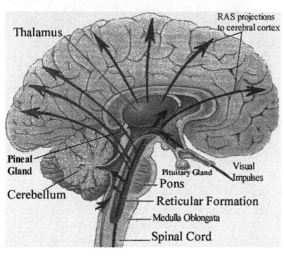

When a person or animal gets used to a stimulus, gets bored with a repetitive sight or sound, the process is called **habituation**. This is an important idea in psychological research. For example, we can test whether a person or animal can detect differences between stimuli using a habituation procedure. Here's how it might work: We present one stimulus over and over again until the subject's response becomes very weak, then we present the other stimulus. If the subject's response increases, we know then that the difference between stimuli was noticed. We can determine if a person or animal can perceive different colors, odors, or any stimuli. This is a common experimental procedure in psychological research with babies and lower animals.

8. Attached to the back of the brainstem is the **cerebellum** (literally: the little brain), which has a number of jobs as its cells process and store information and communicate with other parts of the brain. One of the jobs of the cerebellum is to store the programs for **coordinated body movements**. When we practice a movement – playing guitar, golfing, throwing a ball, riding a bike, gymnastics, and other motor skills – the cells of the cerebellum gradually get fused into a network that will automatically produce the coordinated movement. These coordinated movements do not require thinking; they are performed automatically. Practice may not make perfect, but it does make cerebellum networks. Damage to these cells of the cerebellum means that a person would need to carefully think about every body movement, as if doing it for the first time, every time.

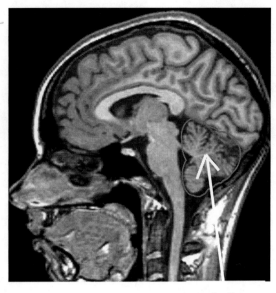
cerebellum

Also, the cerebellum is important for storing memories of **learned body movements**. In a famous experiment, a rabbit was taught to blink when a tone sounded and later the researchers found that the memory for this learned reflex was located in the cerebellum of the rabbit. Damaging that area removed the learned response. (Thompson, 1998).

9. Near the thalamus of the brain are a number of centers (nuclei) where neural pathways come together. This set of nuclei are known as the **basal ganglia**, however, this is a bit of a misnomer since the term "ganglia" normally is used for clusters of neurons outside the brain. The basal ganglia help to smooth body movements. Complex movements, like ballet dancing or even just walking, require smoothing of the muscle movements so we don't jerk at every motion. The cerebellum and basal ganglia work together with the motor cortex to plan, organize, coordinate and smooth our body movements.

Damage to various areas of the basal ganglia results in a number of different muscle movement disorders. These including **dystonia** (sometimes genetic, sometimes acquired), a neurological condition in which muscle contractions cause twisting of body parts, jerky movements, and abnormal positions of the body, **Parkinson's disease**, in which damage to one of the areas of the brain that produces dopamine (the substantia nigra) causes muscles to stiffen, jerk, and uncontrollably tremble and shake, and **Tourette syndrome**, an inherited disorder in which damage to the basal ganglia causes muscle tics and spasms. In these various movement disorders people may have stiff muscles that move or jerk uncontrollably, spasms, tics, tremors, twisting, and quivering, and agitation in which the muscles twitch and shake.

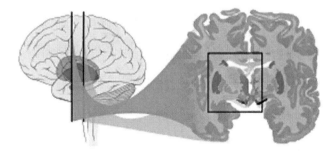
basal ganglia

ꞙinally

This concludes our brief tour of the functions of the brain in your head. The rest of this book will focus on the parts and processes of the brain that influence and contribute to **desire**. Ancient Greek philosopher Aristotle said that by nature all people desire knowledge. So, let's go with that. What is the biological basis for desire? What are the details of the brain's processing that create our cravings for sex, drugs, rock 'n' roll, and more? What is the biological nature of motivation, music, addiction, sex, and emotion? How do brains produce and regulate our desires?

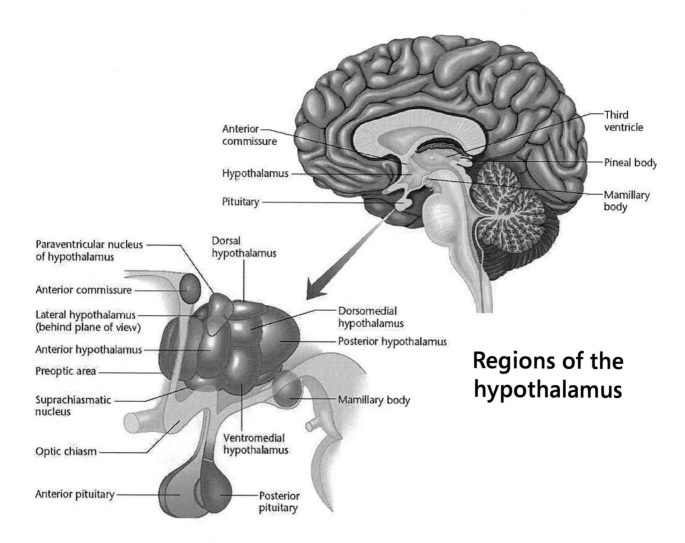

**Regions of the
hypothalamus**

2

Body Motivation

*O*n one episode of the TV show *Seinfeld*, Kramer says to George, "You've got to *yearn*." George stares at him quizzically, and then after a pause says, "Yearn? I don't know that I've ever yearned… I've craved. Oh, boy, have I craved, but not yearned." Then George looks at Kramer and asks, "Do you yearn?" Kramer is now really emphatic; he leans in toward George and heartily exclaims, "Oh, yeah, I yearn, you gotta yeeaarrrnnn!"

To crave, to yearn, to want, to like, to need, to have a hankering, to have a yen, to long for, to fancy, to have the hots for, to desire. What is the nature of our desire? What drives us? What pushes us? What pulls us? What is the biopsychology of desire?

Motivation is a term that refers to what moves us to act a particular way. The word literally means "to set in motion." Naturally, some motivations are driven by survival needs: Hunger, thirst, and other internal **drives** are part of our basic biological make-up honed over many years of evolution. To understand desire, we should begin by looking at basic body motivations, like hunger and thirst. Have you ever been extremely hungry? Or very thirsty? Did you ever just all-out crave food or water? Maybe a certain food, a particular flavor? Did you ever yearn? Where does desire come from? I mean biologically. What makes us crave food and drink? What is the biopsychology of basic body motivation of our desires?

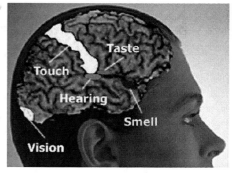

Key Concepts

Let's begin with some fundamental principles, concepts, and terminology. Motivation has been described using certain key ideas:

1. An **instinct** is an inherited tendency toward a certain behavior or pattern of behaviors. **Evolutionary psychologists** have explained a number of human behaviors on the basis of their survival value for our predecessors (and reproduction value, of course, since *surviving* isn't enough to pass on genes – one needs to reproduce!). The **biological drives** such as hunger and thirst had obvious value for the survival of our predecessors, and we can see why they would need to be inherited. But some psychologists have also pointed out that motives such as affiliation, aggression, and achievement have their roots in our evolutionary past, too. That is, these motives had reproduction value for our ancestors.

For instance, people today have an instinct (a natural competency, a natural reaction) to avoid people who cheat in social situations (don't cheaters make you feel icky?). This is because affiliating with cheaters in the past, for our distant predecessors, reduced their ability to reproduce (Cosmides & Tooby, 1992).

Instincts in lower animals are distinct patterns of behavior, such as building a nest, swimming upstream, or a turtle's burrowing to bury an egg. An instinct for humans, however, is not a specific, patterned set of behaviors, but instead refers to inherited tendencies. **Language**, for example is an instinct in humans because our brains are capable of quickly and easily learning any language we experience after birth.

In the 1930s, psychologists attempted to describe nearly every human behavior as an instinct. There was such a long list of instincts suggested by theorists that one expert joked that finding instincts must be an instinct! Today, however, experts say that instincts, in the strict sense of the term, are rare in humans. Lower animals make nests, fly south in the winter, feed their young, and engage in other behaviors that seem totally inherited and unrelated to environment, learning, or to their experiences. Humans, though, are not like that. Humans are much more variable, adaptable, and affected by experiences. Another important point: Calling a behavior an instinct does not explain it, it just labels it. Even if a human behavior like language or hunger or sex or drug addiction could meet the definition of an instinct, we still would like a biological description of how the behavior is caused, regulated, and influenced.

Naturally, evolution determines our basic body make-up. Via **natural selection** certain biological features have evolved because of their advantage in survival and reproduction. Our brain has a certain anatomy and physiology because of millions of years of evolution. We are not born a blank slate. We are not born neutral, like clay to be molded. We are born with specific wiring in the brain that makes it easy to learn some things. These are instincts. The human brain, for instance, has **Broca's area** and **Wernicke's area** with which to process language. The brain's wiring is set by evolution (natural selection). But those brain areas, like all aspects of biology, can be influenced by experience. A baby is not born speaking or understanding language. Language must be learned. However, the baby's brain is wired to make such

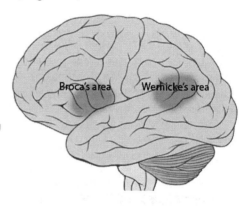

learning easy. Any language can be learned through experience; and, learned easily and quickly because of how the brain is organized. Learning calculus, however, is difficult because the human brain is not wired to easily learn calculus. Knowing calculus did not have any survival advantage among our ancient predecessors.

The property by which the brain can easily learn a task is often called "**hard wired**." For instance, the brain is said to be hard wired for hunger. Such terminology can be useful, but unfortunately is an oversimplification and can therefore mislead. Albert Einstein said, "Make concepts as simple as possible, but not simpler." The idea of hard wiring in the brain is close to being too simple. Brains are **plastic** and respond to personal experiences. Evolution shapes brains, too. While certain motivations and abilities may be hard wired, they also are plastic and modifiable to a large extent. And, wiring in the brain is plastic, too. There is a great deal of interaction between hardware and software in a brain. In many respects it is difficult to separate them. Taking psychoactive drugs, for instance, changes the synapses in subtle ways that modulates chemical responses and therefore firing of neurons. At a microscopic level, the hardware is changed.

2. Intrinsic motivation refers to an animal's tendency to perform a behavior for its own sake, not for the result of the behavior. For example, you may enjoy bouncing a ball, doodling, singing in the shower, helping people, or playing computer games just for the fun of it, not because you get something for engaging in these activities. "Intrinsic" means the motivation is coming from within. Many of our behaviors come from within us, rather than from an outside temptation. We often engage in behaviors that satisfy something inside

Gandhi is a good example of a person with intrinsic motivation.

of us. Psychologists use the term **drive** to refer to the force or desire inside of us that makes us do something. We might say that there is something that "pushes" a people toward a certain behavior when they have intrinsic motivation.

Extrinsic motivation, on the other hand, refers to behavior that is motivated by some payoff, something outside the body. For instance, you may agree to do some boring work in order to get money, or you may behave a certain way to get people to like you, or you might shovel snow from the walk to have a safe path, or do the dishes to have them clean. You don't do these behaviors for the fun; you do them for the tangible result. I'm certain you can think of many examples of extrinsic motivation as you think about the things you do during your normal day. Many of our behaviors that are related to school, work, and social situations are motivated by what we can get from them, not by something pushing us or driving us from inside. The term **incentive** is typically used to refer to the payoff or reward involved in extrinsically motivated behaviors. In such cases, you might say there is something "pulling" you toward a certain behavior. The term "drive," however, is usually used to mean an intrinsically motivated behavior that is originated mainly from inside a person.

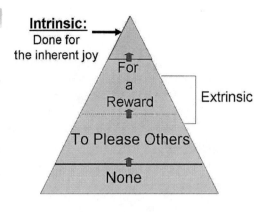

One of the interesting debates in psychology concerns the extent to which people are motivated by **drives** (push) or **incentives** (pull). What is the balance between these two motivations that have different sources – that push or pull us? Do our desires originate from within, are they intrinsic, or are they pulled from us by outside **temptations**? Am I hungry because my body is driven to eat, or is it the TV ad for chocolate cake that I just saw that motivates my desire?

Somewhat surprisingly, it has been found that if a person's behavior consistently leads to a tangible reward (a pull, an incentive), the person sometimes may come to think of the behavior as one that is not interesting in its own right. Intrinsic motivation may in fact in some cases be *decreased* by receiving tangible rewards. If we are constantly receiving a substantive reward for a behavior, we may lose interest in that behavior. It may become boring. Then we would engage in the behavior just for the consequence, not because we enjoy it. Therefore, if we want someone to enjoy a behavior, perhaps we should not make that behavior constantly dependent on an outside reward. Praise, compliments, and fun often increase intrinsic motivation more than do money, treats, or goodies. On the other hand, a recent study found that children ate more disliked vegetables 3 months later if they had been given either a tangible reward or a social reward (Cooke, et al., 2011). So, rewards of all kinds can increase behavior.

In life, as you certainly have already concluded, intrinsic and extrinsic factors nearly always work together to motivate behavior. Hearing food sizzling on the grill can be as motivating as a rumbling stomach. Here's a funny analogy to make the point: A living plant will grow toward the direction of the sunlight it receives. What causes this? Is it the internal nature of the plant, or is it the effect of sunlight on the plant? Of course, it is both! The interaction between the two forces gives rise to the actions of the plant. The plant's inner botanical processes need sunlight, but the light hitting one side of the plant causes the plant to grow and bend in that direction thereby getting more sunlight. Similarly, humans and other animals have internal mechanisms that interact with stimuli in the environment. It is this interaction that motivates us – an interacting combination of push and pull, intrinsic and extrinsic motivation, drives and incentives.

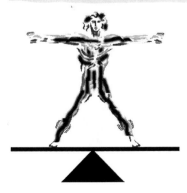

3. Homeostasis is an important concept in body motivation; it refers to a body's internal state of **balance**. Think of it as a steady state or **equilibrium**. Motivation often revolves around a center of balance: When too low, we feel a drive to increase it, and when too high, we experience a need for decrease.

There are many motivations based on this principle. For example, body temperature, thirst, and hunger are homeostatic motives. The body maintains a balance in those conditions; not too much, nor too little. When the body state is too low, a person is motivated to crank it up (when low on nutrients, we feel a desire to eat or drink, for example), and when the body state is too high, the motivation is to lower it (to stop eating or drinking when full).

Homeostasis refers to the state of **balance** that a body must maintain in certain motivational conditions. In each case, the body and brain have some means of receiving information, regulating that information, and then initiating behaviors or body processes that react to that information and correct it, thus bringing the body back into balance. For homeostatic motivation we need a detection system that can monitor the level of a certain stimulus, and we need body processes that will correct the body state when it is out of the optimal range. The central regulating system that evolved in the human brain consists of very complex regions in the **hypothalamus**, the pea-sized area just below the thalamus in the center of the brain. The result of such processes is that the body maintains a balanced state of **equilibrium**. Homeostasis is centered on a certain body level known as the **set point**. Body temperature, for example, must be kept within a certain range. Most motivations operate on this homeostatic set point concept.

An interesting example is **arousal**. Do you like to ride on roller coasters? Why? Do you tap your foot when you are bored? Do you like to watch horror movies and get scared? What's that all about? Well, psychologists have found that people tend to strive for a medium level of stimulation, for a set point in the middle: Not too much arousal, and not too little.

For instance, when a lecture is boring, students begin to swing their legs, tap their pencils, and to talk and fidget. The students are motivated to become more aroused because they are bored. But, when people have too much stimulation, say after a hard, stressful day at work, or following an exciting experience, then people tend to want relaxation and quiet. More arousal in that situation is annoying and bothersome. If you are bored, under-aroused, then a horror movie or roller coaster ride sounds great. But if you've been busy and active all day, then sitting quietly on the beach seems nice. There seems to be something like a body set point when it comes to arousal; we want to maintain a certain level of equilibrium.

4. Researchers have found that people normally perform at their very best at an activity when their level of arousal is somewhere around **medium**; not too high, and not too low. This principle is sometimes called the **Yerkes-Dodson law**. If you need to perform a task and you are under-stimulated, bored, less than thrilled by it, then you are likely to be easily distracted, careless, and sluggish. However, if you are over-stimulated (too nervous, excited, or aroused, for example) then you will more likely be tight, confused, and prone to make errors. If we want top efficiency in performing a task, we don't want to be too high or too low in arousal. For example, that's why in a sport contest opposing coaches call a time-out when a player is to shoot a free throw or kick a field goal. The coach wants the player to think about it in order to increase that player's arousal, and therefore to decrease his or her performance.

Consider the Yerkes-Dodson law when taking tests: Your best performance is likely to result when you are stimulated some, but not too much. If you are too nervous about a test – too aroused – you will choke up, tighten, and make mistakes. However, if you are too relaxed, too care-free about the test, then you will not have enough motivation to pay attention, think carefully, and concentrate on the questions. A medium amount of arousal is not only what people seek, it also gives the most efficient performance.

Of course, the exact optimum level of arousal for performing a task varies somewhat depending on what the task is. In general, tasks that require **creativity** are performed better at a lower level of arousal than tasks that require tedious repetition. You'll need a higher level of arousal to add a table of numbers than to solve a complicated crossword puzzle. The right amount of motivation in order to do your best on a task is somewhere in the middle, but the more creative the task is, the lower the arousal needed for best performance, while the more tedious the task, the higher the level of arousal (more focus) required for top efficiency.

Yerkes-Dodson Law

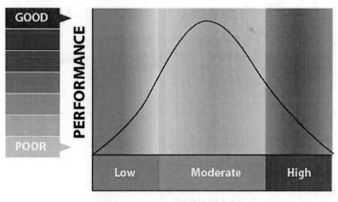

Body Temperature

An excellent example of the key concepts discussed above is the body's motivation to maintain a steady, appropriate body temperature that will support survival, health, and activity. Humans, other mammals, and birds are warm-blooded animals (**endothermic**): that means they help maintain body temperature by internal body mechanisms. **Ectothermic** (cold-blooded) animals, such as snakes and lizards, do not have an internal process for regulating body temperature, so they must lie in the sun or burrow underground to influence their body temperature.

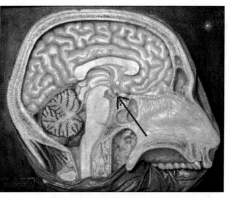
hypothalamus

To maintain a body temperature set point within a pretty narrow range, humans have an internal regulatory system that measures body temperature and then initiates behaviors or body changes that will make adjustments when temperature goes outside the ideal boundaries. The part of the brain that acts as the body's thermostat is an area of the hypothalamus called the **preoptic area**. However, the hypothalamus is not a thermostat that acts as a simple on/off switch; it is much more complicated than that, involving a number of operations and connections with the rest of the brain and with the body. Also, the set point is somewhat flexible and variable; that is, the body temperature set point can be adjusted. For example, when you are **asleep**, your body temperature set point is lowered and then when you awaken the set point temperature goes up to a higher level.

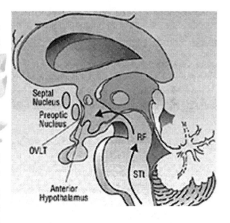

In the **preoptic area** of the **hypothalamus** there are receptor cells that are sensitive to **warm**, and there are other cells that are sensitive to **cold**. These neurons can react to the temperature of the blood in that area of the brain, but they also receive signals from other parts of the body, particularly from the skin. So, the homeostatic set point system begins with the monitoring or detecting of body temperature. Specialized cells in the brain and body have that ability. Of course, detecting body temperature is not enough. The next step is for the brain to initiate biological processes and behaviors that can raise or lower body temperature when it goes outside the ideal set point range by adjusting the production of heat, or the loss of heat, by the body.

Thirst

Thirst is another good example of a homeostatic drive – one that requires balance or equilibrium. In this case the set point is a rather narrow range because water is a critical element for so many life functions; that is, the human body needs a certain amount of water, not too much nor too little, to function well. As you now understand, a homeostatic drive needs a system of detecting when the levels are too low or too high, and also needs a means by which to make corrections. The body and brain have evolved a nice, efficient regulatory system for maintaining healthy levels of water in the body.

But, here's something weird: Did you know that you have two different kinds of thirst! Well, more precisely, there are two types of water depletion in your body that need mechanisms by which to homeostatically control them. The body needs two systems of detecting water loss because there is water both inside the body's cells and also in the fluids outside the cells. Low levels in one system are not necessarily related to low levels in the other system, so the body needs two types of thirst. That is, these two water systems can act independently; therefore your body needs two different homeostatic mechanisms for detecting them – two kinds of thirst.

The first type of thirst is related to cellular water content, that is, the water in the cells of your body, and is called **osmotic thirst**. Cells use water for many different biological functions and the amount of water in the cells must be regulated within a narrow range. When the cells of the body lose water it is by osmosis into the bloodstream because the blood is too concentrated.

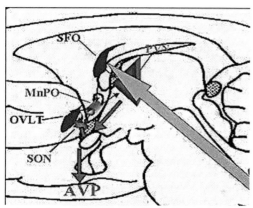

A section of the hypothalamus showing the location of the OVLT, median preoptic nucleus (MnPO), and the SFO.

Eating salt can increase this water osmosis from the cells, for example. The result is a craving for water that is called osmotic thirst. The purpose is to provide more water for the body's cells so they can perform their biological functions with highest efficiency.

The process of osmosis (losing water from the cells) is detected by a part of the brain called the **OVLT** (organum vasculosum lamina terminalis) which is on the side of the hypothalamus bordering the third ventricle in the brain. The neural signal then travels from the detecting region, the OVLT, to an area of the hypothalamus known as the **median preoptic nucleus**, which then signals the body to drink water by sending chemical and neural signals to the pituitary gland and other brain regions.

The second type of thirst refers to the water content of the blood and is called **hypovolemic thirst**. This second type of thirst is based on the volume of water outside the body's cells. Water is lost from the extracellular fluids via sweating, diarrhea, vomiting, and loss of blood. In each case the water volume outside the body's cells decreases, which naturally interferes with biological functions such as the smooth flow of blood through the veins. This **hypovolemia** is detected by receptors both in the veins near the heart and also in the kidneys. When water content of the blood is low, the receptors near the heart respond to the stretching of the vascular walls. The reduced blood volume in the heart is detected by those receptors and a signal is transmitted via the **vagus nerve** to an area of the brainstem known as the **NST** (nucleus of the solitary tract). From there the signal is transmitted to the median preoptic nucleus of the hypothalamus which is in charge of sending out signals to initiate drinking.

A second signal is also involved with hypovolemic thirst. Lowered extracellular water volume is also noted by receptors in the kidneys, which then signal the release of a hormone called renin. The hormone renin in turn increases the production of a similar hormone called **angiotensin II**. Circulating through the bloodstream, angiotensin II stimulates an area of the brain near the hypothalamus known as the **SFO** (subfornical organ). This part of the brain is not separated by the **blood-brain barrier** that protects nearly all areas of the brain from particles in the bloodstream. Therefore, the SFO, since it is unprotected by the blood-brain barrier, can be stimulated by the hormone angiotensin II. Get it? The SFO is stimulated by angiotensin II, which was produced by renin, which was released by the kidneys when receptors there detected a lowering of water volume. The SFO then signals the median preoptic nucleus of the hypothalamus (you guessed that, didn't you?), which then signals the brain to crave water and initiate drinking. In the case of hypovolemic thirst, the craving will be for water that contains salts and other nutrients. When a person has taken in enough water, then receptors in the mouth, stomach, intestines, and liver start the **satiety** process to stop drinking.

Hunger

You might naturally expect **hunger** to be another good example of a homeostatic drive, like temperature and thirst – a drive that requires balance within a certain range or set point. And, yes, to some extent that is

so. However, hunger is so complicated that it goes far beyond the basic homeostatic principle. Hunger, for example, does not revolve around a simple amount of a substance, like thirst, because there is the issue of variety with hunger; that is, we need a variety of nutrients in our food diets. That is the function of taste – to give us cravings for a variety of nutrients. We need salt, fat, and sugar, for example. (How about vegetables? Yes, carrot cake, zucchini bread, and pumpkin pie! Minnesota native Garrison Keillor, author and host of radio's *Prairie Home Companion,* said, "Sex is good, but not as good as fresh, sweet corn").

Hunger is tremendously influenced by variables outside a simple body maintenance regulation – variables such as thinking (cognition), social situations (a big-meal holiday), flavor (yummy cheese), and emotions (depression or anxiety, for example, can affect hunger). For example, you can always fit in a piece of chocolate cake even after a huge meal! Flavor matters! Also, when you are very nervous, you might easily scarf down a whole box of cookies, or on the other hand, you might have no appetite at all. Stress matters! When you are with friends at a fun party, you may find yourself eating those yummy appetizers, or you may gulp down a huge amount of food while watching the big game. Social situation matters! You might even forget to eat when you are intensely concentrating on some interesting activity. Cognition matters! Hunger is not a simple homeostatic, equilibrium motivation. It is pushed and pulled by cognition, affect, sensations, mood, circumstances, and more. Hunger is a complex motivation.

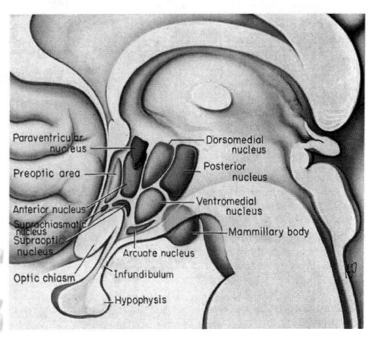

Now to better understand how hunger works, first let's look at the brain's center for regulating eating. Can you guess where that is in the brain? Did I hear you say the **hypothalamus**? You are right! How did you know that? Yes, the hypothalamus is the central regulator of the body's energy system. The whole system – brain, mouth, stomach, intestines, liver, nerves, receptors, hormones – is a complicated scheme of signals that flow in and out of the hypothalamus. The role of the hypothalamus is to integrate body motivations; it is a central monitoring and regulating center in the brain and has often been compared to a thermostat, though it is much more complex. The hypothalamus is made of distinct anatomical areas that regulate the body's energy system, sleep, the circadian rhythm, sexual activity and behavior, and body temperature (Swanson, 1987). One of the jobs of the hypothalamus is to regulate hunger. It does this via interconnections of several of its regions.

Hunger is a good example of a complex drive. It will be a good model for other topics in this book, such as sex, drug addiction, music, and emotion. Complex brain systems receive inputs from numerous body parts and interconnect with many different brain areas in a complex and coordinated manner. Hunger does not have a simple on/off switch! Hunger is complex in that it is influenced by a wide array of factors including emotion, stress, cognition, mood, and sensory signals (seeing an advertisement for a cheeseburger!), as well as by homeostatic nutrition needs that are signaled by the body. The hypothalamus is at the center of this complex system.

But, when we look at the hypothalamus we find that it has many different centers, or **nuclei**, that are intricately interconnected. It's like looking at a bowl of spaghetti noodles in which there are certain areas where the noodles are tightly wound. These nuclei receive inputs from a vast array of brain and body areas and organs and interconnect with each other, with other brain areas, and with the nearby pituitary gland that releases hormones into the bloodstream. The hypothalamus has numerous nuclei where neurons interact in vast networks, and where hormones are produced and released.

So, the hypothalamus is an exceedingly complicated structure – not a simple, single area that is uniform and homogeneous. The hypothalamus is highly interconnected and interacts with other brain areas as well as with the **endocrine system** (glands that secrete hormones). The hypothalamus can react to hormones as well as to neural signals originating from the brainstem, the limbic system, the cerebral cortex, and other body parts and organs. Hunger, of course, is only one of the many functions of the hypothalamus, the master regulator of body drives and motivations.

Hunger Brain Centers

An age-old question: "If you ate pasta and antipasto, would you still be hungry?"

There are several interacting areas of the hypothalamus that are involved in hunger and eating behavior. The first two hypothalamus regions implicated in hunger were discovered by neuroscientist **Karl Lashley** in

1938. The first, called the **lateral hypothalamus**, is thought to be involved in starting or initiating hunger and eating. When Lashley damaged this lateral hypothalamus in rats, he found that they significantly reduced their eating. This behavior is known as **aphagia** (literally "not eating"). When the lateral hypothalamus is stimulated electrically, an animal will begin eating immediately and rapidly. This tiny region appears to be a primary regulator of initiating hunger and eating. It receives signals from the body via the bloodstream and the brainstem, and also from other regions of the hypothalamus. The lateral hypothalamus controls chewing, salivation, swallowing, acid secretion, and insulin production. It is very actively involved as the main "go" area for eating, but is not alone, as we shall see.

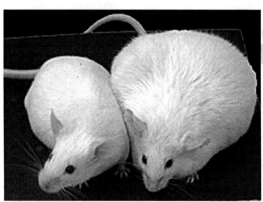

A hyperphagic rat caused by damage to the ventromedial hypothalamus.

The second area of the hypothalamus critical to regulating hunger that was discovered by Lashley is called the **ventromedial hypothalamus (VMH)** or **ventromedial nucleus (VMN)** of the hypothalamus. This small area came to be known as the stop eating center, or the **satiety** (satisfied) center of the brain. (Incidentally, the VMH is also involved in fear, temperature regulation, and sexual activity). When Lashley lesioned this area in rats' brains he found that the rats overate to excess and became obese. This condition is known as **hyperphagia** (literally "over eating"). And, when this area was electrically stimulated in a rat's brain eating would decrease markedly. A mnemonic device was soon devised to help students remember the roles of the two areas of the hypothalamus that had been identified as important centers for hunger: Lat makes you fat, ven makes you thin! Cute, but unfortunately not entirely correct! Following more extensive research, the role of the ventromedial hypothalamus in hunger has been questioned and diminished; research clearly indicates that the VMH does not exactly "stop" eating, but rather changes it so that animals become more finicky. Also, other areas of the hypothalamus that are connected to the ventromedial area it turns out are also important in regulating the satiety of hunger.

It was originally thought that the lateral hypothalamus was a "start" eating center and the ventromedial nucleus was a "stop" eating center, and that they acted together in a balanced arrangement that kept a person's body weight roughly steady over long periods of time. As you might suspect, Lashley's research had stimulated a great deal of interest in the biology of hunger by other researchers and theorists, and the plethora of research findings in this area soon led to the idea that the hypothalamus acted as if it had a **set point** for hunger; that is, the hypothalamus seemed to increase eating when an animal's weight went below a certain range, and then decreased eating behavior when the animal's weight was above that range. This, of course, seemed like a typical homeostatic system. It was speculated that the hypothalamus set point for hunger was set genetically or perhaps was influenced by early eating patterns in infancy. The idea was that a person's hypothalamus will regulate maintenance of a certain body weight (within a narrow range) over long periods of time, and therefore dieting will be difficult – because the **hypothalamus** is pushing the body to maintain its **set point**. It turns out that this conception is partially correct, at least in its general themes.

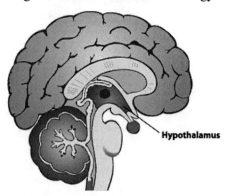

Hypothalamus

However, today it is understood that hunger and body weight are influenced by many more factors than this rather simple conception allows, that there are other brain areas involved in the body's energy metabolism, and that brain regulatory centers are not simple switches that turn hunger on or off. Psychologists today are more cautious about considering hunger to be a homeostatic drive. Some experts have openly denied that hunger and eating are homeostatic or that there is a set point for body weight. For example, Bolles (1980) argued that eating is influenced by so many factors that body weight settles around a point that is only moderately stable and is influenced by appetite, food availability, the taste of food, and other factors. Bolles says that **obesity** is more common today because external conditions and norms have changed, not because brain set points have changed; there is no *set point*, but rather a **settling point** similar to sea level.

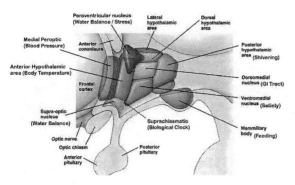

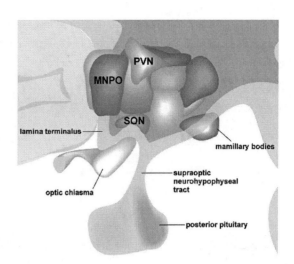

Areas of the hypothalamus including the lateral hypothalamus (LH), ventromedial (VMH), arcuate nucleus (ARC), and paraventricular nucleus (PVN).

Contemporary research findings support the notion that hunger is much more complicated than it was first imagined. Importantly, two other areas of the hypothalamus have been found to play critical roles in hunger and eating. The **paraventricular nucleus (PVN)**, like the lateral hypothalamus, is involved with initiating or starting eating, but also helps regulate various metabolic processes, such as body temperature, fat storage, and cell metabolism. These biological processes help the body to use the nutrients taken in by eating.

Another area, the **arcuate nucleus,** is an area of the hypothalamus that is vital for monitoring the nutrients in the body. For example, the arcuate nucleus responds to a chemical in the bloodstream that is released by the stomach as it empties. This brain region is located at the bottom of the hypothalamus and has a curved shape, which gives the arcuate nucleus its name. The arcuate nucleus sends signals to the PVN and to the lateral hypothalamus to aid in controlling eating and metabolism. It is in the arcuate nucleus that we find the key neural and hormonal systems for the regulation of hunger. Most scientists today consider the arcuate nucleus of the hypothalamus to be the primary control center for hunger and satiety. The arcuate nucleus coordinates the need for food with signals from the body indicating nutritional conditions. Two circuits in the arcuate nucleus promote or suppress appetite in order to maintain homeostasis.

Located in the lower portion of the brain, the arcuate nucleus is one of the few brain areas that is not blocked by the blood-brain barrier. Therefore, chemicals in the bloodstream that are released by the stomach, liver, and intestines can stimulate cells in this region of the hypothalamus. There are two main chemicals in the arcuate nucleus that stimulate hunger: **Neuropeptide Y (NPY)** and **agouti-related protein (AgRP)**. These chemicals initiate hunger and eating behaviors. For example, mice that over-express AgRP become obese. These two chemicals activate cells in the brain that start hunger, apparently by inhibiting the cells that suppress, or slow down, hunger. But these

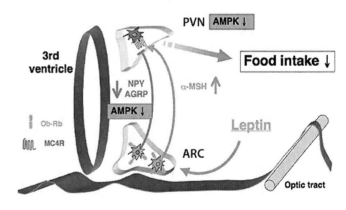

two chemicals, NPY and AgRP can be inhibited by other chemicals, too, such as by **insulin** (released by the pancreas to break down glucose) and **leptin** (released by fat cells to signal they are full).

Both insulin and leptin, therefore, help to calm down the eating urge by inhibiting NPY and AgRP. And, just to make things even more complicated, hunger is driven primarily by the POMC system. **POMC (stands for pro-opiomelanocortin) is a chemical found in the hypothalamus that can break down into various hormones.** The arcuate nucleus of the hypothalamus has **POMC neurons** that act on a system of receptors called **melanocortin** (a hormone produced from POMC in the pituitary gland) **receptors**. The POMC-melanocortin system inhibits eating. By the way, POMC neurons are also found in the **brainstem**, which shows that the hypothalamus is not the only part of the brain involved in modulating or influencing hunger and energy homeostasis of the body.

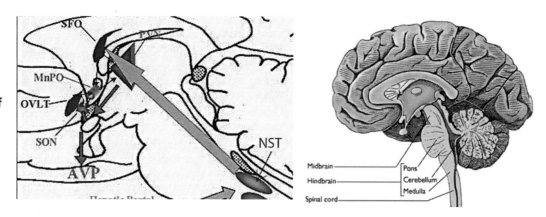

The NST is part of the medulla of the brainstem.

One of the primary inputs to the **hypothalamus** comes from an area of the brainstem known as the **NST** (nucleus of the solitary tract), which is also involved in regulating thirst by reacting to low water volume in the blood. The NST receives its signals via the **vagus nerve**. For example, stomach volume and other indicators of energy consumption and the needs of the body send neural signals up the vagus nerve to the brainstem. The NST organizes this incoming information and informs areas of the hypothalamus via neural circuits.

It's not so much that the brain has start and stop centers, but rather there are redundant brain mechanisms that modulate and influence energy homeostasis through a number of biological processes. Think of various areas of the hypothalamus and brainstem as **dials** rather than on/off switches. Not only the hypothalamus, but also the **brainstem** should be thought of as a brain area that regulates energy metabolism by modulating taste, hunger, and thirst.

Hunger Signals

Comic Buddy Hackett: "As a child my family's menu consisted of two choices: take it, or leave it."

Here are some of the sources to the **hypothalamus** and **brainstem** where body energy systems are centrally regulated that scientists have so far uncovered:

1. Glucose: As a major source of energy for nearly all organisms from bacteria to humans, glucose (blood sugar) is a simple sugar that is also the primary source of energy for the brain in performing mental activities; when glucose levels are low, cognitive processes are impaired. The liver and the brain separately are both are able to monitor glucose levels and alert the arcuate nucleus of the hypothalamus. The liver does this via the vagus nerve and then the NST in the medulla. When glucose levels are low, the hypothalamus receives signals from the liver and also from the brain and consequently initiates eating behavior. Animals injected with a substance that causes glucose deficiency start eating nearly immediately and eat three times as much as normal (Novin, VanderWeele, & Rezek, 1973). This process is known as **glucoprivic hunger** (gluco = sweet; *privia* = condition of loss or deprivation). So, low glucose levels in the brain or in the liver will trigger the brainstem and hypothalamus to start eating.

2. Fatty acids: Besides monitoring glucose, the liver is also able to monitor the level of fatty acids and send a signal to the NST of the brainstem, a process known as **lipoprivic hunger** (*lipo* = fat; *privia* = condition of loss or deprivation). The heart, skeletal muscles, and some other body cells use fatty acids for energy, but the brain relies solely on glucose for energy. When fatty acid levels are low, the hypothalamus receives the signal to initiate eating. Blocking the metabolism of fatty acids will increase the amount eaten (Ritter & Taylor, 1990).

3. Ghrelin: This hormone is often called the "**hunger hormone**." Released by the stomach as it empties, ghrelin is a peptide chemical that travels through the bloodstream, passing easily through the blood-brain barrier, and is detected by the **arcuate nucleus** of the **hypothalamus**. Ghrelin levels in the blood rise before each meal and drop sharply after eating (Cummings et al., 2001). Ghrelin is a main "go" chemical in the bloodstream that signals the brain to initiate eating.

There is an **enzyme** that works with ghrelin that scientists abbreviate **GOAT**. It is believed that this enzyme, GOAT, is necessary for ghrelin to do its job of increasing appetite. Researchers are now testing methods to block GOAT from attaching to ghrelin in the hopes of diminishing the "hunger hormone" from increasing eating behavior in obese people (Yang et al., 2008).

4. Neuropeptide Y (NPY): A brain neurotransmitter, NPY was discovered in the 1980s and is now known to be involved in a number of physiological processes, including energy, learning and memory, and epilepsy. Its main function appears to be to increase energy storage and conserve energy by increasing food intake, decreasing physical activity and sexual motivation, and reducing body temperature. NPY is used by the arcuate nucleus to signal the lateral hypothalamus and the paraventricular nucleus to initiate eating. Rats injected with NPY will continue eating even under adverse conditions such as getting an electric shock to the tongue or experiencing bitter food (Flood & Morley, 1991).

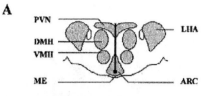

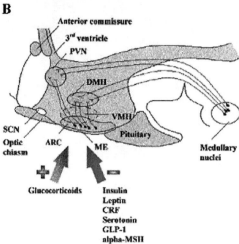

5. Orexin: One of the neuropeptide hormones produced by the hypothalamus, orexin (also known as **hypocretin**) sends projections throughout the brain. Orexin increases the craving for food by its interaction with other substances such as ghrelin. Orexin is also a major factor in metabolism and sleep regulation. For instance, orexin promotes wakefulness and when deficient causes sleep attacks such as seen in the disorder **narcolepsy**.

6. Anandamide: This is a brain neurotransmitter chemical found primarily in the limbic system that, like orexin, also stimulates hunger. By the way, the active ingredient in **marijuana**, **THC**, has a molecular shape very similar to anandamide, and therefore binds with the anandamide receptors in the brain, thus stimulating hunger and giving the "munchies" to a person who has ingested THC.

7. Insulin: Released by the pancreas, insulin is a hormone that helps body cells get energy from glucose. Diabetes results when the pancreas cannot produce enough insulin (type 1) or when the body cells are insufficiently responsive to insulin (type 2). In such cases, glucose in the blood will not be used and the person will still feel hungry. When insulin is released by the pancreas, it travels through the bloodstream to the arcuate nucleus where it inhibits the NPY and AgRP neurons from signaling hunger; therefore, insulin is a "stop" eating chemical signal.

8. Leptin: Over long periods of time, body weight and body fat are regulated primarily because of a hormone called leptin (*lepto* = slender) that is secreted by fat cells and stimulates cells in the hypothalamus to inhibit eating. The amount of leptin in the blood is about four times higher in obese individuals than in non-obese people (Considine et al., 1996). Leptin is not an immediate response to food intake, but rather is a long-term signal. Like insulin, leptin slows eating by inhibiting NPY and AgRP neurons in the arcuate nucleus of the hypothalamus.

In 1994 it was discovered that rats lacking leptin because of a genetic mutation became extremely obese (Friedman et al.). When the rats were injected with leptin, they reduced their food intake and their brains adjusted to a lower set-point body weight – the rats became normal weight. Leptin treatment in humans who have a similar genetic mutation (a rare cause of obesity) was also found to be very effective. However, leptin injections for obese people who do not have the genetic cause is not effective since their brains are insensitive to leptin.

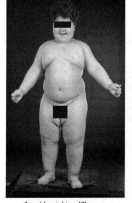

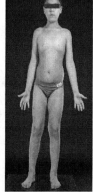

Incidentally, researchers found that when leptin was delivered directly to the **hippocampus** in rats, a part of the brain involved with learning and memory, the animals consumed less food and decreased their body weight. Leptin delivered to this region of the brain also impaired the ability of the animals to learn about the spatial location of food. These findings remind us that cognition also plays a role in eating and control of body weight.

Leptin also stimulates cells in the brain's pleasure pathway, particularly the **ventral tegmental area** of the brainstem. Previous research has shown that eating activates areas of the pleasure pathway, which makes good sense since we know that people find eating to be a pleasurable activity,

3yr old weighing 42kg   7yr old weighing 32kg

A leptin-deficient boy before and after treatment.

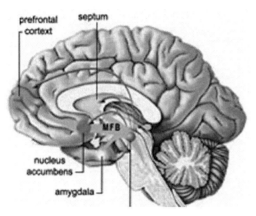

and that evolution certainly made energy intake a rewarding activity. Brain imaging research has found that obese people have impairments in the dopamine pathways that regulate systems associated with reward sensitivity, conditioning and control (Volkow, 2010). So, obesity likely involves a problem in the brain's pleasure pathway.

Interestingly, some research has found that the hormone **estrogen** acts similarly to **leptin** in stimulating brain areas that put the brakes on hunger (Gao, 2006). That is, estrogen suppresses appetite via the same brain regions that respond to leptin. Perhaps this finding will lead to some new treatments for weight loss. And, finally, leptin also slows eating after stimulating cells in the **NST** of the **brainstem**. The hypothalamus is not the only brain area involved in hunger and body cell metabolism. Evolution has given the brain redundant systems for many different functions.

9. Stomach volume: There are receptors in the stomach that respond to stretching. If you swallow a balloon and it is pumped up, your stomach will stretch. Certain receptors in the stomach will then respond by sending neural signals via the vagus nerve to the NST in the medulla of the brainstem. From there the arcuate nucleus will be notified of the increased stomach volume. This will slow eating behavior. Stomach volume, however, is a very limited signal. A stomach full of just water or a pumped-up balloon will not be very satisfying! You will still be hungry for real food. It turns out that the mouth, stomach, and intestines work together to give a *full* sense of satiation (pun intended!).

10. Nutrient-indicating peptides: There are many chemicals (peptides) released by the stomach and intestines in response to particular nutrients that have been ingested. About a dozen have been found so far, peptides that are released in response to fats, proteins, or carbohydrates. These peptides signal other body parts to release the appropriate enzymes to digest the nutrient, and in some cases inform the brain, too, about which nutrient needs have been met.

The best known of these dozen or so peptides is **CCK** (cholecystokinin), which is a hormone that is released when fats are detected. CCK stimulates receptors on the vagus nerve and hence the NST of the brainstem receives the message which then is sent to the hypothalamus. When CCK was injected into the bloodstreams of obese individuals, they ate less at each meal, but ate more frequent meals (Pi-Sunyer et al., 1982). Another example is peptide YY (**PYY**), a hormone released by the intestines that also is an appetite suppressant. PYY stimulates the arcuate nucleus of the hypothalamus via the bloodstream, not through neural circuits. Once at the hypothalamus, PYY inhibits the NPY neurons.

Taste

The definition of "edible" by humorist Ambrose Bierce: "Good to eat, and wholesome to digest, as a worm to a toad, a toad to a snake, a snake to a pig, a pig to a man, and a man to a worm."

Did you ever have the flu or a similar illness that made you feel nauseous, and at about the same time have a distinctive flavor in your brain, say peanut butter, pizza, mayonnaise, or maybe a margarita or gin and tonic? If so, you probably developed what psychologists call a **taste aversion**. Later, you just couldn't stand the taste, the smell, or even the thought of that particular flavor. It made you feel nauseous long after your illness was gone. A taste aversion can last for many, many years. This is an example of a type of learning that psychologists call **classical conditioning**. Two stimuli coming together at about the same time cause a learned association in the brain. Experiments by **Ivan Pavlov** showed that a neutral stimulus can come to have a similar effect as a natural stimulus if they are paired together often enough. Pavlov paired the sound of a bell with food placed in a dog's mouth and found that later the dog would salivate when hearing the bell. This learning process is called classical conditioning. We can learn to like tastes or dislike tastes via this process.

In the case of learned taste aversion, the flavor of a particular food is paired with a nauseous, unpleasant feeling of illness, and later the flavor elicits an aversive, disgusted response. This can happen with any flavor, really. What was your taste aversion, and how long did it last? I learned an aversion to shrimp once, and it lasted eight years! Another time it was pizza sauce. How about you? As you can imagine, taste aversion is an evolutionary adaptation that keeps animals from eating foods that can make them sick or even die. A caveman who ate a food that made him sick and then ate it some more was not likely to stay around very long. So, taste aversion evolved as a mechanism for survival. Thanks, evolution!

Taste aversion has been studied extensively by a psychologist named **John Garcia** and therefore is sometimes called the **Garcia effect**. One of Garcia's practical uses of learned taste aversion was to condition wolves and coyotes (predators) to avoid eating lambs and calves (their prey) by treating their food with a chemical that made the coyotes sick. So, for example, a coyote ate a piece of lamb meat that had been laced with lithium chloride (causes nausea!). Taste aversion occurred. Later, the sight and smell of lambs made the coyote feel nauseous and he backed away from his prey. In the field after taste aversion occurred, some lambs even chased away the reluctant wolves, a pretty funny sight! Ranchers were happy. The wolves and coyotes, however, had to find other food sources, at least for quite a while.

The Garcia effect has been used more recently in the **Mexican Wolf Recovery Program**. There are only about 40 Mexican wolves in the wild and each time more are released ranchers complain because they are a threat to cows and sheep. Now psychologist Dan Moriarity is using conditioned taste aversion to train the animals to dislike the taste of sheep (Dingfelder, 2010). A chemical that induces nausea was mixed into mutton parcels that were given to the wolves. Every animal that ate the bait later refused to eat meat from sheep. This procedure could help wildlife management immensely.

Comedian Fran Lebowitz says, "Food is an important part of a balanced diet." Humans are **omnivores**, meaning their primary diet includes both plants and meats. Animals that primarily eat plants, such as cows, deer, sheep, kangaroos, and insects, are called **herbivores**. When meat is its primary source of food, the animal is called a **carnivore**, such as a lion, cat, alligator, or wolf. Omnivores such as pigs, crows, chimpanzees, and us, have evolved digestive tracts that allow a wider range of food for sustenance. Both plants and animals may taste appealing to an omnivore. Taste results when specific proteins bind with receptors known as **taste buds** on the tongue. Scientists today recognize five categories of taste buds: sweet, salt, bitter, sour, and **umami**. The last one, umami, was recently discovered and is described as meaty or savory; you get this flavor from Parmesan cheese or mushrooms, for example.

However, most scientists today believe that taste buds are not entirely specific to one taste, but rather that the taste buds respond to a range or spectrum of molecules, but with most intensity to a specific stimulus, for example, bitter. These particular taste buds evolved because they help humans to select a diet that is healthy, that provides proper sustenance and nutrition for the body's energy system. The body needs sugar and salt, but should avoid bitter and sour foods that might be poisonous or spoiled. Genetics directs the number of taste buds each person has, and therefore influences taste preferences. But preference obviously is also influenced by culture and familiarity with certain foods. As you become more familiar with a particular taste you come to like it more. Each culture has foods that are common and the people within a culture come to prefer those foods. Do you like sushi? Some people love sushi, others consider it bait!

Of course, we can grow tired of a specific taste, too, if we have it too much. **Taste-specific satiety** refers to the fact that the more of a particular taste or food that a person eats, the less appealing that food becomes. This condition results from neural signals in the **NST** portion of the medulla in the brainstem. Your **brainstem** wants you to eat a balanced meal! Taste-specific satiety likely evolved in order to keep our diets in good variety. Don't you get sick of a flavor that you eat over and over again? Okay, I'm not talking about chocolate; I guess there are exceptions to everything!

Amazingly, research has shown that this type of **habituation** to a particular flavor can occur simply through imagination! When people imagined eating a certain food, they later consumed less of it (Morewedge, 2010). The lead researcher of this study said, "These findings suggest that trying to suppress one's thoughts of desired foods in order to curb cravings for those foods is a fundamentally flawed strategy. Our studies found that instead, people who repeatedly imagined the consumption of a morsel of food - such as an M&M or cube of cheese - subsequently consumed less of that food than did people who imagined consuming the food a few times or performed a different but similarly engaging task. We think these findings will help develop future interventions to reduce cravings for things such as unhealthy food, drugs and cigarettes, and hope they will help us learn how to help people make healthier food choices."

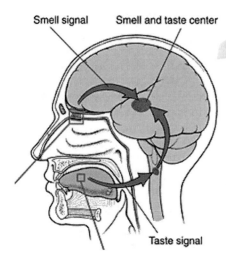

Smell signal   Smell and taste center

Taste signal

From Cervantes: "Hunger is the best sauce in the world."

In case you're wondering, yes, there is some evidence of a **learned taste preference**. Some studies have found that an animal can learn to like the taste of a food that provides a nutrient that the animal needs. Also, infants apparently will eat a somewhat balanced meal if they are allowed to choose from different healthy foods. To some extent the body can monitor nutrient intake and then create a desire for the taste of foods that contain a nutrient that is needed.

In one early experiment, rats were given a diet deficient in a vitamin and later they preferred a food enriched with that vitamin. When that food was given a distinctive flavor, the rats continued to desire that flavor even when the food did not provide the vitamin (Scott & Verney, 1947). However, subsequent research showed that the "wisdom of the body" is very limited and can be overtaken by taste preferences. Rats, for instance, will not select nutritional foods if given a choice of chocolate or cinnamon. Humans, too, will forsake healthy needs for cinnabons, ice cream, blueberry pie, or french fries!

Obesity

Comedian Steven Wright deadpanned, "I went to a restaurant that serves breakfast at any time. So I ordered French toast during the Renaissance."

The World Health Organization has declared obesity to be a global epidemic. About 2 billion people, one out of three people over 15, are overweight or obese. For the first time in human history there are more people on earth who are overweight than who go hungry. **Obesity** is defined as a medical condition in which body fat is so excessive as to be a health risk. Health problems such as diabetes, stroke, Alzheimer's disease, colon cancer, high blood pressure, and heart disease are much more common among overweight people. In 2011 the American Stroke Association reported a dramatic increase in the number of strokes among young and middle-aged Americans as a result of overweight childhoods.

Not only do obese and overweight people have more health problems, but their life-spans are reduced, too. Reductions in life span range from 2 to 10 years on average for people who are overweight. The best known and perhaps the only scientifically proven method of significantly increasing life span is calorie reduction. Not only does weight loss increase life span, but some preliminary findings suggest improvements in cognition are a result of cutting calories. For example, elderly adults who reduced their calorie intake by almost one-third for a period of three months showed a twenty percent increase in memory (Witte et al., 2009). Of course, that is a huge reduction in calorie intake; much more than nearly anyone would be willing to attempt. Still, weight loss does increase life span across the board.

In recent years, all developed countries have seen increases in the percentage of their populations who are overweight or obese. In the United States, the obesity rate has doubled since 1980 (Ogden, 2006). Two-thirds of adult in the U.S. are considered overweight or obese. The reason? People are eating richer foods and exercising less. Changes in diet and the types of foods that are available are part of the problem. Contributing to the problem

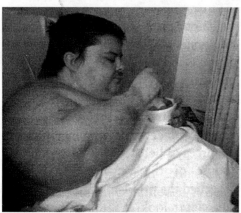

Prader-Willi syndrome.

is that myths about obesity are very common today and seem difficult to shake. For instance, studies have made it quite clear that lack of will-power is not the cause of obesity (Volkow & Wise, 2005), yet this is often cited by the public and is suggested by comedians who make light of obesity.

There is a rare genetic disorder, occurring in about 1 out of 20,000 births, called **Prader-Willi syndrome** that was discovered in 1956. In this disorder, certain genes on chromosome 15 from the father are missing (deleted) or unexpressed. Normally, these paternal genes are expressed while the corresponding genes on the maternal chromosome 15 are unexpressed (such situations are called **genomic imprinting** when only genes from one parent are expressed; genes are expressed through the production of proteins). This means the child with Prader-Willi syndrome does not have any expression of the deleted genes. The result is a large number of symptoms – physical, behavioral, and cognitive – such as a characteristic facial appearance, learning difficulties, sleep disorder, delayed puberty, and many others. This disorder also results in abnormalities in the functioning of the hypothalamus leading sometimes to extreme hyperphagia and obesity. Prader-Willi children have high levels of ghrelin and an insatiable appetite. They can become morbidly obese.

Incidentally, a sister disorder called **Angelman syndrome** (named after Dr. Harry Angelman) occurs when the some genes on the maternal copy of chromosome 15 are deleted and the paternal genes are imprinted and not expressed. Angelman children have a number of developmental delays, physical symptoms, an abnormal EEG with seizures, and behavioral problems, but also present a very happy disposition with frequent laughing. They are contented and enjoy play, but have extremely limited use of speech.

A cheerful disposition is also seen in **Williams syndrome** which is caused by a deletion of genes on chromosome 7. Williams syndrome children have general intellectual impairment and poor spatial perception, but good verbal ability. Neither Angelman syndrome nor Williams syndrome is associated with eating disorders as seen in Prader-Willi syndrome.

Williams syndrome.

An old Spanish proverb says, "The belly rules the mind." But, author Robert Byrne said, "Anybody who believes that the way to a man's heart is through the stomach flunked geography." There are many factors that influence body weight, and **heredity** certainly is one of them. In one investigation, rats were selectively bred to be **obese** and the rats had genetic abnormalities in their **arcuate nuclei** making them less receptive to **leptin** (Bouret et al., 2008). The lead researcher concluded, "The results show that obesity can be wired into the brain from early life." Studies show a **heritability factor** of about 50-70% for **obesity** (Maes, Neale, & Eaves, 1997).

Many **genes** have been discovered that presumably influence excessive weight gain (Thorleifsson, 2009). Hofker and Wijmenga (2009) reported 15 chromosome loci associated with body mass index. Such genes include: ***Ob(Lep)*** is a gene found on chromosome 7 that codes for leptin and when mutated causes extreme obesity; The ***TUB* gene** is highly expressed in the hypothalamus and likely acts as a **transcription factor** (modulating other genes) in influencing eating behavior; The ***FTO* gene** is carried by half the people with European ancestry. People who have one version of this gene are 70% more likely to be overweight than people who carry the other version. The *FTO* gene also is associated with brain loss (Ho et al., 2010); The ***MC4R* gene** has been associated with human obesity and insulin resistance (Loos et al., 2008). Besides eating behavior, this gene also is involved in metabolism and sexual behavior (Chambers et al., 2008). It is very important to note that heredity is not fate. For the vast number of us, life style, diet, exercise, sleep, social life, and other factors are incredibly important factors in influencing our body weights. Heredity is one contributor, an important risk factor, but does not guarantee a person's body mass index.

Humans **evolved** over a period of time when food was relatively scarce. Therefore, humans developed a biological system that stores fat for energy use when food is not available. Today, of course, for most humans food is available nearly all the time. The result is that the body is motivated to eat when food is available in order to store it for later use. Overeating will, therefore, be common. The brain wants to eat when there is food available. Evolution has provided humans with a brain and body that are intricately designed to guard against weight loss, but not so much against weight gain. On the contrary, our hunger system is designed to eat when food is available and to store energy for later use. The results are catching up with us. Not long ago certain foods were only available seasonally. Today, well in developed countries you can eat nearly anything anytime.

Body fat is carried in cells known as **adipose tissue**, and therefore obesity is scientifically known as **adiposity**. As you are well aware, people have created thousands of different diets in an attempt to help people reduce eating, lower body weight, and decrease adiposity. However, as you probably also know very well, all of these various diets have been notorious, spectacular failures. Dolly Parton, like many people, had trouble controlling her weight. She lamented, "I tried every diet in the book. I tried some that weren't in the book. I tried eating the book. It tasted better than most of the diets."

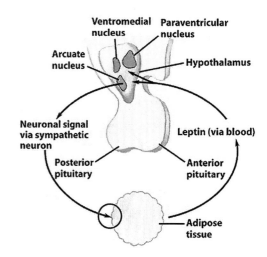

With nearly every diet that has been tried, when there is weight loss, invariably the weight returns after a year or so. TV and movie actor and comedian Jackie Gleason, who was chronically overweight said, "The second day of a diet is always easier than the first. By the second day you're off of it." Diets are massive failures, likely because they do not attack the roots of the problem. An old adage says, "Eat as much as you like, just don't swallow it." Because of the failure of diets, obese people today often go to extreme lengths to control their weight including wiring the jaw closed, sucking out fat cells, and surgically reducing the size of the stomach (**gastric bypass surgery**). Wow! Weight loss is obviously a very tough problem and a highly desired goal. What does science have to offer?

One of the attempts to treat obesity is the introduction of drugs approved for weight loss. These are typically in a class known as **appetite suppressants**. Unfortunately, not only are these drugs mostly ineffective, but they often cause serious side effects including heart valve leakage, liver damage, heart attack, and stroke. Many such drugs have been taken off the market in recent years. An example is **sibutramine** which showed some benefits, but the side effects were too serious and the drug was withdrawn by the pharmaceutical company that manufactured it. Since the brain neurotransmitter **serotonin** is involved in hunger and eating behavior, medicines that inhibit the reuptake of serotonin and therefore increase its activity in the brain have been tried for treating obesity. The results were good for a subset of overweight people: Those who crave carbohydrates. Other overweight subjects did not benefit.

Leptin treatment is similar in that it helps only a small subset of overweight people: Those who have the genetic form of the *Ob(Lep)* **gene** and are leptin deficient. Attempts also have been made to use peptide YY to treat obesity, but these trials have not been successful and subjects experienced severe side effects. A quite different approach that has recently been suggested is to treat overweight as an **inflammatory** problem of the body cells. Obesity researchers Sears and Ricordi (2011), for example, recommend an **anti-inflammatory diet** to control appetite. Because eating stimulates the brain's reward pathway (**the mesolimbic pathway** includes the **ventral tegmental area** of the brainstem, the **nucleus accumbens**, and areas of **the limbic system**) producing pleasure, some attempts have been made to treat obesity and over-eating the way addictions are treated. This primarily means targeting the dopamine receptors that populate the pleasure pathway. Early trials have shown some success and medicines will likely be on the market in a few years.

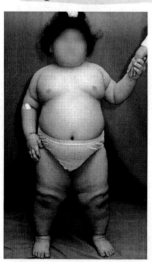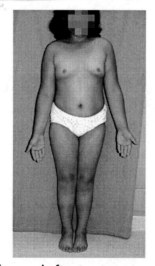

A leptin-deficient girl before and after treatment.

Obesity is linked to numerous factors. Scientists today are investigating possible treatments in three areas:

(1) Researchers at the Harvard Medical School have presented what they call a "**right brain hypothesis**" for obesity (Alonso-Alonso & Pascual-Leone, 2007). Their research shows that the **right prefrontal cortex** plays a critical role in the control of eating. They have shown that activity in the right hemisphere is diminished in obese people. This brain area may be involved in giving value to foods. In fact, research on decision-making supports such an idea. Perhaps obesity can be treated by increasing activation of the right prefrontal cortex.

(2) In many respects, obesity resembles **drug addictions**. Investigations of the brain's pleasure pathway that uses dopamine as a major neurotransmitter have found that both obese people and alcohol addicts have a reduced number of dopamine receptors (Wang et a., 2001). Perhaps the overuse of food or alcohol are an unconscious means of attaining greater stimulation of the pleasure pathway that is achieved by other people by ingesting smaller quantities. Obese people may eat more in order to stimulate dopamine activity in their pleasure pathways just as drug addicts do.

(3) Doctors in Pittsburgh have received FDA approval to use **deep brain stimulation** to treat obesity. In the procedure, a thin electrode is inserted into the patient's hypothalamus and a battery pack implanted in the chest sends electrical signals to the brain. Scientists at the University of Toronto were the first to use the procedure in 2006. The procedure is still experimental and only used in extreme cases of obesity that have not responded to other treatments (Halpern et al., 2008).

ℰating 𝒟isorders

Two categories of eating disorders are defined by psychiatrists, and they are commonly referred to as anorexia and bulimia. In **anorexia nervosa**, a person does not eat enough. The person refuses to maintain a normal body weight, has an intense fear of becoming fat, and seemingly has a disturbance in body image. For example, people with anorexia often claim to be fat when in fact they are very thin. Women with anorexia also experience **amenorrhea**, the absence of a menstrual cycle. European researchers found that 11% of anorexics, compared to 4.5% of controls, carried a certain form of a gene for an appetite hormone (Harvard Mental Health Letter, 2003).

In **bulimia nervosa**, a person **binges** (eats a large amount at one time) and then **purges** (removes the food from the stomach by self-induced vomiting or the use of laxatives). As in **anorexia**, the patient with **bulimia** has a disordered view of his or her body, and self-evaluation is unduly influenced by body shape and weight. Bulimic women are more likely to have suffered childhood sexual or physical abuse (Kent, 2000). Eating disorders are very serious, and can result in permanent biological problems and even death. Models, gymnasts, and dancers have reportedly died from anorexia, not only demonstrating the seriousness of this disorder, but also indicating the relationship of eating disorders to certain types of activities in which a thin body is highly valued.

Eating disorders are seen almost exclusively in adolescents and young adults, and occur about ten times more often in women than in men. This **gender difference** is believed to be due both to biological (hormonal) differences between the sexes, and to the emphasis in many cultures that the ideal woman's body should be very thin. Anorexia might be viewed as a weight phobia. People with eating disorders are often dissatisfied with their bodies, have **perfectionist** attitudes and behaviors, strive for high achievement, show black or white thinking, judge themselves harshly, have difficulty separating from their families and establishing individual identities, problems in interpersonal relationships, and substance abuse.

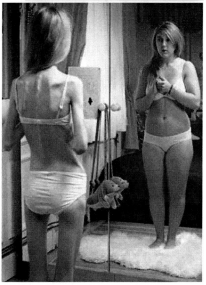

However, the desire to be thin is *not* seen in women everywhere in the world. In West Africa, for instance, women are encouraged to be overweight and often take fatty foods and substances that will increase their body size. Being obese is a sign of wealth and high status for those women. A Nigerian doctor said, "The world is a funny place. In America you are rich, you have everything, and the women want to become so thin as if they had nothing. Here in Africa, we have nothing, the women who buy these products have nothing, but they want to become fat as if they had everything." A group of teenage girls in Niger was asked what they thought was the ideal body shape and they unanimously picked an obese woman. This illustrates the effect of **cultural attitudes** on behavior and psychological disorders. Anorexia is unknown in many developing countries.

Culture alone is obviously not enough to cause an eating disorder. It appears that some people are more likely to develop this disorder than others, if exposed to certain social and cultural conditions. One study found that the brain transmitter serotonin, as well as other brain chemicals and estrogen, may be important for development of eating binges (Klump, 2007). Another study found that the brains of people with **bulimia** had a reduced ability of **serotonin** to bind to receptors in certain brain regions (Kaye et al, 2001). Many people with an eating disorder also suffer from depression. The brain chemical dopamine was also found to have increased activity in the brains of women with eating disorders. Both serotonin and dopamine are closely tied to mood, appetite, and impulse control.

Genetic risk appears to be a factor. A director of an eating disorder clinic concluded, "Many people do seem to have a kind of hereditary susceptibility, but that doesn't mean that they will develop an eating disorder. It may be that women who inherit this vulnerability have to be especially careful about dieting, because it could trigger eating disorders (Bailer, 2005).

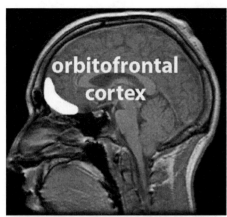

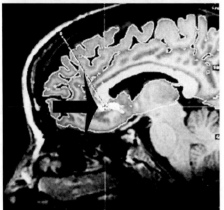

Top: medial orbitofrontal cortex.
Bottom: subgenual cingulate cortex.

Brain imaging studies have found some differences and some **abnormalities** in the brains of people with eating disorders. For example: Schafer et al. (2010) found differences in the frontal lobe in people with bulimia or binge eating disorder. The authors concluded that the data implied a crucial role of the **medial orbitofrontal cortex** in bulimia and binge eating, and speculated that the structural abnormality might be associated with dysfunctions in either reward processing or self-regulation. Vocks et al. (2010) found that women with anorexia nervosa had different brain activity, particularly in the amygdala, than did women without anorexia when looking at photographs of women's bodies. Miyake et al. (2010) also found amygdala activity when women with eating disorders processed negative words about body image.

Wagner et al. (2010) found that both women with anorexia and those with bulimia had brain activity that showed difficulty discriminating the emotional significance of a stimulus. Bruce et al. (2010) found that obese children had over-activation of the **pleasure pathway** in the limbic system, including the **nucleus accumbens**, when viewing pictures of food. This study suggests that the origins of neural dysfunction in obesity may begin early in life. Van Kuyck (2010) reviewed numerous brain imaging studies and concluded that many brain areas have been implicated in anorexia including the frontal, parietal, and temporal lobes, and the **subgenual cingulate cortex** (an area below the corpus callosum where the frontal lobe curls under and meets the limbic system, which has vast connections to the **hypothalamus** and is involved in governing appetite, sleep, and depression). This review of research shows the extremely large scope and complexity of **anorexia**. The authors suggest that there might be a neural circuit or pathway associated with this eating disorder. Wouldn't it be nice if we could find just one, single brain area for eating disorders? But, wait, there's even more…

Researchers at the National Institute of Mental Health found higher levels of neuropeptide Y and peptide YY in people with eating disorders, indicating dysfunction in the **hypothalamus**. Research has also found difficulties in the frontal and temporal lobes (Uher, 2005). The **frontal lobe** has circuits that help modulate or control limbic system functions and may be important in influencing eating behavior. Scientists have also found chemical similarities between people with eating disorders and those with **obsessive-compulsive disorder (OCD)** and **clinical depression**. These neurotransmitters, such as **serotonin**, were found to be decreased in patients who had recovered from anorexia.

And, as you might guess, abnormalities in the expression of chemicals in the POMC system have been found in anorexia (Ehrlich, 2010). **Brain-derived neurotrophic factor (BDNF)** is a protein that helps to support and to grow neurons. BDNF is found in many places in the nervous system, but particularly in the hippocampus and cerebral cortex. This chemical is involved in many disorders from **Alzheimer's disease** to **depression**. It also plays a role in feeding regulation and has also been found to be implicated in anorexia and bulimia (Mercader, 2010). Another protein that supports neurons is called **nerve growth factor (NGF)**, and it, too, has been suggested as a player in eating disorders (Chaldakov, 2009).

Eating disorders, like many other psychological disorders, often overlap with other syndromes. This is called **comorbidity** (co = together; morbid = illness). For example, as noted above, many people with an eating disorder also suffer from obsessive-compulsive disorder (OCD) and depression (Anderluh, 2003). In fact, eating disorders are often treated with antidepressant medicines. Perfectionist personality traits are risk factors for eating disorders, and mothers of patients with eating disorders had high levels of perfectionism (Woodside, 2002). Substance abuse, panic disorder, phobias, and other psychological disorders are common in women with eating disorders.

To some extent comorbidity occurs because mental disorders are subjective categories that define mental illnesses on the basis of symptoms. But symptoms often overlap. It is wise to think of people with mental illnesses as people with problems. It is not wise to think that mental illnesses are fixed, concrete conditions that are the same from person to person. In fact, the terminology we use often confuses this issue. We say that a person "*has*" anxiety, as if anxiety is a thing that people catch. When we say that a person has a mental illness, we simply mean that the person is reporting complaints about his or her emotions, behaviors, or cognition. Don't put mental illnesses into discrete categories. There are tremendous overlappings of symptoms.

Though difficult to treat, eating disorders do respond somewhat to behavior therapy, cognitive-behavioral therapy, antidepressant medications, and other therapies (Peterson, 1999). However, there is a relatively low rate of improvement with these problems, partially because only people with the most severe symptoms seek out help (Keel, 2002). Some new research has found that anti-seizure medicines can help binge eaters (McElroy, 2003). Also, a recent scientific comparison of non-medical treatment for **binge eating** found a success rate of better than 50% for therapist-led group cognitive-behavioral therapy compared to only 18% improvement for a self-help group (Peterson, 2009).

Another study found the success of cognitive-behavioral therapy maintained at above 50% after a period of more than a year for all kinds of eating disorders (Fairburn, 2009). A day treatment program for adolescents with anorexia showed good results (Goldstein, 2011) and even deep brain stimulation (implanting an electrode into the brain to deliver electrical stimulation) was successful for one woman who suffered both depression and eating disorder (Israel, 2010).

A treatment regimen called the **Maudsley method** (because it is based on a program at the Maudsley Hospital in London) has shown some promise. This program is for children and adolescents who have had anorexia for fewer than three years. In the first phase, parents and siblings learn strategies for coaching and encouraging patients to eat more. Second, family dynamics are identified that might get in the way of recovery and changes are implemented. Finally, patients and families work to improve relationships to help the patient become more independent. Though treatments for eating disorders do not have a high rate of efficacy, the Maudsley method is the most effective therapy today for patients for whom the disorder is not long lasting enough to become chronic.

Recent surveys have shown that **binge eating** is even more common than the two traditional eating disorders described above. About 2% of men and 4% of women engage in frequent binge eating. As already mentioned, obesity has become a national epidemic in the United States. About one out of three children are overweight. The problem is more serious among poor people since their budgets require them to buy the cheapest foods, which are the least nutritious and the most fattening. As with bulimia, binge eating involves instances of extreme overeating; but in this case, without the elimination or purging. Many binge eaters are normal weight because they find methods such as exercise or eating less between binges to keep their body weight down.

Willpower

From Oscar Wilde: "I can resist everything except temptation."

Many people wonder, when it comes to cravings and desires, why don't people just use their **willpower**? For example, in the familiar phrase: Just say no! Why don't people who are addicted to food, substances, or behaviors just say no? Say no to eating, say no to drugs, say no to gambling, and so on? Why don't people just use their willpower?

First, **willpower** is a brain process like any other psychological or cognitive ability or skill. Willpower does not come from nowhere. It comes from the brain. Some people are better at controlling their desires than are other people. Why? The same reasons people differ in all psychological processes – heredity, experiences, hormones, learning, situations, biological states, and so on. Willpower is like other psychological processes. It is controlled by the brain which is influenced by multiple factors both innate and experiential.

The first psychological studies of willpower were done by famous social psychologist **Walter Mischel** in the 1970s. At Stanford University, Mischel measured the ability of children to **delay gratification**. In the best known version of the experiments children were left alone in a room with a bell. They were told they if they rang the bell the experimenter would return and give them one marshmallow. However, if they could wait for the experimenter to come back, they would receive two marshmallows. This became known as the **marshmallow test**. Mischel found that some kids caved in early, while others were able to wait up to 20 minutes. How about you? Are you able to see long-term gains for behavior now? Or, do you give in to immediate temptation?

The children in Mischel's experiment were tracked into **adolescence**, and can you imagine? The 4-year-old children who were able to **delay gratification** were better adjusted and had higher test scores than the kids who caved to the immediate incentive. This finding led psychologists to think that maybe teaching self-control to children would have long-term benefits for them. But, how can we teach **willpower**?

Mischel provided one answer: He found that if he told the children to think of the marshmallow as a yummy treat, they then caved in more readily. However, if he told them to think of the marshmallow as a cloud or a snow ball, or some other "cold," abstract representation, then they were able to delay gratification longer. Also, if they thought of the **long-term outcome** as more desirable (or "hot"), that helped boost the willpower to delay gratification. So, it appears that willpower can be taught to some extent. Perhaps learning how to view temptations as cold abstractions and to think of long-term goals as yummy may help people who have dependencies.

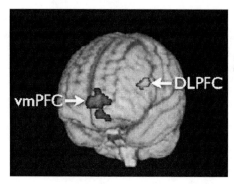

Now, just where do we find willpower in the brain? You might guess the frontal lobe, and you would be right. The **prefrontal cortex**, which is important for working memory (holding ideas and concepts in mind), is key to delaying gratification as an executive control center. Also, the **dorsolateral prefrontal cortex** is associated with inhibiting impulses, which is important for willpower. And, the **ventromedial prefrontal cortex** is a decision making brain region that takes information about the values of rewards and punishments in order to decide the best course of action.

People with damage to the ventromedial prefrontal cortex have difficulty seeing the long view and persist in short term behaviors that are rewarding without concern for possible future catastrophes. Some psychologists have suggested that **addictions** can be viewed as failures of areas of the prefrontal cortex to suppress the impulsive, short term desires that emanate from the lower brain areas such as the limbic system and particularly the **amygdala** (Bechara, 2005). Furthermore, research shows that these frontal brain areas can become **overloaded** and be less capable of exerting willpower (Baumeister, 2008). So, it seems our willpower can be depleted if it is over-worked! When we are cognitively overloaded, we are less able to delay gratification. So, helping addicts might mean keeping their brain control centers from being too busy.

Liking vs. Wanting

Now here's an idea that's terribly interesting and important, but not yet well-studied by scientists, and not even known or considered by most people! Here it is: Could you want something, but not like it? Maybe want a drug or food, but not like it? Or, the other way around: Could you like an object or substance, but not want it? Could 'wanting' and 'liking' be separate processes? If we "want" something, does that mean we necessarily "like" it?

You guessed it – there is now good evidence that the brain has different pathways for **wanting** and for **liking**. And, yes, these two pathways do overlap, but apparently the brain has evolved two somewhat dissociated systems for the wanting a substance and for the liking of a substance. Why didn't we all think of this? We all should have noticed this particularly in the 20th and 21st centuries when advertising and drug addictions have become so overbearing. Yes, ads can make us want things that give us no pleasure at all, and people can want a drug that gives them no satisfaction hedonically (sensual pleasure). *Liking* something is different from *wanting* something. Desire apparently has two components: a craving and a hedonic pleasure. You can want a substance or object that, in fact, does not provide you with pleasure. Motivation (wanting) is part of the pleasure pathway in the brain, but not the whole thing. We can be motivated to buy objects, ingest substances, or engage in behaviors that, in fact, do not give us pleasure.

The sensation of pleasure is relative. The taste of sugar, for example, although sugar has the same sensation it is deemed more pleasurable when we are hungry than when we are full. Although temperature is a steady physical factor, a hot bath feels much more pleasant when we are cold than on a hot day. Liking is a subjective, pleasant (hedonic) experience, feeling, or sensation that results from immediate receiving of a rewarding substance, such as a sweet taste. Wanting, on the other hand, is a motivational state, often accompanied by an incentive. Wanting is not a sensory pleasure, but a motivation, a craving.

Wanting and liking normally go together, and, apparently, the two pathways in the brain do overlap one another a great deal. However, wanting can be blocked while liking continues. Drugs that block dopamine receptors in the **mesolimbic (pleasure) pathway** reduce the wanting of a substance such as sugar or cocaine, or an activity, such as sex. But the sensual pleasure, or liking, of the substance or activity can still be present. Researchers typically measure liking in laboratory animals by detecting certain facial expressions that are innately connected to pleasurable responses (lip-licking reflexes that are similar in rats, monkeys, apes, and human infants when tasting sugar). Rats that are

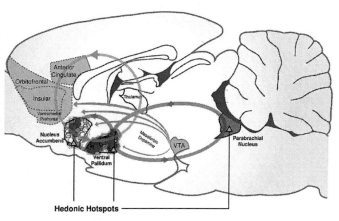

Hedonic Hotspots

electrically stimulated in the lateral hypothalamus show increased eating behavior, but they do not show facial expressions of pleasure; on the contrary, the facial expressions are sometimes of aversion or dislike.

Similarly, blocking the dopamine receptors in the pleasure pathway in humans does not reduce the subjective ratings of pleasure that people give to substances such as amphetamines; the 'wanting' may be blocked, but not the 'liking.' People who smoke cigarettes may get no pleasure at all from smoking, yet they continue to *want* to smoke. Sometimes a brain likes the rewards that it wants, but sometimes it just wants them without the liking component (Berridge, 2009). Also, it was found that **morphine addicts** would push a button to deliver a dose of the drug that was too small to have any pleasurable effect; yet, the brain seemed to want it. Wanting without liking. That's right: It seems that the brain can produce a *want* without a *like*!

Researchers Berridge & Robinson (2009) found that wanting and liking correspond to separate, but overlapping brain pathways. **Liking** begins in the **brainstem**. Even infants born with no cerebral cortex, limbic system, or amygdala (**anencephalic infants**, who cannot develop a forebrain prenatally because of a genetic mutation) still show characteristic facial expressions for sweet and for bitter substances. Areas of the brainstem connect to other brain regions extending into the limbic system. The liking pathway is also known as the **mesolimbic pathway** or **pleasure pathway** and has so-called **hotspots** including the **nucleus accumbens** and the **ventral pallidum** (near, and just in front of the lateral hypothalamus). For instance, the researchers reported that they found neural building blocks of both desire and dread in the nucleus accumbens.

The researchers also reported that the liking (pleasure) pathway was more dependent on **opioid** (similar to opium or heroin) neurotransmitter substances or **endocannabinoids** (similar to cannabis, the active substance in marijuana) in the brain. Neurons in the **ventral pallidum** fire faster when rats eat a sweet, sugary substance and also fire faster if the rat has been deprived of salt and then eats a salty substance. But, these neurons do not fire faster when a rat is eating salt if the body is not salt deprived. So, this brain area in the **pleasure pathway** is responding to intake based on the state of the body's needs. When cells in the ventral pallidum are destroyed, the sense of **liking** is abolished and replaced by dislike. In humans, the sight of disgusting, rotting food stimulates cells in the front part of the ventral pallidum, while the back portion seems to respond to the "liking" of a taste.

The **wanting pathway**, on the other hand, passes through some of the same brain areas as the pleasure pathway, but diverges into the **hypothalamus**. The wanting pathway apparently is more likely to use **dopamine** as a transmitter substance. Mice that have an overactive dopamine system show increased wanting behavior but do not show expressions of increased liking. Brain manipulations to make animals want more food often result in the animals liking food less. Researcher Berridge concluded that it is easier to activate the wanting pathway. To generate increasing pleasure – to make you like something more and more – it is necessary to activate different **opioid** brain areas at the same time.

This new conception – dividing "wanting" and "liking" into two overlapping systems – has been used by theorists to propose new ways to think about obesity and eating disorders (Berridge, 2009; Zheng, 2007; Finlayson, 2007). Scientists are realizing that if wanting and liking are two different brain systems, then a person could be eating for calories (want), or could be eating for the taste (like). That is, there could be two different motivations for obesity or eating disorders. Experts are now considering different options in the treatment of motivational problems based on this new idea. You may not like it, but then again, you might just want it!

"When you move in right up close to me, That's when I get the chills all over me,
Quivers down my backbone, I get the shakes in my thigh bone,
Shivers in my knee bone, Shakin' all over."
– Shaking All Over by The Guess Who

"Come on baby light my fire, Try to set the night on fire."
– Light My Fire by The Doors

David Reimer

"I'm pickin' up good vibrations, She's giving me excitations."
– Good Vibrations by The Beach Boys

"I can't get no satisfaction, Cause I try and I try and I try and I try,
I can't get no, I can't get no, I can't get no satisfaction, no satisfaction."
– Satisfaction by The Rolling Stones

Chapter 3

Sex

*C*onsider the astonishing case of **David Reimer**: In 1965 identical twins Bruce and Brian were born in Winnipeg, Canada. At 8 months of age, because of a problem with urinating, the baby boys were presented for circumcision. But, something went terribly wrong. The urologist was using a cauterizing needle and had set the voltage too high. Little baby Bruce's penis was destroyed. The distraught and confused parents consulted with doctors and experts for months about what to do with a son whose genitals were deformed. At that time, the leading ideas about **gender identification** argued that an individual's sexual identity and behaviors were not determined by genetics, but rather came about through socialization, through experiences in the family and in the culture. Psychologist **John Money** at Johns Hopkins University in Baltimore was the top authority in this area and he advised that the best course for the parents was to raise Bruce as a girl. And, so they did.

Bruce became Brenda and began childhood raised and treated as a girl. His testes were removed and he received estrogen treatment for breast development, as well as additional surgery on his genitals. Brenda's mother said that as a young girl Brenda was adjusting perfectly fine to her new gender. But, in fact she was not. John Money reported that everything was fine, that Brenda was a normal young girl; apparently Brenda's parents were lying or exaggerating about her gender development. In truth, Brenda was a complete tomboy with many male behaviors and was even called "caveman" by her schoolmates. She was unhappy with her gender and by early adolescence Brenda decided she was a boy. She was then told by her father what she'd already guessed: She was a genetic male. Soon after, Brenda changed her name to David and chose to have surgery to remove her breasts, reconstruct a penis, and live her life as a man. Thus began the life of David Reimer.

At age 25 David Reimer married and adopted his wife's three children. Shortly after, sex expert **Milton Diamond** persuaded David to tell the world about his experience so that doctors and scientists could make better decisions in such cases in the future (Diamond & Sigmundson, 1997). David's story was reported in *Rolling Stone* magazine and in the book, *As Nature Made Him: The Boy Who Was Raised as a Girl* (Colapinto, 2001). David's story raised public consciousness about this issue, and persuaded scientists to reconsider the determination of gender identity.

Top: John Money.
Bottom: Milton Diamond.

While his gender identification was at that time much improved, David Reimer still suffered from deep anger and depression, and also had a family with severe psychological troubles. His mother attempted suicide, his father was an alcoholic, and his twin brother, Brian, suffering from schizophrenia, died from an apparent suicide, an overdose of antidepressants, in 2002. On top of all that, David was unemployed and unhappy with the life he'd been dealt. His wife suffered from the stress, too, and one day in 2004 she told David that she wanted a separation; she was going to leave him. David went into an uncontrollable rage, walked out on his wife and refused to tell her his whereabouts, and shortly afterward killed himself with a shotgun. David Reimer's case aroused great curiosity and debate, as you might imagine, and it heightened the now widely accepted realization that genetics are important contributors to our gender identities.

Sex Determination

From actress Shirley MacLaine: "Sex is hardly ever just about sex." Another clever saying: "Sex is hereditary. If your parents never had it, chances are you won't either."

Sex is the term we use to refer to the characteristics by which we divide individuals into categories called male and female. To most, this seems like a perfectly reasonable and clear dichotomy. We assume the world is divided into two groups, men and women, and that these are distinct, well-defined categories. However, in many cases this dichotomy is not clear cut at all. There are many varied definitions of male and female, many criteria by which to classify a person as a man or a woman. Such criteria include genetics, hormones, physical features, clothes and presentation, parental assignment at birth, internal organs, external genitals, behaviors, and self-identity. These various criteria are not always congruent with each other in a particular individual. There are many people who do not neatly fit into the categories of male and female; the issue is much more complicated than most people assume.

Sex determination begins with genetics. At conception, a woman's egg (**ovum**) is fertilized by a man's **sperm cell** (about 20 times smaller than the egg). The two **gametes** (egg and sperm) each carry genetic material,

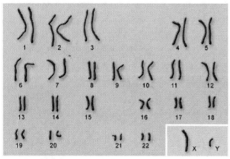

autosomes   sex chromosomes

chromosomes, in the form of long strands of deoxyribonucleic acid (**DNA**) in the nucleus of each cell. The sperm cell uses its tail to swim to the ovum, usually in a fallopian tube, where fertilization takes place. The sperm cell penetrates the egg, and the membrane of the egg then changes so as not to allow any other sperm cells to enter. The chromosomes from the sperm and egg then join together in the nucleus of the fertilized ovum. The normal number of chromosomes for humans is 46. In the parents, half of these are selected into the egg and half into the sperm by a process called **meiosis**. Thus, the normal human egg and normal human sperm cell each carry 23 chromosomes. The resulting **zygote**, the union of ovum and sperm, has 46, and this total set of chromosomes is called a **karyotype**.

Scientists classify chromosomes into pairs, one from mom and one from dad, and then number the pairs by their size. Chromosome pair #1 is the largest, #2 is the next largest, and so on. This numbering system is used for 22 pairs of chromosomes, which are called **autosomes**. But, one pair of chromosomes is set aside for special consideration because these chromosomes carry the chemical recipes for genetic sex determination. That is, these **sex chromosomes**, as they are known, carry the genes for determining the characteristics that distinguish male from female. The truth about genetic sex determination is quite amazing, and quite different from early theories. Ancient Greek philosopher Aristotle, for instance, taught that warm sperm made males, while cold sperm led to females. What actually happens is a bit more complicated.

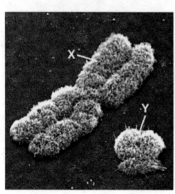

A woman has two sex chromosomes that are known as **X chromosomes**, one from each parent in ovum and sperm. The X chromosome is rather large as chromosomes go. A normal woman is designated as (46, XX). A man gets one X chromosome from his mother, in the egg, but also has a smaller chromosome called a **Y chromosome**, which came in the sperm cell from his father. So a normal man is designated (46, XY). Every normal egg produced by a woman will have 23 chromosomes, one of which is an X chromosome (either the one she got from her mother or the one from her father). Similarly, every normal sperm cell will carry 23 chromosomes: 22 autosomes and one sex chromosome. But the sex chromosome carried in the sperm cell can be either an X or a Y, since men have one of each. Men got their X chromosome from their mother and their Y chromosome from their father. Therefore, an ovum (egg from the mother) with an X chromosome will be fertilized by a sperm cell carrying either an X chromosome or a Y chromosome.

So, the offspring can be either XX (the recipe for female) or XY (the recipe for male). But, interestingly, many variations occur in this scenario.

Chromosome Abnormalities

As described above, the normal human karyotype is 23 pairs of chromosomes: One chromosome from each pair comes from mom, and one from each pair comes from dad. However, some people have a different number of chromosomes, not 46. These conditions are known as **chromosome abnormalities** and arise from errors in the process of meiosis, the process by which chromosomes are selected into the sperm and ovum, or from errors in cell division during embryonic **mitosis**, the process by which cells copy themselves. Many variations of such errors occur, and the vast majority of chromosome abnormalities compromise the development of the embryo and it will not be viable, it will not develop. Some fetuses with chromosome abnormalities, however, do survive. The most common is **Down syndrome** (trisomy 21), a total of 47 chromosomes. Down syndrome occurs in both boys and girls, results in a typical physical appearance, and involves intellectual disability.

A **supermale** (47, XYY) is a male who has received an extra Y chromosome, typically as a result of an error in the process of meiosis. This situation is not affected by parental age, as Down syndrome is. Some experts do not want to call supermale a syndrome since the XYY male is normal in phenotype. About 1 in 1000 male births are XYY, and the vast majority are physically normal and unaware of their genotype. However, there are a number of traits that are correlated with XYY. Supermales, for instance, are taller by about 3 inches than they would normally have been, due to genes on the Y chromosome. Some studies show higher rates of learning disabilities, lower IQ scores, acne, and developmental delays among supermales, but these findings are not robust and many XYY individuals do not show any differences from 46, XY males (Graham, 2007).

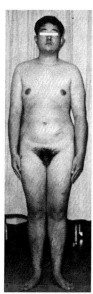

Karyotype From a Male With 47,XYY

Superfemale syndrome (47, XXX) also can arise from an error in meiosis. This condition is sometimes referred to a triple X syndrome or trisomy X, and similar conditions include XXXX and XXXXX syndromes. Since no Y chromosome is present, such individuals are always females. Typically, there are no unusual physical features or medical problems because each cell only has one active X chromosome. In the majority of cases these women do not appear any differently than XX females, though they may be a bit taller, have earlier onset of menstruation, and in some rare cases have distinctive facial features and skeletal problems (Linden, 2002).

Turner syndrome (45, X0), or **monosomy X**, is a condition in which a female inherits only one sex chromosome, an X. Such females have characteristic physical and cognitive traits, such as being short with a broad chest, a low hairline, low set ears, a webbed neck, non-functional ovaries, difficulty with mathematics and visual-spatial tasks, and a number of health problems such as diabetes, heart disease, and hypothyroidism. Hormone therapies are often provided to help manage symptoms (Donaldson, 2006). About 99% of Turner syndrome fetuses are spontaneously terminated in the first trimester. This condition occurs in about 1 in 2000 live female births.

The most common, and perhaps the most interesting sex chromosome abnormality, is **Klinefelter syndrome** (47, XXY). Individuals with this condition have the genetic recipes for both male and female. In fact, this person will have some phenotypic features of both sexes, and can present a sexual identity as either, though the vast majority of cases present as male. Affected individuals nearly always have fertility problems, small penises, and small breast development. There are many variations in physical, health, behavioral, and cognitive features in Klinefelter as there are with all the chromosome abnormalities, and hence there are no universal markers in all affected individuals. Often there is less body hair and muscle development, as well as delayed language ability, but there are so many variations that generalizations are quite misleading. Also, all the chromosome abnormalities involve a variation known as a **mosaic** in which a person has a different number of chromosomes in different cells of the body due to an error in cell division shortly after conception. In a mosaic, for example, some body cells can have 46 chromosomes while other cells have 47.

Left: Klinefelter syndrome.
Right: Turner syndrome.

Sex Differentiation

During development of the fetus, the normal, default anatomical development is female body organs. Everyone would be female if nothing changed that path of development. However, genes on the Y chromosome (if one is present in the embryo) can trigger the anatomical development of male physical features. For the first six weeks of prenatal development, the XX and XY embryos appear identical. But then **sexual differentiation**

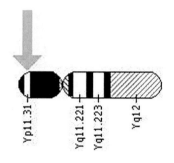

of the organs begins in the fetus. If two X chromosomes are present, then ovaries and related female body parts will emerge. However, a different scenario unfolds if there is a Y chromosome present. There is a gene on the Y chromosome known as the **SRY gene** (sex-determining region Y) that produces SRY protein, a transcription factor that unleashes a cascade of biological events that modify the development of the reproductive body parts. Male organs, **testes**, that will later produce sperm, will develop as a consequence of SRY. The testes then release hormones, mainly **testosterone**, that continues the process of **masculinization** of the fetus.

An interesting condition arises if there is a **mutation** in the **SRY gene**. Such an error in the DNA sometimes prevents the SRY gene from producing testes. Thus, **masculinization** is prevented, and the fetus develops female genitalia. This condition is one variation of a group of similar abnormalities called **Swyer syndrome**. Such individuals are XY, that is, they have the recipe for male, but since the recipe was not manifested, they have female body parts. At birth they appear to be perfectly normal females. At puberty, however, they will require hormone treatments for development of the breasts and secondary sex characteristics since their ovaries will not have matured properly.

Swyer syndrome.

The standard view of sexual differentiation is that **testosterone** from the testes directly **masculinizes** the fetal brain. However, there is evidence that differences between the sexes may be stimulated by genes even before the gonadal hormones are present (Dewing, 2003). Also, there are instances of XX males who do not have the **SRY gene**. There must be one or more genes other than SRY that contribute to the sexual differentiation. Many candidate genes have been identified that may contribute to male/female differences. For example, the **DAX1 gene** on the X chromosome affects early development and (in a mutated form) may inhibit the SRY gene. Also, a gene known as **Sox9** can cause a bone disorder that occurs in many sex-reversed males. Researchers DiNapoli and Capel (2008) wrote, "Recent work has demonstrated that the fate of the gonad is actively contested by both male-promoting and female-promoting signals. Sox9 and Fgf9 push gonads towards testis differentiation. These two genes are opposed by Wnt4, and possibly RSPO1, which push gonads toward ovary differentiation." So, sex differentiation is a complicated process involving hormones and numberous genes.

Sex is difficult to define since there are so many variables that can alter the typical course of development. Regardless of the difficulty, society and individuals, of course, persist in attempts at categorizing people as male or female using one criterion or another. The International Olympics Committee (IOC), for example, had attempted in the past to classify athletes as male or female using the presence of a Y chromosome for male, and then later using the SRY gene to define male. Neither of these criteria is perfect, and both have been abandoned since there are multiple alterations that produce valid exceptions. To deal with issues of what the IOC calls "disorders of sex development" medical commission chairman Arne Ljungqvist said, "There cannot be a general rule; the rule needs to allow for a case-by-case evaluation. Each case is unique. They are not many. They are all individual."

Traits vs. Recipes

As you can see from the above example of Swyer syndrome, a person can carry a Y chromosome but still develop relatively normal female body parts. The physical characteristics of a person are known as the **phenotype**. But, the genetic recipe the person carries is called the **genotype**. Swyer syndrome, recessive genes, and many other conditions are good examples that we do not necessarily develop the traits for which we carry the recipes. Mutations and other events also can result in incongruence between genotype and phenotype.

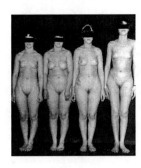  

AIS: All these women are XY, but their body cells are insensitive to the androgen hormone.

Middle: Model Christie. Right: Jazz Singer Eden Atwood.

Take the case of **androgen-insensitivity syndrome (AIS)**: In AIS, a person carries the Y chromosome, but has a disorder in which some or all of the cells of the body are insensitive to male hormones. This condition is due to a genetic lack of androgen receptors. AIS is divided into three cases labeled complete (C), partial (P), or mild (M). In CAIS, the person has a female phenotype, but a male genotype (as in the photos above).

This person is female in physical appearance but carries the male **chromosomal** pattern. At birth, the baby appears female, has all the external female body parts in working order, but carries the **XY** genotype. Because of the presence of a Y chromosome, ovaries will not develop due to the presence of the **SRY gene**. Therefore, although the CAIS individual appears female in external features and has normal female response to sexual activity, she will not be able to naturally reproduce since she does not have ovaries. The **CAIS** individual is female in nearly every way; only the presence of the **Y chromosome** would give this person a label of male. In partial and mild cases of AIS, however, the phenotype can be male or female, or a bit of both. A person with CAIS not only appears female, but typically is taller than average, has very clear complexion, long slender legs, well-developed breasts, and narrow hips. As you might guess, it has not been unusual for such XY women to find careers as fashion models (Diamond, J., 1992).

Another interesting example is **congenital adrenal hyperplasia (CAH)**. This is an autosomal recessive condition that interferes with adrenal gland functioning. In a small number of these cases the individual can develop an **intersex** (atypical or ambiguous male and female physical characteristics) condition. In such cases, a genotypical female (XX) can experience an overabundance of male hormones resulting in the development of male genitalia. The result is a female who has a small penis. The newborn baby may appear male, though the genotype is female. This condition can be treated with hormones prenatally, if it is recognized during the pregnancy.

The term **hermaphrodite** has been used to refer to a person or animal that has the sexual characteristics of both male and female. This is not a totally accurate description of any humans since even the very rare instances in which a person has body tissue of both ovaries and testes, such people do not function as both male and female, as do some lower animals. The term **pseudohermaphrodite** is often used for people whose ovaries or testes are consistent with their chromosomes, but they have sexual characteristics different from what is expected. These terms, however, do not fit all conditions (CAIS is one) and have been challenged, as has the term intersex, which was introduced in 1923. Some medical groups are now using the term "disorders of sex development" instead.

So, we see in many cases male and female are perhaps not as clear cut as many assume, and that the development of sexual characteristics is dependent on a wide range of factors. The chemicals of the endocrine system, the hormones, are also important players in this story.

Ƀormones

Androgens, discovered in 1936, are a class of hormones that stimulate or control the development of male characteristics. The word hormone, in fact, means "to stimulate or excite." **Testosterone** is the best known and primary type of androgen. In the male fetus, testosterone triggers the development of the physical sex organs (testes) and increases muscle mass. Adult brains also respond to testosterone, which influences **libido** (the sex drive), aggression, and visual-spatial cognitive processes, while decreasing verbal ability. In women, testosterone has also been linked to libido.

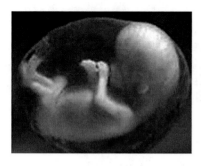

Prenatal testosterone levels affect social and emotional behaviors, too. Scores on a test of **empathy** were lower on average in children who had been exposed to higher levels of testosterone prenatally (Chapman, 2006). Level of prenatal testosterone is also correlated with **facial width**. Men with wider faces show more **aggression** (Weston, 2007). And, research has found that men with wider faces were more likely to exploit the trust of others, and that others were less likely to trust men with wider faces (Stirrat & Perrett, 2010).

Estrogen is commonly referred to as the female hormone because of its role in promoting the development of female secondary sexual characteristics such as the breasts and in regulation of the menstrual cycle. However, estrogen is also present in males and plays a number of roles including assisting in the maturation of sperm. The testes and the ovaries both produce androgens and estrogens, though in different amounts. Estrogen has also been found to influence moods; for instance, women with low or fluctuating levels of estrogen experience depression and sometimes obsessive-compulsive disorder.

A type of estrogen called **estradiol** is important for **masculinizing** the male fetus and plays a role in sexual differentiation of the brain both prenatally and later in life. In males, estradiol is a metabolic product of testosterone and in that role contributes to male sex differentiation. But estradiol is a female hormone, so it is involved in the development of female secondary sex characteristics and supporting the reproductive organs.

Males and females differ in **testosterone** concentrations early in **prenatal** development. These hormonal differences appear to influence numerous traits and behaviors including motor, cognitive, visual, and personality characteristics. A prominent researcher recently summarized the research findings: "Male and female fetuses differ in testosterone concentrations beginning as early as week 8 of gestation. This early hormone difference exerts permanent influences on brain development and behavior. Research has shown that hormones are particularly important for the development of sex-typical childhood behaviors, including toy choices, which until recently were thought to result solely from socio-cultural influences. **Prenatal testosterone** exposure also appears to influence **sexual orientation** and **gender identity**, as well as some, but not all, sex-related cognitive, motor and personality characteristics. Neural mechanisms responsible for these hormone-induced behavioral outcomes are beginning to be identified, and current evidence suggests involvement of the hypothalamus and amygdala, as well as interhemispheric connectivity, and cortical areas involved in visual processing" (Hines, 2010).

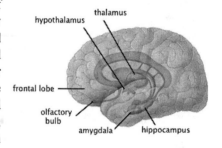

As mentioned above, testosterone is significantly involved in masculinizing the fetus, a consequence of biological actions triggered by the **SRY gene** on the Y chromosome. In adults, **testosterone** also been shown to increase **libido** (sex drive) in both males and females. Women, for example, have higher levels of both testosterone and estrogen in the middle of their menstrual cycle when they are ovulating, and are more likely to initiate sexual contact at that time. However, testosterone levels in both men and women also increase after sexual activity. After menopause, women's levels of testosterone and estrogen decrease, as does their sexual activity. Castration, removal of the testes in males or the ovaries in females, reduces sexual activity and interest, and also reduces aggression in men. The specific relationship between hormones and sexual activity, however, is tremendously variable from one case to another. Though higher levels of **testosterone** increase libido in an individual, it is also true that different people can have similar amounts of sexual activity though they have large differences between them in testosterone levels. Sexual activity depends on a number of factors including learning, previous experiences, and situations, not just on hormones.

It is difficult to study the effects of **hormones** in a tightly controlled manner in humans, so research on lower animals is more common. Rats, for example, have sex many times a day and are not embarrassed to perform in front of scientists. When female rats are given **testosterone**, they are more likely to mimic male sexual behavior and mount other females. If a male rat is **castrated** or given a chemical that blocks the action of **androgens**, the male will present himself sexually to other males. Testosterone is important for masculinizing the brain and behavior, but the final step requires the estrogen hormone estradiol.

The process of **bonding** in the mating of male and female is also influenced by **hormones**. Bonding has been studied primarily in lower animals since it is easier and considered more ethical to manipulate variables in them rather than in human subjects. For example, mate bonding in prairie voles, a species that is **monogamous**, has been studied recently (Young & Wang, 2004). During vole's mating, **dopamine** is released in the **reward pathway** of the brain. If dopamine is blocked by a chemical, then mate preference will not develop in the voles.

Sexual mating also releases two hormones that are chemically similar, **oxytocin** and **vasopressin**, both found to be important for mate bonding. Oxytocin has been found to more effective for females, and vasopressin for males. **Oxytocin** increases in humans during sexual activity, and has been found to be influential in recognizing faces (Ferguson, 2000), which, of course, is an important component for **bonding**. In one study, men who used an oxytocin nasal spray were superior at recognizing women's faces whom they had seen previously (Rimmele, 2009). **Trust** also increases with oxytocin exposure (Kosfeld, 2005). If you want someone to trust you, give them a spray of oxytocin in the nose!

Because of all these interesting research findings, **oxytocin** has been called the "love hormone," "bonding hormone," or "trust hormone." A recent study (Bartz et al., 2010) had men take either oxytocin or a placebo intranasally and then watch a video of people talking about emotional events. While watching the video the men rated on a scale how positive or negative they thought the person in the video was feeling. The results showed that **oxytocin** did improve the **empathic** accuracy of the men, but only for men who were less socially proficient. The authors suggested that the findings show that oxytocin may not be a universal pro-social enhancer, but helps only some people be better in social situations.

Perhaps even more important is a **gene** that is responsible for a **vasopressin receptor** (Pitkow, 2001). Males with two copies of a particular version of this gene were found to be twice as likely to experience a marital crisis (Walum, 2008). Also, young adults with distress in their pair-bonds had elevated levels of oxytocin (Taylor, 2010). Consistent differences have been found in the distribution of **vasopressin** receptors and the axons of neurons containing vasopressin between monogamous species and promiscuous species, even when the species are closely related. And finally, vasopressin also appears to make males more aggressive toward other males (Young, 2009). These findings and many similar results indicate quite clearly that oxytocin and vasopressin are important ingredients that contribute to the **social pairing** of males and females, and probably to monogamy.

Our **evolutionary** history, as one would imagine, had a significant shaping influence on sexual desire and behavior and affects us through genes and hormones. For example, women who are in the middle of their menstrual cycles (when they are most fertile) show a preference for masculine faces, and they also make fewer and shorter phone calls to their fathers at that time, but show no change in contact with female relatives (Lieberman, Pillsworth, & Haselton, 2010). These instinctual behaviors increase the likelihood of mating and having a healthy offspring, and decrease the chances of inbreeding.

Pheromones

Karl von Frisch (1886-1982), an Austrian **ethologist**, discovered that a chemical released by a certain species of fish when under attack was detected by other members of that species and warned them of danger. Frisch called the chemical "scary stuff." In his ground-breaking research on honey bees, Frisch noted that odors released by a Queen bee maintained the social order of the bee hive (von Frisch, 1953). These are good examples of odors affecting behavior. Lower animals show a robust response to air-borne chemicals, which are known as **pheromones**. The term was introduced in 1959 and means "to transport hormones" or "to bring excitement." Pheromones are secreted chemicals released from one animal to others, such as indicating a food trail, that when received tend to stimulate certain behaviors.

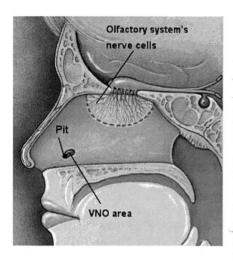

There are different types of pheromones. *Sex pheromones* are released by animals to signal availability for breeding or to indicate a particular phenotype. Pheromones are detected biologically by a cluster of receptors in the nose called the **vomeronasal organ** (VNO). This brain area is proportionately a large part of the brain in lower animals but quite small in human brains. Some scientists speculate that the genes that regulate this brain area in humans are mostly non-functional because color vision took over much of the role of sexual signaling in our evolutionary history. In lower animals, the VNO sends signals to the hypothalamus and the amygdala, key components of the limbic system in the lower brain. Some scientists question whether these connections are active in the human brain. People do have a VNO and a small pit in the nasal cavity that accesses it, though the connections to the brain are probably not active. However, pheromones can still influence humans since there are receptors in the human olfactory system (smell) that are similar to those in lower animals that elicit such a response (Brechbuhl, 2008).

While the human response to sex pheromones is nowhere near that of lower animals, there is some evidence that odors do play a role in human sexual response. For example, both men and women reported increased sexual activity when wearing cologne or perfume that contained underarm odors (McCoy & Pitino, 2002). Also, men rated the odor of women's T-shirts as more attractive if the women were in the middle of their menstrual cycles (Kuukasjarvi, 2004). This was not true if the women were taking birth control pills, which suppress ovulation. Men's testosterone levels increased after being exposed to the scent of an ovulating woman (Miller & Maner, 2010). Women rated the odor of men's T-shirts as more attractive if the men were different from the women in certain genes that contribute to the immune system (Wedekind, 1995). This reaction probably evolved in order to decrease inbreeding and increase variability in the species.

Interestingly, research has shown that women not only smell differently during ovulation but they also act differently, and men seem to notice. For instance, women dress more attractively during ovulation, are more attracted to men other than their partners, and their voices and scents are more attractive to men. It was even found that lap dancers made more money in tips when they were ovulating (Haselton & Gildersleeve, 2011). Also, men react with more vigilance and jealousy when their female partner is ovulating. And, finally, one study found that women who were ovulating were better at predicting which men were gay (Rule et al., 2011). Hormones certainly are interesting!

Sexual Behavior

Woody Allen: "Sex is the most fun you can have without laughing." Ellyn Mustard: "Except for 75% of the women, everyone in the whole world wants to have sex."

Sexology is the systematic study of human sexuality. It encompasses all aspects of sexuality, normal and pathological. This, as you are likely aware, is a very modern field of study. Most people today are a bit shy or embarrassed by scientific research or discussion of sexual behavior. This shyness was even much more present in the past, even among scientists. For instance, in the 1940s, biologist **Alfred Kinsey** (1894-1956) remarked

Pioneer sex researcher
Alfred Kinsey.

that science knew more about the sexual behavior of bees than the sexual behavior of humans. Kinsey, however, was not so shy, and he decided to begin research to correct that inadequacy. He and his team interviewed thousands of people about their sex lives. The books that reported the results of Kinsey's interviews were immediate best sellers. So, the shyness and embarrassment about sex that people demonstrated apparently was not an indication of a lack of interest in sex. In 1947, Kinsey founded the Institute for Sex Research at Indiana University, now called the Kinsey Institute for Research in Sex, Gender and Reproduction.

Earlier research and writing about sexuality was often full of errors, opinions, and wild conjectures. The first influential book about sexual disorders, *Psychopathia Sexualis* (1886), consisted of a series of case histories written by psychiatrist **Richard von Krafft-Ebing** (1840-1902). While this text appeared to take an objective look at sexual behavior, including the introduction of terminology, it also advanced some incorrect ideas based more on morality and opinion than on medical or scientific facts. Krafft-Ebing wrote, for instance, that nocturnal emissions (ejaculations of sperm during sleep) were abnormal disorders that required treatment. A typical treatment required a man to wear a penis ring during sleep that consisted of a metal ring with razors or spikes on the inside; while wearing such a ring, an erection would be prevented by the severe pain that resulted. What early researchers did not know is that erections are a normal and natural part of **REM sleep** as the body's autonomic nervous system is activated, quite apart from whatever the man is dreaming about.

Krafft-Ebing's book was influential and was the first to introduce certain terminology used even today, such as sadism, masochism, pedophilia, heterosexual, and homosexual (for which the book elaborated a biological cause), and it also proposed a genetic cause for **transsexualism**. At about the same time as Krafft-Ebbing's book, sexologist **Havelock Ellis** (1859-1939) wrote the first medical textbook on homosexuality (1897). While this book took an objective, scientific look at the subject of being gay, the general public was not so neutral about the topic – a bookstore owner was arrested merely for offering Ellis's book for sale!

Kinsey's interviews were important in giving sexology at least a start at more empirical accuracy. The books published by Kinsey in the late 1940s and early 1950s reported sexual behavior that not only fascinated the public, but in many cases caused genuine surprise. Apparently couples were engaging in sexual behaviors that were not talked about (oral sex, for example, was more common than couples openly admitted). Kinsey's reports were also controversial, for a number of reasons, but largely because he participated in sexual encounters with his co-workers and interviewees. Kinsey said he did this for objectivity and to gain the trust of his subjects. The manner in which he collected information about adult sex with children has also been questioned.

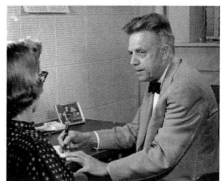

Kinsey interviewing a subject.

Kinsey reported his results primarily in two books: *Sexual Behavior in the Human Male* (1948) and *Sexual Behavior in the Human Female* (1953). The general public was immediately interested in the publications, though they were controversial. Sex books sell. An anonymous quote says, "Dirty books are seldom dusty." However, some people were outraged by the mere fact that sex was being openly talked about, and others were shocked by the fact that the findings challenged wide-spread public beliefs about sexual behavior. Like Havelock Ellis before him, Kinsey disapproved of using the terms heterosexual and homosexual, and did not believe a clear dichotomy was warranted. Kinsey wrote, "Males do not represent two discrete populations, heterosexual and homosexual. The world is not to be divided into sheep and goats. It is a fundamental of taxonomy that nature rarely deals with discrete categories." He reported that 37% of males had at least one homosexual experience. Too, Kinsey estimated that 50% of males and 26% of females who were married or living together had extramarital affairs. Also, according to his interviews, 22% of males and 12% of females had an erotic reaction to a sadomasochistic story. Though oral sex was illegal in many places in the United States, Kinsey reported that it was a common sexual behavior among married couples.

Easily one of the most frequent questions the public asks sexologists is how often couples have sex. There is an old joke about **sexual frequency** that goes like this: *For couples in their 20s and 30s, sexual frequency is **tri-weekly**. For couples in their 40s and 50s, sexual frequency is **try weekly**. And, for couples in their 60s and 70s, sexual frequency is **try weakly**.* So, the answer when *pronounced* is always the same!

Well, is the joke correct? According to current statistics from the Kinsey Institute, the average sexual frequency for people in their 20s is twice a week plus a fraction. For couples in their 30s, the average is a bit more than one and a half times per week. And, for couples in their 40s, the average is about one and a third times per week. Those are averages; the range is extreme, from zero on up (by the way, about 1% of people are asexual; they do not have sex). Sexual frequency does decline with age, but older people still maintain sex lives in almost all cases. Women past menopause (average age 51) do report a decline in sexual interest and in frequency of sexual intercourse. By the way, these present day numbers are very similar to those reported by Kinsey some sixty years ago. Comedian George Burns said, "Sex at age ninety is like trying to shoot pool with a rope."

Sexual Response

Mae West: "Sex is an emotion in motion." Robin Williams: "See, the problem is that God gives men a brain and a penis, and only enough blood to run one at a time."

While Kinsey's research was daring, it was, after all, just interviews. Even more daring was the idea of studying and observing sex in the laboratory. Not very long ago there were no credible scientists willing to pursue such research because of its delicate nature, their fear that it would damage their reputations, and the inability to find funding for such research. However, of course, the barrier was eventually broken and sex did enter the scientific laboratory. William Masters and Virginia Johnson were the pioneers in this arena. Though their research was careful and accurate, and certainly offered new information, still they had difficulty finding journals willing to publish it, and were often not taken seriously.

Masters and Johnson observed couples having sex in a laboratory setting while physiological recordings were taken. While their research was extensive, including the development of a number of therapies to treat sexual dysfunctions, their primary finding is known as the **human sexual response cycle**. By recording physiological measurements, Masters and Johnson revealed a cycle of response that a body experiences during a sexual encounter. The human sexual response cycle is divided into these four stages:

1. The excitement phase.

In preparation for intercourse, when becoming aroused, various changes occur in the bodies of men and women. Increases in heart rate, respiration, blood pressure, and muscle tension occur. Blood flows to the genitals and breasts. The penis, clitoris, and nipples become erect. The genitals begin to lubricate, and women's breasts enlarge. Such sexual arousal in humans is very much dependent on situational variables. Opportunity matters. In lower animals, the excitement phase is primarily regulated by a surge of hormones. In humans, the circumstances are significantly important; conversation, physical appearance, music, and other variables can increase or decrease sexual arousal.

2. The plateau phase.

Sexual arousal will begin to taper off after a bit of time; it reaches a plateau. Arousal will be maintained at a high level for a little while as the body is now prepared for intercourse. Changes have occurred in the male genitals to make it possible to ejaculate, and changes in the female genitals make penetration possible. This period of time might last only seconds, perhaps minutes, or maybe longer depending on many variables; there is no set guideline. Masters and Johnson did not put a time limit on sexual activity. They said that if the partners are satisfied, then it was long enough. If they were not satisfied, then it wasn't enough time.

3. The orgasm phase.

During orgasm, the penis experiences rhythmic contractions that will produce ejaculation of sperm into the vagina, which also experiences similar muscle contractions. Lasting only a few seconds, orgasm is accompanied by an intense feeling of pleasure that is unique. Other pleasures can be similar to orgasm, but lack the extreme intensity.

Virginia Johnson and William Masters and their graphs of the human sexual response cycle.

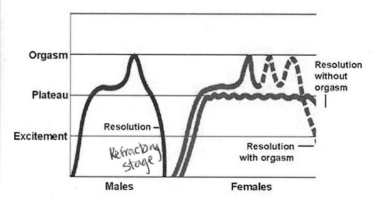

4. The resolution phase.

Following orgasm, the body's physiology gradually returns to its previous condition. During this resolution stage, men experience what is called a **refractory phase** during which they cannot have another orgasm. Some time must pass. Women do not have a refractory phase. How much time must pass for a man to experience arousal again depends on the particular individual and many other factors. One of them is the presence of a new partner. The refractory period will be shorter if a new mate is present. This fact is called the **Coolidge effect** based on a story that was told about President and Mrs. Coolidge visiting a farm. Whether it is true or not, the story goes like this: When shown a henhouse of chickens that experienced extensive sexual activity, Mrs. Coolidge asked, "Is there just one rooster?" "Yes," replied the farmer. "Well, tell that to Mr. Coolidge when he comes by," she remarked. Later when the President appeared at the henhouse, the farmer did as he was asked. President Coolidge then inquired, "Is it a different hen each time?" When the farmer answered in the affirmative, the President said, "Tell that to Mrs. Coolidge."

Brain Areas and Chemicals

Sexual activity is so complicated – motivation, arousal, performance, emotion, pleasure – that one would expect many brain areas to be involved. And, yes, that is the case: Many different brain areas, typically in coordination with one another, are necessary to carry out and regulate all the various elements of sexual experience. Thinking is involved, of course, but sexual activity has more to do with desire, emotions, and drives than with reasoning, therefore the **limbic system** seems a good place to look for areas of the brain that are involved.

Researchers have found areas of the **hypothalamus**, a motivation regulating center, and the **amygdala**, a brain region involved with emotions, and other nearby brain areas to be crucial for sexual activity. These brain regions are in communication with the endocrine system (release of hormones) via the **pituitary gland** and with the thinking cortex via connections with the frontal lobe. The hypothalamus and amygdala receive incoming sensory signals from vision, smell, touch, and other senses, and from the brain and body via hormones and neural signals. This is a very active, interconnected part of the brain, and we can easily see how sex is influenced by so many different variables.

Sexual activity in both males and females is accompanied by activity in an area of the hypothalamus called the **medial preoptic area (MPOA)**. If this area is electrically stimulated in rats, sexual activity increases in both sexes. Large lesions in the preoptic area of the hypothalamus abolish sexual behavior in male rats, and testosterone therapy does not restore it (Heimer & Larsson, 1967). When this region is destroyed in male monkeys, they

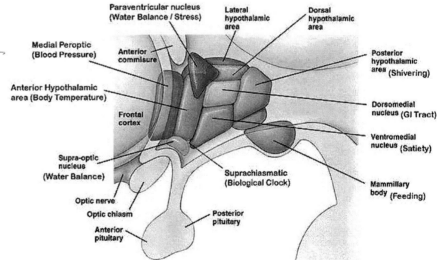

no longer attempt to copulate, but they do masturbate in the presence of a female (Slimp, 1978), indicating that the MPOA is more important for sexual performance than for motivation or arousal.

For males, another region of the hypothalamus called the **paraventricular nucleus** is important for sexual performance and for initiating an erection. This part of the hypothalamus secretes the hormones **oxytocin** and **vasopressin**. For females, the **ventromedial hypothalamus** is active during sexual activity. When this region is destroyed in female rats, there is a decline in the female's response to male sexual overtures. Female, but not male, sexual behavior in rats is disrupted by lesions in the **anterior hypothalamus**, too (Paredes, 1970). So, the hypothalamus is intimately involved in sexual activity for both males and females, though the specific areas differ a bit for the two sexes.

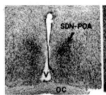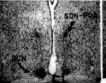

The SDN area of the hypothalamus is larger in males than in females, but is larger in females exposed to the hormone testosterone.

Parts of the brain or body that differ in their morphology between males and females are referred to with the term "**sexually dimorphic.**" Dimorphic means "having two forms." Several brain areas have been found to be sexually dimorphic. For example, a small area of the hypothalamus, within the MPOA region, is five times larger in male rats than in females. This area is called the **sexually dimorphic nucleus (SDN).** Its size is dependent on the amount of prenatal testosterone the fetus was exposed to — more testosterone equals larger SDN.

Also, a male rat's level of sexual activity is related to the size of the **SDN**, and if the SDN is destroyed, the amount of sexual activity is reduced (De Jonge, 1989). The SDN is connected to a number of other brain areas in such a manner that researchers have concluded that the SDN very likely is important for integrating incoming information and then coordinating the physiological and behavioral responses to those incoming signals (Roselli, 2004).

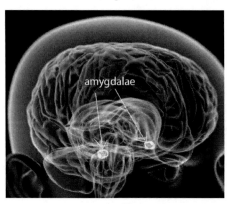

As mentioned above, the amygdala, an emotion-related area of the limbic system, is also involved with sexual activity. The **medial amygdala** is active during sexual activity in rats. This brain region apparently releases the brain neurotransmitter **dopamine** into the MPOA of the hypothalamus (Dominquez, 2001). Dopamine levels are associated with sexual motivation and with sexual performance in males, influencing erections and ejaculation. People who take medicine to increase their brain's dopamine levels report increased sexual activity. A major dopamine pathway runs from the brainstem to the frontal lobe. The job of the amygdala, it seems, is to respond to sexually-arousing stimuli and then signal the **MPOA** of the hypothalamus. The posterior portion of the medial **amygdala** is dense with **sex hormone** receptors and is larger in males than in females. Destruction of this area in rats reduces male, but not female, **libido** (sex drive). Women with temporal lobe epilepsy who experience an electrical seizure often report an increase in sexual arousal, perhaps through stimulation of specific areas of the amygdala and hypothalamus.

A small brain area that is located at the base of the forebrain, the **nucleus accumbens**, is a major hotspot in the **pleasure pathway**. It has many connections to the frontal lobe as well as to areas of the limbic system and to the brainstem. The nucleus accumbens is involved in addiction, reward, laughter, and sexual arousal. This brain area is sometimes called the "**pleasure center.**" During sexual activity, the nucleus accumbens increases in dopamine level. For a male rat, the presence of a female rat increases dopamine activity in the nucleus accumbens.

Dopamine is one neurotransmitter involved in sexual motivation, performance, and pleasure. Another brain chemical that plays a role is **serotonin**. In males, ejaculation is associated with increases in serotonin in the hypothalamus, which apparently contributes to the refractory period that males experience after orgasm. The role of serotonin is also suggested by the fact that people who take **antidepressant** medicines, drugs that increase serotonin activity, often report problems in sexual performance such as inability to achieve an orgasm.

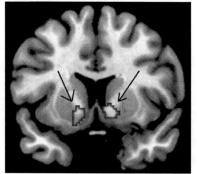

Nucleus accumbens.

Sex Differences

Billy Crystal: "Women need a reason to have sex. Men just need a place." Dorothea Dix: "The reason husbands and wives do not understand each other is because they belong to different sexes."

Men and women are like one another in many more ways than is usually recognized or discussed; of course, people are more interested in talking and writing about the differences between men and women. There are differences between male and female brains, and measurable differences in many psychological domains. However, the differences are small in most cases, and there is tremendous overlap between the two sexes in almost every behavior that is measured. While there are significant differences in several brain functions, these are averages and not meant to indicate anything near a complete dichotomy. The differences in mathematical ability, for example, have been overblown. For most ability levels, there are very few differences with males showing an advantage at some math tasks, while females have an advantage at others. In the U.S. at present, there is near equality in mathematical ability between males and females, the exception being at the very high ability level where boys outnumber girls. Almost all the research shows that the Mars/ Venus analogy is a bit overdone.

Mental Rotation Test—Are these two figures the same except for their orientation?

The difference that has been perhaps the most studied is that on average men have better **visual-spatial skills** than women. This difference has been found in study after study and appears even in babies and young children. In one recent study that looked at the differences in the architecture of several visual areas of male and female brains the author concluded, "The differences give males potentially more space in which to process additional information, a finding consistent with superior male processing in particular visuospatial tasks, such as mental rotation" (Amunts, 2007). **Mental rotation** refers to the ability to imagine in one's mind the rotation of two or three dimensional objects. Men consistently do better than women on such tasks, perhaps because the lower parietal lobe is larger on average in men (Frederikse, 1999). This is the part of the brain that was quite large in Albert Einstein's brain and is known to be involved in visual-spatial processing. Women do better on mental rotation tasks if they had a male co-twin (Vuoksimaa, 2010), apparently due to intrauterine exposure to testosterone from the male fraternal twin. Women also do better with such tasks if they have played video games that require spatial ability.

While male brains are larger on average, the ratio between brain size and body size is about the same for males and females (Ankney, 1992). Women's brains are smaller but more densely packed with neurons. Some sex differences have been found in the white matter and in the connections in the **corpus callosum** in men versus women (Kun-Hsien et al., 2011). Some research has found that women have a larger corpus callosum on average, but not all studies support that view. **Sex hormones** appear to affect the functioning of the **hemispheres** (Weis & Hausmann, 2010). It was found that the influence of the dominant hemisphere on the non-dominant hemisphere was reduced in women during their menstrual cycles. Apparently sex hormones can influence functioning within hemispheres, also.

Men's brains are more often lateralized, that is, are more active on one side than the other while performing a task, while women's brains tend to be more active in both hemispheres. Many studies have found larger brain structures, such as the corpus callosum, that communicate between the two hemispheres, in women's brains, though this has not been found consistently and there is still some controversy about it. Brain imaging studies show that women are more likely to use both hemispheres when processing language while men are more likely to use only the left hemisphere (Kansaku, 2000).

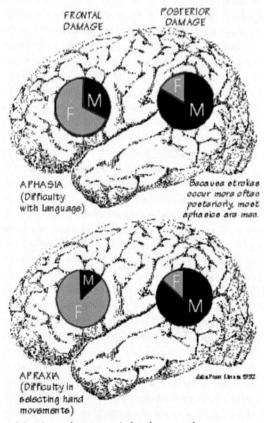

Men's and women's brains on the average show differences in language and hand movements.

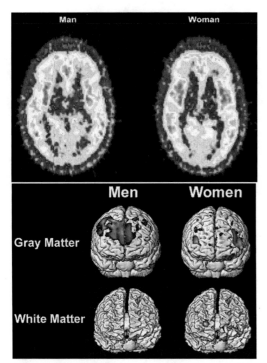

Top: Different activity occurs in men's and women's brains during learning.
Bottom: Men use more gray matter and women more white matter when solving intelligence problems (Haier et al., 2005).

It has been observed that different brain activity occurs in men and women during learning, and, too, it was found that while men tend to use their **parietal lobes** for spatial tasks, women use the **frontal lobes** (Andreason & Cahill, 2009). Thus, while men and women score equally on IQ tests, they may be achieving their results in slightly different ways.

While men excel at visual-spatial skills, almost all research shows women do better at **verbal tasks**, tests that require using language, though it depends on the specific test how much difference there is between men and women. By the way, the same is true for **spatial** tests; women do as well, or even better, than men on certain variations of spatial perception, and men's scores are higher than women's on certain tests of verbal ability. However, on average, the language areas on the left side of the cerebrum, Broca's and Wernicke's areas, are larger in female brains (Harasty, 1997).

Brain images show expanded regions of the left hemisphere's language and auditory areas in women's brains, and larger areas in the lower parietal lobe in men. This difference in verbal ability favoring women and visual-spatial ability favoring men is the most robust sex difference found by psychological researchers, but do not forget there is tremendous overlap between the two sexes even in these functions. The playwright George Bernard Shaw was once asked who were smarter, men or women. He replied, "Which man and which woman?" Of course, when we say women are superior at verbal skills and men at spatial perception, we mean on the average.

Another robust difference between the sexes that involves behavior is that

men have much higher rates of aggression, presumably because of higher rates of testosterone. The rate of homicide is thirty times higher for men (Daly & Wilson, 1988), and boys are much more likely than girls to participate in aggressive play and sports. Women, while less likely to engage in physical aggression, are equally likely to use verbal aggression as are men. Also, men are more likely to view their aggression positively, while women experience more regret and guilt after an aggressive action. One study reported two genes that are involved in the brain's activity of the neurotransmitter serotonin were linked to extreme aggression in men (Univ. of Pitts. Med. Ctr., 2006). Also, ratio of index finger to ring finger is influenced by prenatal exposure to testosterone (more testosterone leads to shorter index finger), and finger ratio was found to be correlated with aggression in adult men but not in women (Bailey & Hurd, 2005).

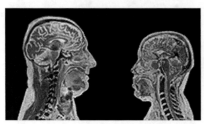

Some small differences in the sensory systems of men and women have been found. One study noted differences in the perception of color and reported, "It is well known that men and women may experience, perceptually and cognitively, the appearance of color differently" (Pardo, 2007). While women are better at perceiving differences in colors, men are better at visually noticing movement. Women have a more sensitive sense of smell, on average, but men are better, as noted above, at visually detecting spatial configurations and navigating in the environment. Men and women respond differently to stress; while men withdraw when stressed, women tend to seek social support. This finding was accompanied by increased activity in the brain's face recognition area for women under stress, but not for men (Mather et al., 2010).

There are a number of psychological disorders that show large sex differences. Eating disorders, depression, most anxiety disorders, and borderline personality disorder are all considerably more common in women. Men, on the other hand, have more developmental problems such as dyslexia, autism, ADHD, and speech disorders, as well as drug addiction, and antisocial personality disorder. To some extent, perhaps to a large extent, these differences are the result of brain differences. As two prominent researchers concluded, "Structural and functional sex differences in brain areas, together with changes in sex hormone levels and their receptors in development and adulthood, are closely related to sex differences in behavior and neuropsychiatric disorders" (Bao & Swaab, 2010).

Several genes have been located that appear to code for sex differences in the brain. Genes of the **Y chromosome** sometimes lead to sex differences in traits such as hemophilia, baldness, color-blindness, and some forms of intellectual disability, all conditions that are seen more often in men.

A review of the literature in this area concluded, "Sex differences in neural expression of X and Y genes significantly contribute to sex differences in brain functions and disease" (Arnold, 2004). But hormones, obviously, are also a main contributor to sex differences. **Hormones** influence brain *development* prenatally, shortly after birth, and again at puberty, and affect brain *functioning* throughout life (Caldwell, 2006).

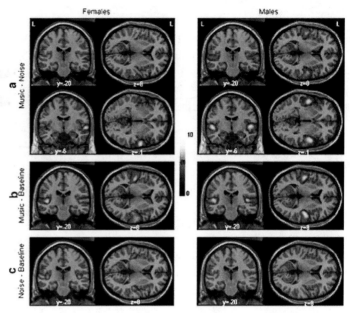

Ruytjens, et al. (2007) found significant differences in the responses of men's and women's brains to music and to noise.

Men who take **estrogen**, for instance, show an increase in verbal ability (Hulshoff Pol, 2006), while men who produce lower levels of **testosterone** during development have lower scores on tests of **visual-spatial ability** (Hier & Crowley, 1982). **Testosterone** injections in both men and women increase their scores on visual-spatial perception tasks (Janowsky, 1994). Girls with higher levels of **testosterone** act like tomboys and show interest in more active play and in toys considered to be stereotypically male, such as trucks and balls. Of course, child-rearing practices, and cultural and social factors play an important role in these differences, but the evidence indicates that **sex hormones** are important influences on sexual arousal, mating, bonding, behaviors, and even cognition. Parents are constantly amazed that their children choose stereotypical boy/girl toys and play in stereotypical male/female patterns despite their attempts to guide their children in more gender-neutral directions. Interestingly, a couple in Toronto recently refused to tell people the sex of their child, Storm. It will be fun to see how that turns out. It did generate a lot of controversy – people care a lot about such issues.

Sexual Orientation

Just how many people, or what percent of the population, are gay depends on how gay is defined. Researchers use different definitions of gay ranging from sexual attraction to sexual behavior to sexual identity. These are all separate, somewhat independent issues. That is, they do not correlate with each other perfectly. Gay behavior, for example, often occurs among incarcerated men who would clearly be defined as straight when outside of prison, and even while in prison they would be defined as straight in their sexual identity and attraction to the opposite sex. Depending on which component of sexuality is stressed in defining gay, the rate of homosexuality in the population can range from 1% to 21% (Savin-Williams, 2006).

The term "**sex**" refers to male and female, and "**gender**" refers to the behaviors and other qualities associated with sex, though the terms quite often are used interchangeably. Males and females in different cultures have different behaviors; that is, what is male in one place may be female in another. The term "**gender identity**" is today used to refer to one's idea of being male or female; that is, some people have the biology of one sex, but the mental idea of being the other sex. **Gender role** is the term used for the behaviors or social norms that are deemed appropriate to either males or females within a particular culture.

But, quite apart from sex and gender is the idea of **orientation**. For the most part, this refers to the fact that a person may prefer a partner of the same sex or of the other sex.

Kim Petras, German pop singer born male had sex change surgery at age of 16 – the youngest person ever to undergo the procedure.

Though **orientation** is not a clear dichotomy – there are **bisexuals**, after all – it still is interesting to ask what factors contribute to sexual preferences. As you likely know, there are commonly used terms for different sexual orientations: Men who prefer same-sex partners are called **gay**, and corresponding women are called **lesbians**. Heterosexuals are known as **straight**.

For many years experts believed that **gender identity** and **sexual orientation** were both primarily shaped by early childhood experiences in the family and society. In fact, not long ago sex experts believed in **gender neutrality**, the idea that gender is neutral at birth, that our sexual identities are shaped by experience. However, scientific research has offered no evidence for this notion. An early review of the research found no empirical support for the idea that parental influences, seduction by an older person, a weak father, or any other early experiences influenced the development of homosexuality (Bell, 1981). A recent review of the research concluded, "There is no proof that postnatal social environment has any crucial effect on gender identity or sexual orientation" (Bao & Swaab, 2010). Okay, so what then does cause sexual orientation and gender identity?

Today researchers are looking for that answer in genes, hormones, and brain structures. Genes get some support from twin studies. The concordance rate for identical twins is about 50%, while the rate for fraternal twins is about 20%. A gene on the **X chromosome** is a serious candidate, though experts have concluded that at least two genes are implicated (LeVay, 2011).

The idea that **hormones** are important contributors to sexual orientation gets support from animal studies. Same-sex preference has been demonstrated by manipulating hormones in the early development of a number of species including rats, hamsters, some birds, ferrets, and pigs. Homosexual orientation is seen in most species; about ten percent of male sheep naturally prefer male partners, and female gulls occasionally form lesbian pairs, for example. However, administering testosterone does not change orientation, but just increases sexual activity.

Female rats are more likely to mount other receptive females if they were **androgenized** before, or just after, birth. Mounting is most common in female rats that shared the uterus with several brothers; fewer males present prenatally resulted in less often mounting by the females (Clemens, 1974). Recently it was found that male homosexuals tend to have more **older brothers**, yet having more non-biological older brothers does not correlate with higher rates of male homosexuality (Bogaert, 2006). This finding suggests that maybe hormones are involved. Also, lesbians are likely to show the finger ratio typical of heterosexual men (shorter index finger than ring finger), and also have an inner ear response that is unique. Both finger ratio and inner ear response are influenced by prenatal **testosterone**. In addition, some experts have hypothesized that extreme **stress** during a critical period of pregnancy can cause an increase in hormones that shape areas of the hypothalamus that influence homosexual orientation. There is some evidence that women who experience extreme stress during pregnancy have a slightly higher rate of homosexual children.

Several brain structures have been found that differ between straights and gays. Researcher **Simon LeVay** discovered an area in the preoptic region of the hypothalamus that is smaller in gays and lesbians (LeVay, 1991). This brain area has a complicated name: **third interstitial nucleus of the anterior hypothalamus**. Incidentally, this part of the brain is also smaller in sheep that prefer same-sex partners. In straight humans, this brain region is three times larger in men than in women. But gay men have a pattern that looks like that of straight women. This part of the hypothalamus apparently is related to straight sexual behavior since if this brain region is damaged in non-human primates it disrupts heterosexual behavior.

Another difference has been reported in one of the brain areas that connects the cerebral hemispheres, the **anterior commissure**. This area is typically larger in women than in men and recently was found to be larger in gay men, too (Allen, 1992). Also, when looking at the left and right hemispheres, men typically have a more asymmetrical brain, while women's brains are more symmetrical. Brain imaging research has found that gay men tend to have more symmetrical hemispheres, similar to straight women. Homosexuals score more like the other sex on tests of verbal ability and mental rotation (Neave, 1999). That is, gay men score high on verbal tests, while lesbians score higher than straight women on visual-spatial problems. Gays and lesbians show amygdala responses similar to the other sex, also.

Research has also found differences in the **amygdala** and the **cerebral hemispheres**. Research using PET scans and MRI looked at the size of right and left hemispheres and the connections of the amygdala in a group of 90 people. The research discovered that gay men's brains looked like straight women's, and gay women's brains looked like straight men's (Savic-Berglund & Lindström, 2008). The straight men and gay

Do gay men have less testosterone on average? If so, why so horny?!

women showed an asymmetry toward the right hemisphere, whereas the volumes of the two hemispheres were symmetrical in gay men and straight women.

Also, the researchers found that the number of connections made within the left and right hemispheres of the **amygdala** showed sex differences and that gay subjects were similar to the opposite sex straights; that is, gay men (HoM) had brains that looked like those of straight women (HeW), and gay women had brains that looked like those of straight men. The differences found were in brain areas that were unlikely to have changed based on experience, so the researchers concluded that these brain differences were likely the result of innate differences between gays and straights. Later research by the same team showed that gay men's brains responded to the smell of **hormones** in a similar way to the response of straight women's brains (Savic et al., 2005).

Furthermore, lesions to the medial preoptic area (MPOA) and the anterior (AH) of the hypothalamus have been shown to alter partner selection in rats. The authors of one such study wrote, "Males with bilateral destruction of the MPOA/AH changed partner preference after the lesion and spent significantly more time with the stimulus male than with the receptive female. Coital behavior of males with bilateral destruction of the MPOA/AH was significantly reduced. Results are seen as further support for MPOA/AH as a crucial structure in the integration of sensory cues that determine partner preference" (Paredes, 1970).

In humans, some differences have been found in the parts of the brain that create and release hormones. For example, a part of the brain that secretes vasopressin, which is called the **superchiasmatic nucleus (SCN)** is larger in gay men (Swaab, 1990). This tiny brain area is located at the front of the hypothalamus just above the optic chiasm. When rats were treated with a chemical that inhibited testosterone conversion in this brain area both prenatally and shortly after birth, they developed many more neurons in the SCN and showed bisexual behavior. The researchers wrote, "This observation supports the

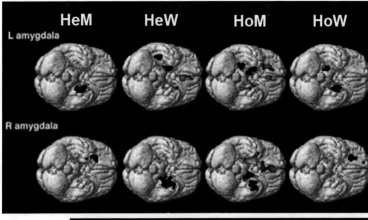

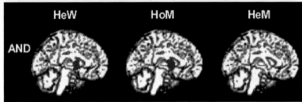

Top: Brains of gays were similar in the amygdala to brains of opposite-sex straights.
Bottom: Gay men responded the same as straight women to the smell of androgen hormones.

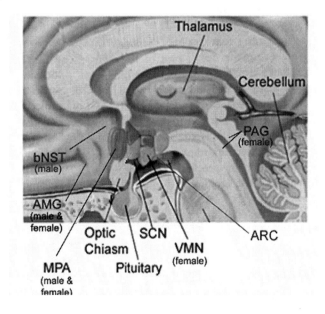

hypothesis that the increased number of vasopressin neurons found earlier in the SCN of adult homosexual men might reflect differences that took place in the interaction between sex hormones and the brain early in development" (Swaab et al., 1995).

Apparently sexual orientation and gender identity are complicated issues with many influences. Researcher **Simon LeVay** has summarized the research on orientation and concludes that genes, hormones, and neural structures all play critical roles (LeVay, 2011). But, here's a fact that may surprise you a bit: Though researchers have found significant evidence of the biological nature of homosexuality, some gays and lesbians are very upset about this! Researcher Dick Swaab was even attacked by an angry group of homosexuals who complained about his research on the biology of sexual orientation. You are probably wondering: Why in the world…?! Can you guess? While most gays and lesbians support the neurobiology research, a minority believe that such findings will be used against them. They fear that when the precise biological roots of homosexuality are discovered that being gay or lesbian will then be defined as an illness or a disorder, and that attempts will be made to "correct" the condition. Interesting, wouldn't you say? People and issues are much more complicated than one might at first assume!

Gender Issues

Billy Lee Tipton was an American jazz musician and band leader born in 1914. **Billy Tipton** played piano and saxophone, recorded two jazz albums, and was a talent broker and musician in Spokane, Washington until retiring in the 1970s. He was married and had adopted three sons. He died in 1989. While the paramedics were trying to save his life, Billy Tipton's son William was looking on. It was then that William discovered that his father was a woman.

Billy Tipton had been born Dorothy Lucille Tipton. At the age of 19 she started dressing as a man to fit in with other jazz musicians playing in clubs. It was difficult for women to be accepted into the circuit of jazz players, so she took her adopted father's nickname, Billy, and began using binding and packing to present herself as a man.

Billy had numerous relationships with women, although, of course, he could never be legally married; still, several women had documents identifying them as Mrs. Tipton. In some of his early relationships, his female partners knew he was a woman and his friends believed Billy was having lesbian relationships. However, in his later relationships, Billy hid the fact that he was a woman from his "wives." Billy told the women that he had been in an accident and was injured and therefore had to wrap himself every day. The couples had sex in the dark and preferred only touching, though Billy sometimes used a prosthetic.

Just exactly why Dorothy Tipton led her life as a man, no one knows for certain. His last wife, Kitty, has given contradictory stories, even as to whether or not she knew that Billy was a woman. Another of Billy's wives, Maryann, claims that she did not know that Billy was a woman and that they had a normal sexual relationship. Billy Tipton did not seem to be a transsexual who wanted to be a man (he didn't seek out counseling or surgery), nor did he seem to be a cross-dresser purely for sexual purposes. He seemed to adopt a male life-style primarily for the efficiency of being a jazz musician, though it is difficult to think that a career could be a strong enough motivation to change genders. It is certainly a curious story, and perhaps makes you wonder how many Billy Tiptons are out there now.

Sexual Disorders

Psychiatrists define mental disorders in a book called the Diagnostic and Statistical Manual of Mental Disorders. Because of its long name, this book is popularly called the **DSM**. There are three categories of sexual disorders included in the DSM: sexual dysfunctions, paraphilias, and gender identity disorders.

Sexual dysfunctions are problems experienced by individuals or couples during normal sexual activity. These include difficulties with desire, arousal, performance, or orgasm, and parallel the phases of the human sexual response cycle as described by Masters and Johnson, who also studied these sexual problems and developed a number of treatments for them. Sexual dysfunctions include a man's inability or difficulty in achieving an erection (**erectile dysfunction**), when a man ejaculates too soon for a woman's pleasure (**premature ejaculation**), a woman's inability to achieve orgasm (**orgasmic dysfunction**), and when a woman's vaginal muscles tighten before sexual intercourse (**vaginismus**). These sexual dysfunctions are mostly highly treatable disorders. For example, Masters and Johnson report a cure rate of 100% for vaginismus. They use a treatment that conditions the woman's muscles to relax. Similarly, premature ejaculation, the most common of the sexual dysfunctions, is easily treatable with a procedure called the **squeeze technique**. The problem is not discovering treatments for these disorders, rather, the problem is that people feel embarrassed about sexual dysfunctions and therefore are reluctant to seek treatment. Masters and Johnson estimated that nearly 50% of married couples have some sexual dysfunction, most of which go untreated.

A second type of sexual disorder is called a **paraphilia**, which refers to unusual ways of achieving sexual gratification. As you might guess, what is considered unusual varies from culture to culture and from time to time. What is a paraphilia in one society at one time is not in another. The paraphilias include **fetish**, in which a person must use an object (a shoe or nylon stocking, for example) or a part of the body (a foot) in order to achieve sexual satisfaction. Other paraphilias include **exhibitionism** (a person exhibits his genitals to strangers) and **voyeurism** (a person secretly watches other people engaged in sexual activities).

Treatment programs for paraphilias have been relatively successful. For example, Maletzky (1998) reports that cognitive-behavioral treatments had success rates from 78% to 96% for various problems such as **pedophilia** (sexual attraction to children), exhibitionism, and fetish.

A third category of sexual disorder is **gender identity disorder**. This circumstance arises when an individual's biological sexual characteristics do not match his or her mental idea of gender. A person's mental (or psychological) concept of himself or herself as a man or a woman is called **gender identity**. This concept is at least partially developed early in life. By the age of two, children have a very strong concept of themselves as boys or girls. Normally, of course, gender identity is congruent with a person's biological status as male or female. However, in some cases there is a mismatch between the biological and psychological. In adults this is called **transsexualism**. Don't confuse this disorder with **transvestism**, which is a kind of fetish in which a man needs to wear women's clothing in order to achieve sexual satisfaction, or with **homosexuality**, in which a person's gender identity is fine, but he or she is sexually attracted to members of the same sex. Homosexuality is not considered a mental disorder. **Transsexuals** can either have psychotherapy to try to convert their gender identity (a tough task), or they can have **sex reassignment surgery** (a so-called **sex change operation**) that will allow their bodies to match their minds. Thousands of people have had such an operation, and an overwhelming number of them are very pleased with the results. However, the number of such operations has decreased greatly in the past twenty years as transsexuals are turning more to counseling.

Nina Poon, transsexual model.

There is an area of the brain that extends around the thalamus (the relay center of the limbic system), and leads from the amygdala to the hypothalamus. This region is called the **stria terminalis**. Sexual dimorphism appears in this area. There is evidence from animal studies that neurons in this region participate in sexual mating.

One section of this brain region called the **bed nucleus** is typically twice as large in men as in women. However, researchers have found the bed nucleus of the stria terminalis to be reversed in transsexuals; male to female transsexuals have a typical female pattern, while female to male transsexuals have a typical male pattern in this brain region (Zhou, 1995). The sexually dimorphic nature of the bed nucleus is thought to be the result of **androgen** activity prenatally and shortly after birth. In fact, most scientists have concluded that gender identity is shaped very early in life, and, like sexual orientation, is influenced by genes, hormones, and brain structures that develop prenatally and in the weeks and months after birth (Money, 1994; LeVay, 2011).

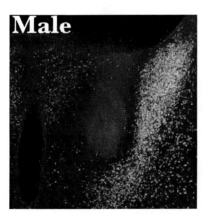

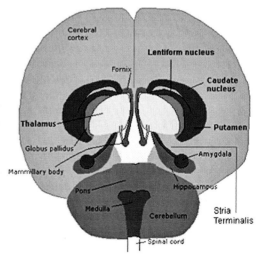

The bed nucleus of the stria terminalis is larger in men and in female transsexuals than in women and male transsexuals.

"Mother needs something today to calm her down, And though she's not really ill,
There's a little yellow pill, She goes running for the shelter of a mother's little helper
And it helps her on her way, gets her through her busy day."
— Mother's Little Helper by The Rolling Stones

"Picture yourself in a boat on a river, With tangerine trees and marmalade skies.
Somebody calls you, you answer quite slowly, A girl with kaleidoscope eyes.
Cellophane flowers of yellow and green, Towering over your head.
Look for the girl with the sun in her eyes, And she's gone."
— Lucy in the Sky With Diamonds by The Beatles

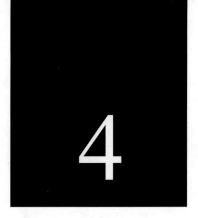

Chapter 4

Drugs

*I*n a suburb of Minneapolis in 2011, a 19-year-old died and ten others were hospitalized after taking a designer hallucinogen called **2C-E**, which on the street is called Europa. The teen who died was reported to have immediately lost control of his body; his eyes fluttered, his arms flailed, he punched a hole in a wall, and he fell to the ground, his body a jumble of seizures. Not far away, in Northfield, Minnesota, a 22-year-old man died from drug overdose on the same day. Also in 2011, the producer of the popular *Narnia* film series died of an overdose of the pain killer **OxyContin** (oxycodone), an opioid similar to morphine.

Such stories are common. Jimi Hendrix, Judy Garland, Janis Joplin, Elvis Presley, River Phoenix, Heath Ledger, Marilyn Monroe, Jim Morrison, Lenny Bruce, Michael Jackson, Kurt Cobain, John Belushi, Sid Vicious, Corey Haim, Brittany Murphy… The number of deaths from **drug overdose** in the United States is over 20,000 each year and is climbing to the point of epidemic, and the number of deaths from all drug induced causes is about 40,000 per year (Heron et al., 2009). In some states in the U.S. drug overdose now exceeds automobile accidents as the most common cause of accidental death. The number of deaths just from overdoses of **prescription pills** now exceeds deaths from guns or alcohol (Hoyert et al., 2006).

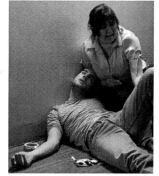

Although TV shows, movies, comedians, and particularly late-night talk-show hosts regularly make light of alcoholism and drug addiction, and although audiences howl with laughter and hoot with encouragement at jokes about alcohol and drug use, there are significant costs and dangers, including severe suffering, brain damage, and loss of life, that accompany the use and overuse of drugs. Despite the fact that drugs alter **consciousness** in ways that are sought by many people, drugs can potentially have very dangerous consequences. **Nicotine** is a stimulant that is highly addictive and dangerous; in the United States about 1,000 people die each day from smoking cigarettes. About two-thirds of fatal auto accidents, spouse beatings, and murders, and more than half of child abuse cases involve **alcohol**. About 10% of adults in the U.S. are dependent on alcohol. The cost of drugs in human lives and suffering is enormous. The pleasurable effects of drugs are immediate, while the damage they do is often long-term.

Furthermore, while there are plenty of movies and media stories about the harmful consequences of drug use, very rarely is attention given to the individual, social, and cultural reasons for such a wide-spread phenomenon. Some of the **neurological** factors involved will be described here. Why do so many people take drugs that alter their awareness and mental experiences? How do overdoses occur? What can be done about this rapidly growing world-wide problem?

*B*rain

A good place to begin in trying to understand drug use/overuse is to look at the primary brain areas and chemicals that are involved. The dominant brain circuit that is stimulated by drugs is the **mesolimbic pathway**, also called the **pleasure pathway** or **reward pathway**. It is called "meso" because it begins in the **mesencephalon**, also called the **midbrain**, a group of structures just atop the brainstem and below the thalamus,

NOV. 2

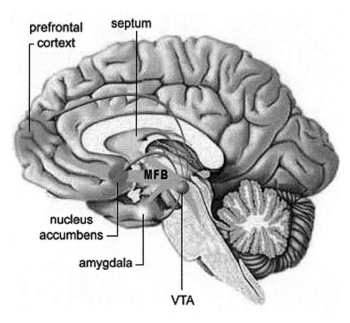

about in the middle of the brain ("meso" means middle), and it is called "limbic" because this pathway passes through areas of the **limbic system**, the group of brain areas including the **thalamus, hypothalamus,** and **amygdala** that are very much involved in emotion, motivation, the body's endocrine system, learning, and memory.

This stream of brain cells and their connections, the **pleasure pathway**, begins at the top of the brainstem and traverses through other areas of the midbrain and through the limbic system and finally sends neurons into the frontal lobe of the brain. Numerous research studies with humans and lower animals have shown that the brain areas along this neural pathway are intimately involved in the pleasurable effects of drug use and drug addiction. Although many other brain areas are part of the overall picture, substance use and abuse is directly, and primarily, tied to these brain regions, to the mesolimbic or pleasure pathway.

The pleasure pathway begins in an area that sits just at the top of the brainstem called the **ventral tegmental area** (**VTA**) or **ventral tegmentum**. This hotspot for pleasure produces and releases the brain neurotransmitter called **dopamine** which is used throughout the pleasure pathway by brain cells downstream from the VTA to perform various functions related to reward and motivation. Although dopamine is a major player in the synapses throughout the pleasure pathway, many other brain chemicals are involved, too. Another important group of brain chemicals used by cells in the VTA are the **endogenous opioids**. The term endogenous means "coming from within" and opioid literally means "similar to opium." So, these are chemicals that naturally occur in the brain and have a molecular structure very similar to that of opium.

Opium is a naturally occurring substance. It comes from **poppy** plants and has a pleasurable, euphoric effect on the brain. The reason that opium affects the brain is because it mimics the **endogenous opioids** that are naturally used in the brain to reduce pain, increase euphoria, give a sense of contentment, and perform other functions related to reward and pleasure. One category of brain opioids consists of chemicals called **endorphins** ("internal morphine"). **Endorphins** are produced in the **pituitary gland** and the **hypothalamus** and they provide a person with a strong sensation of well-being and calm. **Morphine**, which is derived from opium, affects the brain by acting as if it was an **endorphin**. Morphine (the name comes from the mythological Greek god of dreams, *Morpheus*) can be processed chemically to produce **heroin**, a more potent form of opiate. Pain killers such as **OxyContin** (oxycodone) and **Vicodin** (hydrocodone) are opioids created from opium ingredients. So, both dopamine and the endogenous opioids are important chemicals in the brain's pleasure pathway.

The euphoric feeling associated with addictive drugs begins in the **VTA** where **dopamine** is produced and released, and dopamine is then used by various brain areas along the pleasure pathway. Signals from the VTA are sent to areas of the limbic system such as the amygdala, hypothalamus, and hippocampus, and then to the **nucleus accumbens**, another hotspot of activity involved in addictions, sometimes called the pleasure center, though there apparently are several "**pleasure centers**" in the pleasure pathway. The nucleus accumbens is located at the juncture where the frontal lobe curls around underneath and meets the limbic system. The nucleus accumbens uses dopamine as a neurotransmitter and projects neurons to the prefrontal cortex. Increases in dopamine activity in the nucleus accumbens occur with nearly every drug, including nicotine, caffeine, cocaine, alcohol, and heroin. So, the nucleus accumbens is often thought of as a major brain area for drug addiction.

The VTA and the nucleus accumbens are connected to each other by a cable of axons (axons are the long branches of neurons that carry electrical signals from one place to another). This bundle of axons that allows the VTA and nucleus accumbens to communicate with each other is called the **medial forebrain bundle** (**MFB**). The MFB passes through a number of brain regions including the olfactory area (smell), the amygdala (emotion area), and the hypothalamus (motivation area). Stimulation of the brain cells in the MFB results in feelings of pleasure, and hence this connecting cable is sometimes called the **hedonic highway** ("hedonism" comes from the Greek word *hedone* which means delight or pleasure). The pleasure pathway evolved to provide a rewarding experience associated with behaviors that led to survival – eating and sex. Psychoactive drugs hijack the pleasure pathway and stimulate it so excessively that users crave more of the drug. French philosopher Voltaire remarked, "Ice cream is exquisite. What a pity it isn't illegal." He's right – ice cream does tickle the brain's pleasure circuit.

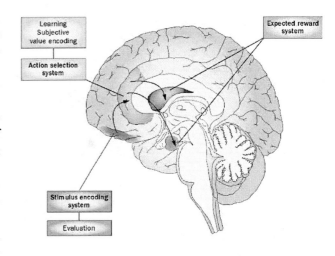

The **pleasure pathway** is primarily a **dopamine** circuit (though other brain chemicals are a major part of the package, influencing the activity of dopamine) that stretches from just atop the brainstem (beginning in the **VTA** where dopamine is produced) through the limbic system, including the hypothalamus and amygdala, to the **nucleus accumbens**. Next, from the nucleus accumbens there are axons that extend up into the prefrontal cortex of the brain. Because the frontal cortex is involved in the pleasure pathway, the whole pathway is sometimes called the mesolimbocortical or mesocorticolimbic pathway. Quite a mouthful! Perhaps it's better to just call it the pleasure pathway!

The **prefrontal cortex** (the front of the frontal lobe) is usually described as being a higher, executive brain area that influences a wide range of psychological phenomena including memory and decision-making, and has connections with multiple brain areas. As you may have guessed by now, the pleasure pathway is sensitive not only to drugs, but to many rewarding stimuli, such as food, water, and sex. The most sensitive areas are where the dopamine neurons are the most concentrated, namely the VTA, the nucleus accumbens, and most particularly, the medial forebrain bundle.

Neurons and Synapses

Psychoactive drugs are substances that affect brain processes and influence psychological functions such as perception, emotions, cognitions, behaviors, and the state of consciousness or awareness. Some drugs come naturally from plants and herbs, some are processed in various ways from natural substances, and some are synthetically created in laboratories. In all cases, drugs affect the brain because they act on the chemistry of the brain. Brain cells communicate with one another (creating neural networks) by chemical actions and reactions. To understand drug use/overuse it is necessary to look at **brain chemistry**.

Drugs typically affect the chemical process that happens where a neuron sends a signal to another neuron. This place (and the process) is called a **synapse**. The synapse is a junction at which a neuron communicates with another cell. The word literally means "to clasp together," but in fact the two cells at a synapse do not touch each other. There is a tiny **gap** or **cleft** between the sending cell and the receiving cell. It is here that a number of chemical transactions take place.

First, a chemical messenger is released from the sending (**pre-synaptic**) neuron, the molecules enter the gap, and then some of the chemical molecules that were released will bind with chemicals that are on the receiving (**post-synaptic**) cell. The chemicals that are released by a neuron at the synapse are called **neurotransmitters**. The chemicals that receive the neurotransmitters are called **receptors**. The chemical reactions of various neurotransmitters binding with receptors may either excite a receiving cell by opening its ion gates, or inhibit the cell by making the gates more difficult to open. So, neurotransmitters are known as either **excitatory** or **inhibitory**. The chemical used throughout the pleasure pathway, **dopamine**, is a neurotransmitter. There are five known receptors for dopamine; that is, there are five chemicals in the brain that will bind with dopamine when it is released by a neuron. These receptors are simply known as D1, D2, D3, D4, and D5. There are at least a dozen **serotonin receptors** known as **5-HT receptors**. Psychoactive drugs may bind with some receptors and not others producing a large number of possible effects depending on which receptors in which areas of the brain are either blocked or activated.

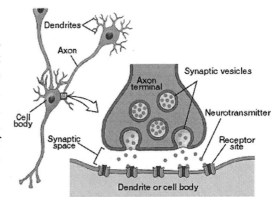

Second, there are chemicals in the synapse that clean up neurotransmitters. There are two means by which this happens: (1) **Enzymes** recycle neurotransmitters. Each neurotransmitter is cleaned out of the synapse by its corresponding enzyme. Interestingly, if a drug interferes with these enzymes, it will increase the amount of neurotransmitter available in the synapse. For instance, MAO inhibitors are antidepressant medicines that increase serotonin activity by inhibiting its enzyme, MAO. Also, an increase in an enzyme will reduce the activity of its neurotransmitter. (2) **Transporters** are chemicals in the synapse that carry some of the neurotransmitter back into the cell from which it came. This process is called **reuptake**. If a drug interferes with reuptake, that is, if it inhibits reuptake, it means that more neurotransmitter will be in the synapse available for binding with the receptor chemical. There are many such **reuptake inhibitors**.

It is common today to divide psychoactive drugs into two categories: Those that increase the action of a neurotransmitter (**agonists**), and those that decrease neurotransmitter activity (**antagonists**). Some drugs mimic a neurotransmitter and bind with the receptors of that neurotransmitter, and some other drugs enhance a neurotransmitter, perhaps by inhibiting its reuptake or decreasing the enzyme that recycles it, and other drugs increase the release of a neurotransmitter at the synapse. In all of these cases the result is that a neurotransmitter is more active at the synapse. Such drugs that increase the activity of a neurotransmitter are called **agonists**. For

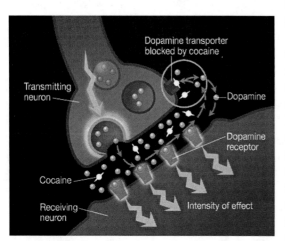

instance, **cocaine** inhibits reuptake of dopamine, meaning dopamine activity is enhanced. So, cocaine is an agonist of dopamine.

Other drugs decrease the activity of neurotransmitters. They could do this, for example, by blocking receptors so that a chemical reaction cannot occur at the synapse, or by decreasing the amount of neurotransmitter that is released, or by increasing activity of the enzyme that recycles a neurotransmitter, or by increasing reuptake. In all of these cases the activity of the neurotransmitter would be decreased. Drugs that have such an effect on the brain are known as **antagonists**. For example, some psychiatric drugs such as **antipsychotic** medicines (also called **neuroleptics**) block receptors, thereby decreasing the activity of certain neurotransmitters such as dopamine. So, neuroleptics are antagonists of dopamine. Just remember: Agonists increase neurotransmitter activity, and antagonists decrease neurotransmitter activity.

Cautions

Before looking at various neurotransmitters and some drugs that affect them, there are some important cautions to be mentioned. First, realize that a drug does not have entirely predictable effects. A drug will affect people differently because of individual differences in heredity and previous experiences, and even the same person will be affected differently by a drug taken at different times because of variations in the situation and in the state of the body and brain. For example, food tastes better to a person who is hungry than to a person who has just eaten. This is sometimes called the **Law of Initial Value**. That is, the effect of a drug depends on the initial state of the person using the drug. Patients who are in serious pain may respond with pleasure and relief when given morphine, but a pain-free person might experience anxiety from the same dose. Drugs have different effects on different people and even on the same person in different circumstances.

Second, pretty much every drug has **dose-dependent** effects. That is, one dose of the drug produces certain effects, but a different dose results in quite different experiences. **Mescaline**, for example, a compound that occurs naturally in the **peyote** cactus, produces euphoria in low doses, but a user will experience visual distortions and intense colors with a high dose. Also, alcohol acts as a stimulant with a low dose, but becomes a depressant with high doses. Another example is **nicotine** which is both a stimulant and a depressant, too, depending on dosage.

Third, it is generally not correct to associate a drug with a particular brain neurotransmitter. Although a certain type of drug may have a primary influence on one particular brain chemical, almost all drugs have complicated effects on neurotransmitters. One reason for this is because drugs are complex molecules that can influence many different brain chemicals. Another reason for this is because brain chemicals depend on each other to some extent; influencing one chemical in the brain causes changes in other brain chemicals. In fact, the brain contains many chemicals that influence the neurotransmitters, so-called **neuromodulators**. These are chemicals that can increase or decrease the release of neurotransmitters or moderate their influence at the synapse. For example, dopamine in the pleasure pathway is more potent if it is modulated by signals coming from the limbic system (emotion brain areas).

So, nearly all of the drugs that people take recreationally, such as alcohol, nicotine, or caffeine, have very complex effects on brain chemistry and the psychological experiences that are produced depend on the drug dose, the initial state of the person, and the user's individual characteristics, including genetics and previous experiences. Keep these cautions in mind as you read the general statements below about brain chemicals and various psychoactive substances that affect them.

Neurotransmitters

Your brain uses nearly a hundred different **neurotransmitters** to convey chemical signals from one neuron to another in a vast sea of neural networks. Any particular neurotransmitter can be found in many different areas of the brain. It is not a good idea to assign a psychological role or function to a neurotransmitter since that depends on where it is acting in the brain. It is a bit like electricity in your house. There are many different functions – lights, toaster, furnace, iron, and so on – associated with electricity. It depends on where and how it is being used. The same for brain neurotransmitters – their role depends on where and how they are being used in the brain.

A drug will affect the brain only if it resembles a neurotransmitter or influences biochemical processes that interfere with neurotransmitters (Wenk, 2010). So, to understand drug effects, we need to look at neurotransmitters and their roles. There are a few neurotransmitters that are most prominent in the brain, and most of those are influenced by drugs. Here are the most important neurotransmitters relative to drug use/overuse:

1. Dopamine. This chemical is produced in two areas at the base of the brain and then released into pathways higher in the brain. One dopamine pathway, originating in the **basal ganglia**, has significant influence on body movement. Therefore, drugs that affect dopamine in this pathway will affect the control of muscles. Huntington's disease, Parkinson's disease, dystonia, Tourette's syndrome, stuttering, and several other movement disorders result from a decrease in dopamine activity in this pathway. A drug called **L-dopa**

helps people in the early stages of Parkinson's disease to make more dopamine, but eventually the cells that create dopamine will be too damaged for this approach to be of benefit. Some recreational drugs affect body movement, too. Furthermore, the volume of the basal ganglia is significantly reduced in cases of **fetal alcohol syndrome (FAS)**.

Another dopamine circuit, the mesolimbic pathway mentioned above, represents pleasure and reward in the brain. All drugs that become **addictive** increase **dopamine** activity in this pathway, from alcohol to barbiturates, to caffeine and cocaine, to mushrooms and meth, to sleeping pills and speed, to Valium and weed, and everything in between. So, dopamine is the primary brain neurotransmitter involved in drug use/

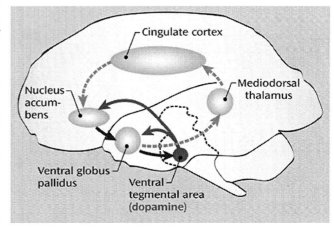

overuse and addiction. Neuroscientist Gary Wenk calls dopamine the "gas pedal of pleasure" (Wenk, 2010). Yes, that's appropriate, but dopamine is influenced by many other brain chemicals. The gas pedal has lots of feet pushing on it. For example, many drugs, such as alcohol and heroin, stimulate the **endogenous opioid** receptors in the brain. Such activations enhance the potency of dopamine in the pleasure pathway.

2. Acetylcholine. The first neurotransmitter to be discovered, this chemical is found in many brain areas and exists nearly everywhere on earth. One of its roles is in the movement (contraction) of the muscles. A natural substance called **curare** is an antagonist for acetylcholine (decreases its influence) in the body (not the brain; it does not pass the blood-brain barrier) and causes the body muscles to be paralyzed, including the diaphragm. A person injected with curare will be able to think, but will not be able to move or to breathe. Some indigenous hunters in South America use **curare**-tipped arrows; their prey die from asphyxiation, paralyzed.

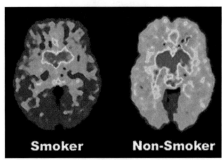

Smoker   Non-Smoker

Tobacco contains nicotine, which stimulates the nicotinic receptors in the brain.

There are two categories of receptors for **acetylcholine**; they are named after the substances that activate them: **muscarine** and **nicotine**. There are many more muscarinic than nicotinic receptors in the body and brain. An example of an antagonist for the muscarinic receptors is a plant known as **henbane** ("bane" is an Old English term for death; legend has it that this plant was named because farmers noticed that their hens died after eating it).

Henbane contains compounds that block muscarinic receptors in the brain. One area where acetylcholine is used is the autonomic nervous system, the neurons that control basic body functions like heart rate. Excessive blocking of acetylcholine receptors, therefore, can be lethal. In fact, that is the stated cause of death of Hamlet in Shakespeare's play of the same name. Appearing as a ghost, the King of Denmark tells his son that it was the King's brother who killed him by pouring henbane into his ears. Henbane would produce death by causing a person to stop breathing or have a heart attack.

During World War II, the German army used a **nerve gas** that was intended to cause death by inhibiting the enzyme that recycles acetylcholine, thus creating a condition of over activity of the neurotransmitter. Remember, if you inhibit a neurotransmitter's enzyme, there will be less re-cycling, and therefore there will be more activity of the neurotransmitter at the synapse. A natural plant that, in fact, has the same effect as the nerve gas is called **Snowdrop**. Chemical compounds in this plant decrease the activity of the acetylcholine enzyme. The result is too much acetylcholine, which can be deadly. The plant is mentioned in the *Odyssey* by Homer, written over 2000 years ago. The hero, Odysseus, is advised to eat an extract of Snowdrop in order to protect himself from a poison similar to henbane. The idea: The poison will block the receptors, but by inhibiting the enzyme there may still be enough of the neurotransmitter to get through and keep the body functioning normally. So, apparently it's true: One man's poison is another man's cure!

Muscarine is a naturally occurring substance found in a number of plants including one species of **mushrooms**. Muscarine acts by stimulating the muscarinic receptors for acetylcholine, so it is an agonist; it enhances the activity of the neurotransmitter. Eating these species of mushrooms can cause hallucinations, perceptual distortions, sleepiness, and even delirium. Author Lewis Carroll must have known of the hallucinogenic properties of these mushrooms since they are mentioned in his book, *Alice in Wonderland*. Amazingly, archeologists found evidence that these mushrooms were used in religious rituals by a cult in North Africa 12,000 years ago.

While the **pomegranate** fruit contains a chemical that is an agonist for the nicotinic receptors, obviously the best-known agonist for acetylcholine's nicotinic receptors is **nicotine**. This chemical is found in a great many plants, but is best known as an ingredient of **tobacco** plants. Nicotine is rapidly absorbed by the body and brain, and is highly pleasurable and addictive. It acts by binding to the nicotinic receptors in the brain, activates the sympathetic nervous system, increases the release of adrenalin, and also releases dopamine, producing a pleasurable effect.

A few examples of Ecstasy pills.

3. Serotonin. Though commonly associated with mood, serotonin is found in many areas of the body and the brain, with about 80% in the gut. For instance, unripe bananas contain serotonin; eating an unripe banana will increase contraction of the muscles in your intestines and cause diarrhea. The receptors for **serotonin** are called **5-HT receptors**, and are sensitive to hallucinogenic drugs. For instance, LSD, mescaline, and psilocybin are agonists of serotonin acting on the 5-HT receptors, and **Ecstasy** (MDMA) increases the release of serotonin at the synapse.

People with mutation in the genes that code for serotonin receptors are twice as likely to commit suicide. Modern antidepressant medicines are mostly **serotonin reuptake inhibitors**, and thereby increase the activity of serotonin at the synapse. This effect seems to raise moods in most people who suffer from severe depression, though the therapeutic value of such drugs for mild depression is still in question.

Chocolate is one of the natural foods that increase **serotonin** activity in the brain. Dates, papayas, and bananas also increase serotonin. Foods that decrease serotonin activity include wheat and rye breads.

4. Glutamate. When you think of glutamate, an extremely common neurotransmitter, think of GO! That's because glutamate is the most common *excitatory* chemical in the brain – it turns on cells at the synapse. This neurotransmitter is involved in about half the synapses in the brain, so it is involved in nearly all drug affects. Glutamate is involved in learning and memory as it helps to lay down new neural networks in the brain. Also, glutamate helps to prune, or reduce, networks that are no longer useful.

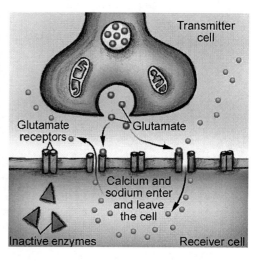

One of the glutamate receptors is called **NMDA**. This receptor has been of great interest to neuroscientists because of its role in forming memories by changing the synapse, a process known as **synaptic plasticity**. Drugs that block NMDA receptors (antagonists) are sometimes used as anesthetics for animals, and also are sometimes used recreationally by humans for their hallucinogenic properties, despite the danger.

Alcohol decreases glutamate activity at selective receptors, while caffeine and PCP (angel dust) increase glutamate activity. Since glutamate is an excitatory chemical, a glutamate antagonist (decreases activity), such as alcohol, will slow down body reactions, while an agonist (increases activity), such as caffeine will act as a stimulant.

5. GABA. When you think of GABA, think STOP! This is an inhibitory neurotransmitter, meaning that it slows, or puts the brakes on, neuronal activity. Glutamate and GABA are both very common in the brain and work together to control excitation and relaxation. They are the yin and yang of neurotransmitters. Since GABA is an **inhibitory** chemical, drugs that are agonists for GABA (that increase GABA activity) have the effect of calming, slowing reflexes, and relaxing a person. Also, GABA inhibits the release of dopamine in the VTA, the hotspot of the pleasure pathway. In fact, about one-third of the cells in the VTA are GABA cells. Research has shown evidence that the GABA cells may play a strong role in the formation of drug addiction (Laviolette et al., 2004).

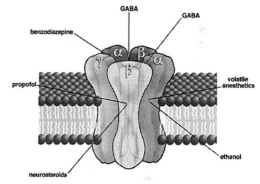

There are many different drugs that affect **GABA receptors**. The effect of these drugs is to slow down the nervous system, and a user will feel relaxed and calm. **Alcohol** has this effect, and so do **anti-anxiety** prescription pills known as **barbiturates** and **benzodiazepines**. Since these drugs all affect the same inhibitory receptors, you can see that it is important not to mix them. If the GABA receptors are over stimulated, the body and brain will slow down so much that death will occur. Mixing **anti-anxiety** pills with **alcohol** has often led to accidental death, as well as to suicide, because the combination overloads the GABA receptor.

Drugs that inhibit GABA will generally have a stimulating effect. For example, caffeine is a common GABA **inhibitor** that students and others enjoy daily. However, such stimulation can lead to periods of overload with shaking, nervousness, and headache. On the other hand, alcohol and tranquilizers increase GABA activity, and hence slow down reflexes and calm the body.

6. Norepinephrine. This brain transmitter is found in neurons low in the brain, near the brainstem. However, these cells project into vast areas of the brain, much more widespread than the pathways of dopamine. Norepinephrine acts a bit like an arousal chemical, preparing the brain to react to pleasure or pain. When norepinephrine activity is reduced, nervous system activity slows down and a person will be tranquilized – will feel relaxed, calm, and slowed. For instance, **reserpine**, a chemical found in the **snake root plant** prevents the transport of neurotransmitters and causes a tranquilizing effect in low doses. However, large doses lead to depression and mood disturbances of such nature that the snake root plant is termed the "**insanity herb**" by Sherpas.

When norepinephrine activity is increased, by drugs such as amphetamines, a person experiences heightened alertness, insomnia, and euphoria. On the rebound, a person will experience fatigue and depression.

7. Endocannabinoids. Did you know that you have natural **marijuana** in your brain? You are under arrest! Okay, not marijuana, but a form of the active ingredient in marijuana known as **THC** or **cannabis**.

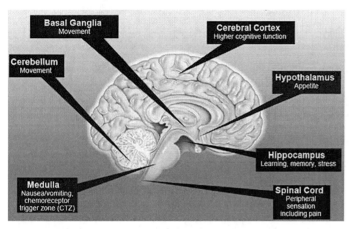

The brain has its own natural chemicals that are molecularly similar to cannabis, and hence are called **endocannabinoids** (*endo* = within; *oids* = similar to). These chemicals, however, in some ways act more like neuromodulators than like neurotransmitters. While transmitters are sent from dendrite to terminal, endocannabinoids participate in **retrograde signaling**; they are released by postsynaptic cells and move **backward** to affect the release of neurotransmitters from the **presynaptic** cell. They are found in brain areas that affect emotion, pleasure, and eating behaviors. Marijuana affects the brain because **cannabis** (THC) binds with the receptors for these natural neurotransmitters because cannabis has a molecular shape very similar to the endocannabinoids.

The endocannabinoid receptors are known as CB1 and CB2. There are at least five known endocannabinoids in the brain. The most studied is **anandamide** (the name means "bliss"), discovered in 1992. Anandamide is thought to be involved in brain mechanisms for pain, memory, pleasure, feeding, and motivation. In rats, injection of anandamide into the nucleus accumbens results in enhanced pleasure responses to food, including increased food intake. No wonder marijuana gives people the **munchies**!

8. Endogenous Opioids. As already mentioned above, your brain has its own form of **opium**. You are under arrest again! The endogenous opioids are chemicals in the brain that act like opium in reducing pain and giving a sense of well-being. Opium works on the brain because it binds with receptors that are naturally present, the receptors for the endogenous opioids. These natural brain chemicals not only increase pleasure and reduce pain, but act on many other body processes such as respiration, hormonal regulation, nausea, and vomiting.

These internal pain killers today are commonly known as **endorphins** (internal morphine). The endogenous opioids were discovered in 1974, and originally called **enkephalins** (inside the head). Today, however, the enkephalins are typically included under the umbrella term "endorphins." Scientists have now identified three separate gene families of endorphins with their own unique types of receptors. The receptor called **mu-opioid** is the most studied and genetic variations in the mu-opioid receptor seem to influence the ease

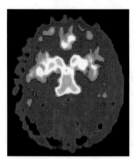

Activity of opiate
receptors in brain.

at which a person can become addicted to opiates, and the type of treatment the person will respond to. Interestingly, alcohol seems also to stimulate the mu-opioid receptor, and alcohol addicts as well as heroin addicts can be treated with medicines that block this receptor. These biochemical findings give us good reason to see why addictions and effective treatments can vary from one person to the next. The mu-opioid receptors can be altered either by heredity or by use of addictive drugs.

The **endogenous opioids** in our brains are generally **inhibitory**, reducing pain and discomfort, are found predominantly in the spinal cord and limbic system (affecting emotions and motivation, too), and share pathways with serotonin and norepinephrine. As already mentioned, neurotransmitters typically act in concert with each other as well as with many other chemicals as they play the neural symphonies in our heads. So, opioid receptors can be influenced not only by opiate drugs, but by chemicals such as nicotine, alcohol, and cocaine.

Definitions

A quick search at the library will stun you by how many different drugs exist. Prescription drugs, herbs, illicit drugs, **designer drugs** (chemically developed to get around drug laws) various plants, mushrooms, processed substances, foods, vitamins, minerals, and so on. There is no precise definition of a drug because the term is used in so many different ways by so many different organizations. However, in general let's say that a **drug** is a substance that when ingested or absorbed into the body alters normal body functioning.

What we are concerned with here are **psychoactive drugs** (also called **psychotropics**), substances that affect behavior, mood, cognition, perception, awareness, and other psychological functions. Psychoactive drugs are chemicals that can cross the **blood-brain barrier** (the biological mechanism that normally keeps large particles, such as bacteria, from entering the brain) and then interfere with neuronal firing and chemistry in the brain. Substances that are **fat-soluble** pass the blood-brain barrier more easily than water-soluble substances. Therefore, the more fat-soluble a drug is, the faster it will be taken up by the brain, the more intense its effects will be, and the quicker it will be removed from the brain. **Nicotine**, for example, is very fat-soluble. Within seconds after inhaling nicotine, the brain reacts to the chemical. This makes nicotine very addictive. Caffeine, too, is very fat-soluble. Some drugs are created in order to be more fat-soluble. **Ecstasy**, for instance, is a drug created by

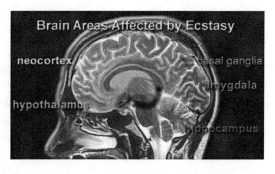

making a molecular change in **amphetamine** that makes it more fat-soluble. Therefore, Ecstasy acts quicker and more potently than does "speed."

Psychoactive drugs have been, and still are, sometimes used for medicinal purposes, but, of course, such substances are very frequently used recreationally by individuals, and ritualistically by cultures, around the world, and have been since prehistoric times. Archeological findings indicate that certain plants were used as **psychoactive substances** by individuals some 10,000 years ago, and various psychoactive plants were used for cultural rituals at least 5,000 years ago. Wine jars from China date to about 9,000 years ago. Poppy seed capsules have been found at grave sites in Europe that are at least 6,000 years old. So, psychoactive drugs have been around for awhile.

After taking psychoactive drugs, many users develop a **craving** for more of the drug. A craving can last for many years, even a life time. Craving is nearly always part of **withdrawal**, the bodily and psychological conditions that follow the cessation of a substance that was previously taken often enough to change the brain's synapses. **Depression** and **anxiety** are also common symptoms of withdrawal. Withdrawal symptoms are the opposite of the effects of the drug. This is called **rebound**. If a drug produces pleasure and relaxation, then removal of the drug results in low mood and nervousness.

Repeated use of a drug changes the chemistry in the brain. It's as if the brain is getting used to having the drug, as if it becomes a normal part of brain functioning. For example, it is common for the brain to produce fewer **receptors** if a drug is repeatedly present at the synapse. In the absence of the drug, a craving will then ensue. The brain is missing a chemical that it has grown accustomed to having. So, brains get used to having a psychoactive substance and will compensate. Later, in the absence of the substance, the brain produces feelings opposite of those produced by the drug. This brings us to the idea of **tolerance**.

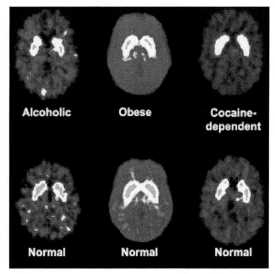

If a drug is repeatedly used, then brain chemistry changes such that the drug is treated as if it is a normal component of the synaptic process. One result of this change is that more and more of the drug is needed to get the same results as previously. The brain has become tolerant to the drug. **Tolerance** is a serious problem since it can lead to overdose. One way this happens is due to the fact that the effects of a drug on the pleasure pathway may not always be the same as the effects in a different brain area. That is, the pleasure pathway may develop so much tolerance to a drug that a large amount is necessary to get high. However, a large amount of the drug may affect other body areas so much to result in death. Some **addicts** willingly go through **withdrawal symptoms** in order to "re-set" their brains so that they can get high on a smaller dose, thereby saving money and averting overdose.

There is another significant cause of **overdose**. If a person repeatedly takes a drug under certain conditions, then classical conditioning occurs. This is the process of learning studied by Ivan Pavlov. A dog can learn to salivate to a bell, for instance. Well, the drug user's brain can also learn to associate various stimuli, such as a syringe needle, a dark room, a bathtub, and virtually any stimulus, with the high produced by the drug. So, tolerance can develop to the learned stimuli. The user must take more of the drug to get a high. However, if the user takes the same dosage of the drug in very different surroundings, an overdose can occur.

From Keith Richards, guitarist from *The Rolling Stones*: "It's an addiction... and addiction is something I should know something about."

Repeated use of a **psychoactive drug** means that changes occur in the brain at the synapses. In many cases this can lead to **addiction**. Addiction means that the user's brain has become so accustomed to the drug that it is dependent on it. Addiction includes intense craving, a preoccupation with obtaining the drug, inability to abstain, high probability of relapse after quitting, and compulsive use of the drug despite the adverse consequences or circumstances. The book used by psychiatrists to diagnose **psychological disorders**, the *Diagnostic and Statistical Manual of Mental Disorders* (popularly known as the **DSM)**, says, "When an individual persists in use of alcohol or other drugs despite problems related to use of the substance, substance dependence may be diagnosed." The DSM has sub-categories of addiction that include alcohol, cannabis, cocaine, inhalants, sedatives, hallucinogens, and more.

It's important to note that many addicted drug users continue using a drug from which they no longer get pleasure. Author Clive James commented, "Like most people who smoked umpteen cigarettes a day, I tasted only the first one. The succeeding were a compulsive ritual which had no greater savor than the fumes of burning money." This means that pleasure is not the only motivation for drug use, at least at the point of **addiction**. A user may begin using a drug for the pleasure it provides, but once addicted users need drugs to feel normal, even though the drugs no longer provide a sense of well-being. Interestingly, neuroscience research shows that the brain areas involved in addiction are not exactly the same as those involved in withdrawal. So, drug use/overuse can have numerous motivating factors, often depending on how long a drug has been used. Scientists sometimes distinguish **physical dependence** (need for the drug) from **psychological dependence** (craving for the drug), but these are somewhat relative and interdependent terms, and in any case, all things psychological have a physical basis, anyway.

Psychoactive drugs

There are a number of different systems for dividing **psychoactive drugs** into various categories. One popular method uses the terms opiates, stimulants, depressants (sedatives), and hallucinogens (psychedelics). While this is a useful way of reducing the huge number of substances into a few manageable categories, unfortunately there are errors that occur in trying to force all psychoactive drugs into these groups. And, many drugs fit into more than one category. For instance, **alcohol** is classified as a depressant, but when first ingested alcohol has a stimulating effect and then later depresses the nervous system. **Marijuana** is considered a hallucinogen in this taxonomy, although many users would consider it more of a sedative or even an opiate. So, the typical classification does not have perfect precision.

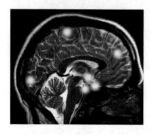

All **psychoactive drugs** that are **addictive** activate brain areas along the **pleasure pathway**, though the specific effects that result from each drug vary tremendously from person to person and from situation to situation. However, there are certain commonalities, certain effects of drugs that are highly typical and predictable. Following are brief descriptions of some of the most commonly used or studied psychoactive drugs together with some typical effects of these compounds on human psychology. However, please note that new drugs are produced so quickly that this list will be out of date by the time you read it! The latest psychoactive drug craze is _____ (fill in the blank).

Opiates

An **opiate** is a drug derived from **opium**, the dried sap of a **poppy** plant, or a similar **synthetic** (laboratory created) drug. **Poppy plants** are grown in many countries in the world, and are legally cultivated for medicinal purposes primarily in India, Turkey, and Australia. The United States is by far the biggest market for legal opiates. It is illegal to cultivate poppy plants in the United States, but this law is not enforced if poppy plants are grown for ornamental purposes. Poppy plants are a big business in some countries, such as Myanmar (formerly called Burma), Pakistan, and Afghanistan (the world's biggest illicit opium producer). For instance, there are over two million addicts in Iran, the highest per capita rate in the world, who depend on drug routes from Afghanistan and Pakistan to bring opium into their country. The number of opiate addicts in the United States is estimated at about 600,000. Opium for illicit trade is grown primarily in two regions that are known as the **Golden Crescent** and the **Golden Triangle**. The Golden Crescent includes parts of Afghanistan, Pakistan, and Iran. The Golden Triangle overlaps the mountainous areas of Myanmar, Vietnam, Laos, and Thailand.

The term **narcotic** is sometimes used as a synonym for opiate, or as a general term for **morphine** and **heroin** (described below). In fact, the term "narcotic" literally means a substance that induces sleep, and the term was used that way at one time, but it is now often used to mean an opiate, or sometimes is used to refer to any illegal drug. So, some people include cocaine and marijuana as narcotics, though they are neither sleep-inducing nor opiates. Anyway, the term is imprecise today, and is typically loaded with a negative connotation.

Opium has been around a very long time and references to it today are found frequently in the popular culture. The use of opium goes back to prehistoric times. Artifacts from archeological sites show images of opium poppy plants from civilizations existing as much as 6,000 years ago. In the book, *The Wonderful Wizard of Oz,* both Dorothy and the Lion fall asleep in a field of poppy plants. Poppy seeds are often used in cooking and for flavoring foods; for instance, you will sometimes find them on a bagel. On one episode of the TV series *Seinfeld*, Elaine failed a drug test because she had been eating poppy seed bagels. Humorous, perhaps, but apparently this is actually possible! The TV series *MythBusters* showed that a person could test positive for drugs after eating four such bagels, and the TV series *Brainiac: Science Abuse* went even further and got a positive reading after only two bagels. Amazingly, in the United Arab Emirates at least one man was arrested for possessing poppy seeds that he took from a bread roll. You see, some countries take opium possession very seriously!

Overdose deaths

The rate of accidental overdose deaths has been on a steady climb in the United States, along with the steady rise in the use of powerful, prescription narcotics:

DEATH RATE PER 100,000

'71 '73 '75 '77 '79 '81 '83 '85 '87 '89 '91 '93 '95 '97 '99 '01 '03 '05 '07

Source: National Vital Statistics System

Opium, the dried sap from the poppy plant, contains many **opiate chemicals**. The main active ingredient in opium is **morphine**, a chemical that is a powerful pain reliever. **Heroin** is a modified version of morphine that is much more potent (it acts faster on the brain). As mentioned above, opiates influence the brain by mimicking natural brain chemicals. The natural substances, the endorphins or endogenous opioids, relieve pain and provide a sense of pleasure and well-being. Heroin is preferred by users because it produces such effects rapidly and potently. However, this means that it is very addictive. Heroin also has other effects on the body that are quite damaging. About half of heroin addicts die prematurely from their habits. Slang terms for heroin include H, horse, smack, junk, tar, mud, snow, skag, and scat.

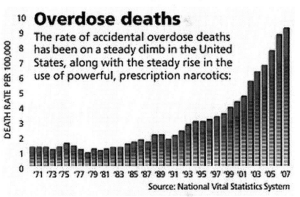

Another opiate ingredient found in opium is **codeine**, also a pain reliever. Codeine is converted to morphine in the liver, though for genetic reasons some people have less liver enzyme to make the conversion and codeine is not very effective for them. Both morphine and codeine are legal, prescription pain killers. However, these substances are often used recreationally, too, since they provide intense feelings of pleasure and euphoria in most users. Codeine is less potent and less addictive than morphine, and withdrawal symptoms are milder. In fact, sometimes heroin addicts take codeine to reduce their withdrawal symptoms when quitting heroin.

✐icotine

Found in a family of plants, and used as an insecticide, **nicotine** is derived for recreational use primarily from the leaves of the **tobacco plant** (duh!). In fact, this drug's name is taken from the name of a particular tobacco plant. Nicotine is a stimulant in humans and is considered one of the most addictive drugs. While nicotine

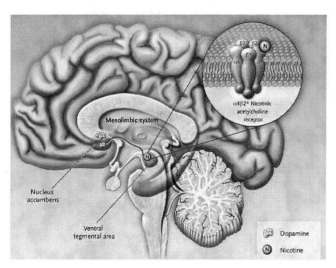

will easily penetrate the skin, it is normally inhaled into the lungs, though most of the nicotine is burned when smoking a cigarette. It is sometimes said that a cigarette has a fire at one end and a fool at the other. As you know, occasionally nicotine is taken via absorption through the lips, gums, or nose, as when a user places chewing tobacco in the mouth or nose.

Nicotine reaches the brain within 10 seconds of inhaling, and crosses the blood-brain barrier. Half-life is about two hours. Smokers who go without nicotine during overnight sleep wake up with a huge craving and heavy smokers light up as soon as they awake in the morning. The euphoria produced by nicotine is greatest after a period of abstinence, so the first smoke of the morning is highly rewarding and re-sets the addiction for the day. Users then unconsciously control the number of cigarettes and the amount inhaled to maintain brain levels of nicotine throughout the day.

How does it work in the brain? Nicotine activates the **nicotinic receptors** of acetylcholine. Such action increases activity of a number of other neurotransmitters, including **dopamine** in the **pleasure** circuit. Cigarette smoke includes other ingredients that increase the activity of dopamine, serotonin, and norepinephrine. Nicotine also activates the sympathetic nervous system, and thus generally has a stimulating effect, increasing the flow of adrenalin. However, like many other drugs, nicotine has complex effects on the brain and body and in some respects can be described as either a **stimulant** or a **relaxant**. In short puffs, nicotine acts as a stimulant, but inhaling tobacco smoke deeply produces a depressant effect (Schelling, 1992). Wenk (2010) adds that low doses of nicotine activate the **left hemisphere** and therefore cause stimulation, while high doses produce more activation in the **right hemisphere** leading to sedating effects.

Nicotine also reduces **appetite**, and some users lose weight while others justify smoking in order to not gain weight. Extremely high doses of nicotine cause nausea, headaches, and even convulsions and death in laboratory animals. People with severe psychological disorders, such as **schizophrenia**, typically are heavy smokers, which leads scientists to hypothesize that nicotine may be relieving some symptoms of certain mental illnesses, much the way alcohol seems to serve a self-medicating function for people with clinical **depression**.

Does nicotine harm the brain or thinking? Well, probably. For example, a recent controlled study that measured brain structures and cognitive abilities in smokers and non-smokers concluded: "These results are consistent with the hypothesis that smoking causes cognitive decline and loss of **gray matter** tissue in the brain over time" (Almeida et al., 2011). Also, a study of rats found that nicotine exposure during **adolescence** had an effect on the brain (Nolley & Kelley, 2007). The researchers discovered that exposing the animals to nicotine retarded the growth of the brain's dopamine system and thereby increased the risk of abuse of other substances, too. So, perhaps teen smoking may alter the pleasure pathway to make it more sensitive to drug abuse. Many studies have indicated that drug abusers have fewer dopamine receptors in the pleasure pathway, thus indicating that drugs are overused in order to stimulate the deficient numbers of cells. Paradoxically, drug use seems to worsen the situation and make continued drug use more likely. That is, using drugs seems to sensitize the brain such that use of drugs becomes more likely.

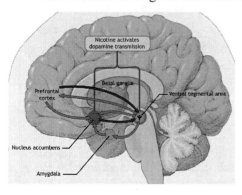

Of course, the dangers of **cigarette smoking** go far beyond nicotine addiction. The health problems associated with the use of tobacco are due to the some 4,000 ingredients in cigarettes. Lung cancer, emphysema, and other tobacco-related illnesses kill approximately 1,000 people per day in the United States. Smoking is the number one cause of premature and preventable death in the U.S. and accounts for about 400,000 deaths per year. During an interview to become an anti-smoking spokesperson actress Brooke Shields said, "Smoking kills. If you're killed, you've lost a very important part of your life." How true, how true.

Tobacco companies have recently been sued on the grounds that their executives knew about the dangers and did not inform their customers.

The courts have upheld such suits and as a result in 1998 tobacco companies made a deal to pay each state in the U.S. a certain amount of money each year instead of dealing with continuous law suits. From the **tobacco settlement** and from taxes on tobacco products the total amount that states receive is about $25 billion dollars per year (yes, that's *billion*; perhaps you noticed, tobacco is a big money business!). Unfortunately, only about two percent of that money goes toward programs to help kids and teens not to smoke and to help smokers to quit.

Alcohol

It's strange, but alcohol has been so widely accepted that it comes practically recommended by many people. Singer Frank Sinatra, who had a problem with alcohol, rationalized, "Alcohol may be man's worst enemy, but the bible says love your enemy." Said by actor, singer, dancer Sammy Davis, Jr.: "Alcohol gives you infinite patience for stupidity." Playwright and wit George Bernard Shaw wrote, "Alcohol is the anesthesia by which we endure the operation of life." And, noted counterculture journalist Hunter S. Thompson remarked, "I hate to advocate drugs, alcohol, violence, or insanity to anyone, but they've always worked for me." Of course, it's a joke – they don't work worth a darn in the vast majority of cases, including for Hunter S. Thompson who committed suicide in 2005.

One of the most commonly used drugs in the world, **alcohol** is a powerful psychoactive substance and one of the oldest recreational drugs. The form of alcohol that people drink is called **ethanol** or **ethyl alcohol**. **Methanol** or **methyl alcohol** or **wood alcohol**, used in antifreeze and fuel, is highly toxic – one sip can cause permanent blindness. **Isopropyl alcohol**, used for cleaning, is flammable, and somewhat toxic.

When first entering the brain, **alcohol** acts as a **stimulant**, exciting brain cells. But this **stimulating** effect is short-lived, and soon alcohol acts as a nervous system **depressant**; that is, it slows down the nervous system. Notice that the term "depressant" in this context does not refer to the mood disorder depression, but refers to the situation in which a substance decreases the activity of the body. In fact, large quantities of alcohol can kill by slowing body functions too much. People think of alcohol as a stimulant because it reduces inhibitions, making users more likely to do things they normally would not. Although alcohol does excite the nervous system when first ingested, its primary effect is depressive.

Alcohol influences many parts of the body and brain, so its effects on mind and behavior are widespread. Alcohol affects motor control, memory, depth perception, spatial perception, ability to detect rhythm and pitch (it's embarrassing to sing or play drums while on alcohol!), smell, taste, ability to perceive time, night vision, and emotional stability. That is a very long list! Alcohol is complex and has wide-ranging effects on the brain and body. Because it reduces inhibitions, alcohol users often show increased aggression, violence, abuse, and hostility, and are less concerned about harmful consequences.

Damage to body organs is a consequence of alcohol, also. After all, it is a poison. An old saying: "A hangover is something to fill the head that was empty the night before." There are more serious consequences to the body than a hangover. Cancer, cirrhosis of the liver, pancreatitis, hypertension, and a myriad of other disorders result from use of alcohol.

Comedian and actor Joe E. Lewis explained, "I drink to forget that I drink." Alcohol has a **global effect** on the brain, influencing regions such as the frontal lobe (judgment and decision making), cerebellum (balance and motor control), and the brainstem (breathing, body temperature, heart rate). The amount of alcohol necessary to cause problems varies from person to person and depends on many biological factors. For example, when taking the same amount of alcohol, women will generally attain a higher level of alcohol in their blood than will men. Body weight matters, too. Metabolism matters, too.

Digestive enzymes influence how much alcohol enters the blood stream. Since enzymes and other body processes are influenced by **heredity**, there is a **genetic component** to **alcoholism**. That is, some people are more likely to become dependent on alcohol because of their inherited physiological make-up (Gordis, 1996; Foroud, 1999). Amazingly, some people have an inherited alcohol metabolism that causes them to become temporarily paralyzed when they drink alcohol! Can you imagine a person becoming paralyzed after a drink?

But not only heredity influences alcohol use/overuse. Of course, social situations, family variables, and cultural factors all play huge roles in alcohol abuse, too. For instance, **binge drinking** is a serious problem among young people in the United States, one that is called an "epidemic" by the National Center on Addiction and Substance Abuse (CASA, 2002). Drinking large amounts of alcohol in a short period of time is very dangerous. A federal task force estimated that 1,400 college students are killed each year in **alcohol-related accidents** (Hingson, 2002).

Alcohol produces a pleasurable effect by first exciting the **opioid receptors** in the brain. Increased opiate activity then triggers dopamine activity in the pleasure pathway. A reduction in alcohol craving in some people can be achieved by blocking opioid receptors. Gremel et al. (2011), for example, found that blocking opioid receptors in an area of the brain known as the **anterior cingulate cortex** reduced alcohol seeking behavior in mice. Medicines that **block opioid receptors** have been approved for human use and do decrease the craving for alcohol among many who are addicted. However, not all alcohol users are motivated by the pleasurable effect of the drug. Some people are addicted to alcohol because it helps them cope with stress. These people don't drink for pleasure; they drink to escape the unpleasantness of stressful situations. Blocking the opioid receptors will not reduce their craving.

Alcohol acts on many of the **neurotransmitters** listed above. Some **glutamate** activity is decreased by alcohol, the result being a **sedating** effect, relaxing, and slowing down the body. With long-term use of alcohol the brain will make more **glutamate receptors** in response to the inhibition of glutamate by alcohol. During withdrawal a person can experience seizures because of the increased number of glutamate receptors. Also, glutamate transmission in the amygdala and nucleus accumbens has been found to be associated with alcohol-seeking behavior in rats (Gass et al., 2011). So, glutamate apparently has a significant role in those brain areas with regard to addictive craving. Furthermore, recent evidence shows that repeated exposure to moderate alcohol disrupts glutamate functioning in the **hippocampus**, the brain region important for learning and memory (Chefer et al., 2011). Perhaps this is one mechanism that helps explain why moderate drinking is associated with cognitive deficits.

The neurotransmitter **GABA**, too, is influenced by alcohol, but in the opposite direction of glutamate. Alcohol increases the release of GABA, which is an inhibitory transmitter, therefore giving the user a reduction in anxiety, relaxation of muscles, slower thinking, and slower reflexes. Furthermore, opioid receptors and endocannabinoid receptors are both stimulated by alcohol, providing a feeling of pleasure and euphoria.

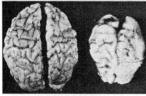

Top: A child with fetal alcohol syndrome. Bottom: Brain of a normal child and brain of a child with FAS.

Alcohol passes easily through the placental barrier, so pregnant women who drink may find that their fetuses are damaged in a number of ways. The result is known as **fetal alcohol syndrome (FAS)**. Such children have distinctive facial features including a short, upturned nose, thin upper lip, no groove above the lips, and a flat surface between the eyes. FAS, which is often the result of binge drinking during pregnancy, also is associated with irritability and attention problems. Sadly, children born to mothers who drink alcohol are significantly more likely to drink themselves later in life. If a woman has three drinks at one time during pregnancy, it doubles the risk of her offspring having a drinking disorder later in life (Alati et al., 2006). Several studies of rats have shown that prenatal exposure to alcohol makes the animals prefer the taste and odor of alcohol and to later consume more (Youngentob et al., 2007).

As mentioned above, there is a genetic component to the susceptibility toward alcoholism. For instance, research has found that people who are addicted have fewer **dopamine receptors** in the **pleasure pathway**. It's as if excessive drinking is an attempt to produce pleasure from a smaller group of chemicals. Also, a brain imaging study found difference is the sensitivity of the pleasure pathway in family members of people with alcoholism (Andrews et al., 2011).

Genetics is one factor that contributes to addiction, but environmental effects, such as **stress**, are important, too. Researchers have recently reported a relationship between early life stress and later alcohol and drug use/overuse. Enoch (2011) concluded: "Genetic and environmental influences on the development of alcohol and drug dependence are equally important. Exposure to early life **stress**, that is unfortunately common in the general population, has been shown to predict a wide range of psychopathology, including **addiction**. Experiencing maltreatment and cumulative stressful life events prior to puberty and particularly in the first few years of life is associated with early onset of problem drinking in adolescence and alcohol and drug dependence in early adulthood." Similarly, Rodrigues et al. (2011) reported that stress that occurred prenatally or shortly after birth altered dopamine systems in various lower brain areas including the pleasure pathway that could predispose a person toward later development of addiction. So, both genetics and life events (such as trauma and stress) can influence brain chemistry in ways that can increase susceptibility to drug use/overuse.

Depressants

Alcohol is the drug most commonly used to slow, relax, or depress nervous system activity, but there are others. The **barbiturates**, for instance, are prescription medicines that produce relaxation and a general slowing of the body, potentially to the point of anesthesia. They are used primarily in the treatment of anxiety. Because of their potential for harm, however, the barbiturates have largely been replaced by the **benzodiazepines**, also prescription **anti-anxiety medicines**. All of these depressant drugs activate GABA receptors in the brain. Since GABA is an inhibitory neurotransmitter, activating GABA receptors produces muscle relaxation, sedation, sleep, slowed reflexes, and calmness. Such medicines are often used in the treatment of anxiety disorders such as panic disorder. Side effects include drowsiness, dizziness, and memory problems.

Such drugs are used recreationally because they provide feelings of relaxation, contentment, and euphoria similar to **alcohol**. Since anti-anxiety medicines and alcohol affect GABA receptors, it is dangerous to combine them. The result could be over-depression of the nervous system, which could result in death. Such deaths are common. Anti-anxiety medicines also are subject to **dependence** and **tolerance**. Extended use of such drugs means the brain compensates and then higher doses are required to get the same effects. Severe and traumatic problems with withdrawal have been reported.

A naturally occurring chemical that is very similar to the benzodiazepines is present in a plant called **kava**. People in countries around the Pacific Ocean use kava regularly, usually as a drink made from kava root powder. Visitors to Fiji, for example, are offered a kava drink in a coconut shell. Sometimes the roots of the kava plant are chewed. It is a popular sedative among western Pacific cultures such as Hawaii, Australia, Polynesia, and Micronesia. A beverage called Kava Cola or Lava Cola is now commercially available and is described as an "anti-energy drink."

Left: Making kava.   Right: Kava drink.

Cocaine

Cocaine is classified as a **stimulant**, one of various substances that stimulate, or speed up, the nervous system. Cocaine is derived from the leaves of the South American coca plant. A white powder that is usually inhaled into the nose ("sniffed" or "snorted;" cocaine is sometimes called "blow") and absorbed into the bloodstream in the nasal passage, or rubbed onto mucous tissues in the mouth, or mixed with water and injected directly into the bloodstream. Repeated snorting leaves a user with a runny nose, nose bleeds, tissue damage, or even collapse or distortion of the end of the nose.

Cocaine is a local **anesthetic** which leaves a numb feeling on the mouth or tongue where touched; in fact, one of the physiological effects of cocaine in the brain is blocking sodium ion channels and preventing action potentials from being formed (same as **novocaine**). The white powder is called cocaine hydrochloride or hydrochloride salt or powder cocaine because the powder is made by processing cocaine with hydrochloric acid.

Powder cocaine arranged in lines to be snorted.

Another method is to remove the hydrochloric acid by a process called **freebasing.** The result, **freebase** or pure cocaine, can be smoked and will reach the brain rapidly via the bloodstream in the lungs. Still another procedure skips some of the steps used in complete freebasing and makes a cracking noise; the result is called **crack cocaine**, also called rock, iron, hard, or simply, **crack**. Powder cocaine can be converted to crack using a spoon, water, baking soda, heat, and a long thin object to extract the oil. The cocaine dries into rock shapes. When smoked, crack cocaine enters the bloodstream and brain rapidly and is more potent than powder cocaine.

Cocaine produces feelings of euphoria and intense pleasure, loss of appetite, increased alertness and energy, confidence, sometimes paranoia, and, as you might know, a craving for more cocaine. It is a highly addictive drug. Highs only last for about 10 minutes, and decreasing dopamine levels in the brain leave a user feeling depressed and anxious. Users typically take cocaine in binges with increasing amounts required because of the effects of **tolerance**. In order to prevent overstimulation users take other drugs with cocaine, such as alcohol, heroin, or marijuana.

Withdrawal symptoms include depression, irritability, restlessness, panic, and sometimes hallucinations. Cocaine produces extreme emotional highs and lows; some people have suggested that the character Dr. *Jekyll and Mr. Hyde* was inspired by cocaine's effects (Wenk, 2010). Cocaine has damaging effects on body organs, too, including loss of the sense of smell, loss of appetite, malnourishment, and intestinal damage. Users who inject the drug may have wounds on their arms called "**tracks**," which are also seen in heroin users.

The primary biological effect of cocaine on the brain is to interfere with the **reuptake** of certain neurotransmitters, primarily **dopamine**. Since reuptake is inhibited, there is more neurotransmitter in the synapse to excite the receiving cell. The **pleasure pathway** is most affected – the result is feelings of euphoria, omnipotence, well-being, and energy (Brick, 1998). As the drug wears off, a period of **depression** called a "**crash**" occurs. Heavy users may suffer personality changes, and **addiction** can readily occur.

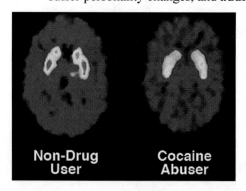

Non-Drug User   **Cocaine Abuser**

Most drug use interferes with brain systems related to attention and **memory**. It is not uncommon to find research results implicating psychoactive drugs in memory impairment and attention difficulty. Cocaine is no exception. For instance, brain imaging studies have found that chronic use of cocaine impairs memory because of reduced activity in the brain's attention areas in the right hemisphere (Bustamante et al., 2011). Similarly, reduction in the brain's **white matter**, the brain areas that connect various regions, have been found in cocaine addicts, although some recovery in some areas was noted in users who had abstained from cocaine use (Bell et al., 2011). Additionally, studies of monkeys indicate involvement of the prefrontal cortex associated with cocaine use and also with cues associated with cocaine use (Howell et al., 2010).

The highly addictive nature of cocaine is believed to be due to changes that it produces in the nucleus accumbens of the brain's pleasure pathway. **Genetic** changes apparently occur, too. For instance, mice given a single injection of either cocaine or Ecstasy later had DNA damage in their blood and damage to their brain cells (Alvarenga et al., 2010). The researchers wrote: "We determined that all doses of cocaine and MDMA tested were able to induce DNA damage in blood cells. Brain cells were affected by all doses administrated."

Additionally, researchers have identified a genetic alteration in a protein that occurs with chronic **cocaine** use (Maze et al., 2010). The researchers found that cocaine overuse interfered with a biological process called **methylation**. This is not a genetic mutation, because it does not change the DNA sequence of the gene. Rather, drug overuse appears to alter the expression, or function, of genes. This is what is meant when it is said that drugs can cause genetic changes. The result is that the brain develops a neuronal pattern that craves more of the drug. A similar process occurs with the overuse of other drugs, too. In fact, a study of heroin addicts found a similar genetic alteration in the opioid receptors. **DNA methylation** has been found to be altered by **alcohol** and **nicotine**, too. So, this is an important finding for developing treatments for drug addiction.

Until 1914 cocaine was used in soft drinks such as Coca Cola. Though illegal, cocaine use in the United States today is very high, especially among teens and young adults; ten percent report using cocaine at least once, and five percent report using cocaine monthly. Cocaine is often the drug of choice for celebrities and wealthy people. Comedian Robin Williams quipped, "Cocaine is God's way of telling you that you're making too much money."

Caffeine

Some T-shirt slogans: *A Morning without Coffee is Like Sleep. OCD: Obsessive Coffee Disorder. Accountants DO NOT do Decaf. Espresso Yourself. I'm a Social Worker – I Need Coffee. If it Weren't for Coffee, I'd Have No Personality Whatsoever. Sleep is Over-rated. Drink Coffee: Do Stupid Things Faster with More Energy. Instant Human: Just Add Coffee.*

A bitter substance found in coffee, tea, and soft drinks, **caffeine** is the most commonly used psychoactive drug in the world. Caffeine comes from many plants, including the nut of the **kola tree**, which is native to West Africa. In fact, the soft drink Coca Cola was originally produced by mixing kola with coca (from which cocaine is derived). Caffeine acts as a natural pesticide in plants, paralyzing and killing certain insects that eat the plants. For humans, as you likely know, the main sources of caffeine are beans from the coffee plant and leaves of the tea bush. Since coffee is brewed to be stronger than tea, more caffeine is ingested by drinking coffee. Chocolate also contains a small amount of caffeine.

Caffeine is not prohibited or restricted by any countries, though it is mildly addictive, does cause withdrawal symptoms and body problems, and in excessive use can dangerous. Mild use is considered relatively harmless in humans, though some animals, dogs and horses, for instance, do not metabolize it as well and it can be damaging. Caffeine quickly crosses the blood-brain barrier and activates a number of biological processes related to arousal and alertness. Heart beat increases, for instance.

Caffeine is a nervous system stimulant, similar to cocaine. Users often take caffeine to feel more alert, reduce physical fatigue, and to ward off sleep. Excessive use can lead to irritability, muscle twitching, anxiety, headaches, and heart beat irregularities – a condition called "**caffeinism**." A caffeine overdose or intoxication, called "**caffeine jitters**," include those symptoms and even more bodily problems, and in extreme cases can lead to hallucinations, delusions, disorientation, and even death. Psychiatrists recognize two behavioral problems related to long-term use of caffeine: sleep disorder and anxiety disorder.

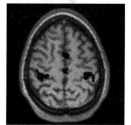

Caffeine acts on the brain as an antagonist (decreases activity) of a neuromodulator called **adenosine**. Caffeine blocks the receptors and thereby decreases the amount of this chemical that can stimulate the receiving cells at the synapse. That is, caffeine molecules bind to the receptors for adenosine without activating them. Therefore, the influence of adenosine is reduced. As a neuromodulator, adenosine influences the activity of neurotransmitters. By blocking or decreasing the activity of adenosine, caffeine increases the activity of glutamate and dopamine.

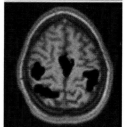

One of the roles of adenosine is to prepare the brain for sleep; adenosine is primarily an **inhibitory** chemical. Since caffeine blocks the action of adenosine, caffeine therefore slows the inhibitory process and promotes **wakefulness**. That does not mean the need for **sleep** is diminished or removed. Caffeine simply puts off needed sleep until another time.

Adenosine is common in the **basal ganglia**, and likely contributes to dopamine activity in the pleasure pathway. Further, caffeine has other, much more complex effects on

Brain on caffeine (bottom) shows more activity.

the brain and body, and also interacts with other drugs such as Tylenol, amphetamines, and histamines. Interestingly, caffeine has been suggested as possibly playing a protective role against **Alzheimer's disease** (Arendash & Chuanhai, 2010). Drinking five cups of coffee or more per day is associated with lower rates of the brain disease that involves build up of proteins that damage brain cells. Maybe caffeine isn't all bad!

Amphetamines

The street drug called "speed" is **amphetamine**, a stimulant that increases alertness and wakefulness, and decreases appetite and fatigue. Amphetamines are prescription drugs, such as Adderall, Benzedrine, and Dexedrine, but are also taken recreationally and as performance enhancers. Withdrawal symptoms include depression, irritability, and fatigue. Amphetamine does not occur naturally, but there are many plants that contain compounds similar enough to produce the same effects on the brain, and there are molecules that occur naturally in the brain that have a similar chemical structure to amphetamine.

Amphetamine causes activation of dopamine, serotonin, and norepinephrine by both causing their release into the synapse and by blocking their reuptake. Amphetamines appear to affect these neurotransmitters only in certain brain areas, however, particularly in the **reward pathway**.

Just as cocaine can be processed, amphetamines can be reduced to their **freebase** form which is called "ice" and can be smoked. The most addictive form is called **methamphetamine**, which has the street names **meth**, crank, and crystal meth or just **crystal** (because it is sold illicitly in bitter tasting crystalline structures). During World War II soldiers used methamphetamines to help maintain their alertness and to stem fatigue and fear. But high doses can cause severe mental disturbance. Adolph Hitler was given injections of meth, and some experts have speculated that the drug may have contributed to Hitler's paranoia. Meth can be produced in labs using somewhat ordinary ingredients, including allergy medicine. The process can be dangerous, however, involving flammable and corrosive chemicals, and it releases noxious odors and fumes. Most meth for the U.S. market is produced in Mexico or California.

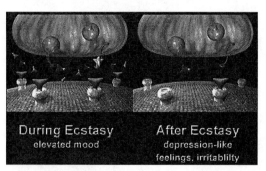

Another version of **amphetamine** is produced by making the chemical more **fat soluble**. The result is the drug **MDMA**, popularly known as **Ecstasy**. Ecstasy is a stimulant and **hallucinogen** that can damage brain cells, as well as cause serious damage to body organs and sometimes death. Ecstasy causes a huge increase in body temperature and often the cause of death from this drug is **hyperthermia**. Men are more sensitive to this condition because they have more muscle mass than women, on average.

Roberts and Garavan (2010) studied brain images of **Ecstasy** users during a cognitive task and concluded: "Evidence suggests that users of Ecstasy have behavioral and cognitive deficits and show increased impulsivity. These results reveal dysregulation in brain regions subserving cognitive control and default-mode processes in current recreational drug users mirroring effects previously observed for 'harder' drugs of abuse." The researchers had earlier shown deficits in learning and memory in Ecstasy users (Roberts et al., 2009).

As noted above, genetic changes have been found with MDMA use. Furthermore, **Ecstasy** has been found to be **toxic** to both dopamine and serotonin neurons in monkeys (Ricaurte, 2002), though the findings are controversial (Mithoefer, 2003). Despite the fact that Ecstasy impairs memory, teens see it as a safe drug. Twelve percent of teens say they have tried it, ranking third behind alcohol (53%) and marijuana (41%). In fact, while use of most drugs has declined among teens, Ecstasy use has increased.

Women selling betel nuts in the South Pacific.

A naturally-occurring mild amphetamine (**cathine**) appears in a plant called **khat** (pronounced *kot*). In many countries of East Africa and the Arabian Peninsula, chewing khat leaves is a legal and common way of achieving euphoria and stimulation. In Yemen, much of the agricultural resources go to growing khat; it is used by 80% of men and 45% of women in that country. Similarly, the majority of people in Somalia chew khat. The plant is a mainstay of the economies of many countries. Khat has lower addiction properties and causes less physical harm than most drugs, but dependence is possible, withdrawal effects occur, and long-term use is associated with loss of self-control. Users have bright green teeth and yellow, blood-shot eyes. Khat is illegal in many countries including the U.S. and Saudi Arabia, but is an everyday experience for people of Eastern Africa and Yemen.

Chewing and selling khat.

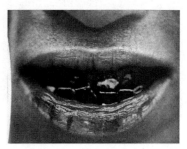

A similar naturally-occurring drug is commonly used in India, Southeast Asia, and Indonesia. The drug comes from the vine leaves of a plant known as **betel**. The betel leaves are combined with areca nuts and chewed. While betel has been and still is used in ceremonial ways, the current practice in Vietnam and many other Asian countries is often a social activity, much like drinking beer and wine or smoking cigarettes in the U.S.

Chewing betel is recommended as a cure for bad breath, toothache, headache, arthritis, and other ailments. Technically, betel is a mild stimulant that produces a feeling of euphoria, relaxation, and excitement. Regular chewers of betel are easily detected since their teeth and gums are stained red! It so happens that in some cultures red-stained teeth are a sign of beauty.

Marijuana

What psychoactive drug was used thousands of years ago, is still used around the world today, is mentioned in the Bible, was probably taken by Jesus, was grown by George Washington, and was encouraged as a farm crop in the U.S. in the 1940s? Yes, **marijuana** – the drug with the most slang names: weed, pot, grass, Mary Jane, baby, black bart, Acapulco gold, Panama red, hooch (also used for liquor), Jane, aunt Mary, Manhattan silver, herba, Jay, magic smoke, mother, locoweed, joint and roach (the marijuana cigarette), tea, dope (also used for heroin, meth, and any drug), and a hundred others. A species of marijuana plant is used to make rope, which is why it was once a crop in the U.S. **Hashish**, the Arabic word for "grass," is created from dried resin from the flower of the marijuana plant.

The active ingredient in **marijuana** is tetrahydrocannabinol (**THC** or **cannabis**) which is a mild hallucinogen. Cannabis can be smoked or ingested. THC works on the brain by stimulating natural THC receptors. But, why are there **THC receptors** in the brain? There must be a natural substance in the brain that those receptors are designed for. Yes, as mentioned above, the brain contains **endocannabinoids**. In 1992 the first such brain chemical was found and was dubbed **anandamide** from the Sanskrit word *ananda* which means "bliss." The THC molecule has a shape very similar to anandamide and therefore binds to anandamide receptors in the brain causing an alteration in consciousness that is pleasurable because it increases dopamine activity.

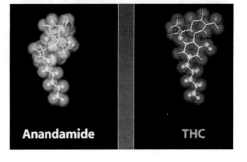

Anandamide   **THC**

Two common effects of **THC**, impairment of memory and an increase in hunger (the "munchies"), are produced because **marijuana** acts primarily on the brain area involved in learning and memory (the hippocampus) and because it influences the hormone **leptin**, which is involved in hunger (Wilson, 2002). While leptin signals the brain to stop eating, cannabis has the opposite effect, reducing the influence of leptin. Also, brain imaging research has shown that marijuana craving is associated with activation in the **reward pathway** (Filbey et al., 2009), indicating that marijuana provides a **euphoric** effect and can be **addictive**. It is difficult to classify marijuana because it causes some **excitatory** behaviors, some **sedative** effects, and in large doses some **hallucinogenic** experiences.

Chemicals that resemble anandamide were found in **dark chocolate** causing the media to suggest that eating **chocolate** might stimulate the brain in the same way that **marijuana** does. Scientists say that not only are the concentrations vastly different (you'd have to eat a thousand candy bars to equal a small dose of marijuana), but that the compounds in chocolate do not have the same effect on the brain as marijuana. The idea that marijuana impairs **memory** is so well known that even TV celebrities make jokes about it. Matt Lauer quipped, "Researchers have discovered that chocolate produces some of the same reactions in the brain as marijuana. The researchers also discovered other similarities between the two but can't remember what they are."

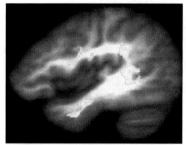

Brain areas damaged by heavy marijuana use.

Marijuana has been known for nearly 5,000 years, is common in many cultures of the world, but was outlawed in the United States in 1937. Some side effects of marijuana include problems in attention, memory, perception, impaired immune system, lung disease, interference with hormones, and difficulty judging time and distance. A small percentage of marijuana users, about 10 to 15 percent, become addicted to the substance. Nearly 100,000 Americans each year go to clinics to try to quit using marijuana (Blakeslee, 1997).

It has been shown that marijuana use during adolescence is associated with a higher rate of **psychosis** later in life. Psychosis refers to psychological disorders in which a person is out of touch with reality. Evidence indicates that in teens who are susceptible, cannabis use can produce brain changes that either cause or aggravate psychotic symptoms. **Schizophrenia** is the most common psychotic disorder. The primary symptoms of schizophrenia – hallucinations, delusions, social isolation, and bizarre behaviors – often begin in late adolescence or early adulthood. It is believed that schizophrenia is partly a genetic disorder, but that it can be triggered or manifested by stress, a virus, a head injury or some other trauma. A 20-year follow-up study found that psychotic symptoms in young adults were associated with exposure to multiple traumas including alcohol and cannabis abuse (Galletly et al., 2011).

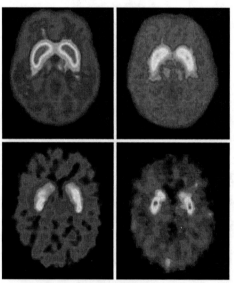

Bottom images show smaller hippocampus and amygdala in marijuana abusers compared to normal (top).

Apparently, **cannabis** can be an instigating factor in **psychosis**. Presumably, ingesting marijuana during the teen years when the brain is not fully matured and is going through a pruning process, can interfere with the laying down of neural networks, thereby disrupting normal functions. The evidence now suggests that cannabis taken during adolescence interferes with the neurotransmitter **glutamate** in the **frontal lobes** of the brain and makes the user more susceptible to psychosis (Bossong & Niesink, 2010).

A study of heavy cannabis users found not only an association with **psychosis**, but also found the **hippocampus** and **amygdala** were smaller (Yucel et al., 2008). The **shrinkage** of these two brain areas is congruent with the findings of **memory** impairment in many studies. The smaller volumes were found in both hemispheres but shrinkage in the left hemisphere was correlated with psychotic symptoms. The authors of the study wrote, "These findings indicate that heavy daily cannabis use across protracted periods exerts harmful effects on brain tissue and mental health."

Another study found evidence for dysfunctions in working memory in early cannabis users (Becker et al., 2010). Numerous studies have found that cannabis is related to **memory** deficits, but this recent research showed that it is very likely that teen use of marijuana, a critical time for glutamate to do its job of synaptic plasticity, is particularly harmful to the brain's memory functions. The authors concluded, "Our findings suggest that an early start of cannabis use is associated with increased cortical activation in adult cannabis users, possibly reflecting suboptimal cortical efficiency during cognitive challenge. The maturing brain might be more vulnerable to the harmful effects of cannabis use."

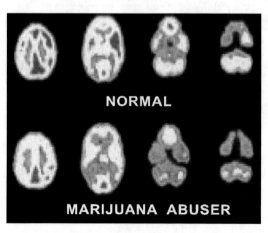

NORMAL

MARIJUANA ABUSER

While most research has honed in on memory deficits associated with marijuana use, a recent study found that **decision making** was impaired in heavy marijuana smokers and that they were less sensitive to feedback (Wesley et al., 2011). This brain-imaging study tracked activation in many brain areas while subjects played a strategy game. The marijuana users had less activity in several brain regions compared to a control group.

Additionally, abnormalities in the **white matter**, the part of the brain that sends signals from one area to another, were found in **adolescents** who either used marijuana or inhalants (Yucel et al., 2010). Furthermore, a recent brain imaging study of adolescent marijuana users found abnormalities in cortical thickness in two brain regions, the **prefrontal cortex** and the **insula**, an area on the inside of the temporal lobe that is important in processing taste sensations and emotional reactions (Lopez-Larson et al., 2011). The authors wrote, "Our results suggest that age of regular use may be associated with altered prefrontal cortical gray matter development in adolescents. Furthermore, reduced insular cortical thickness may be a biological marker for increased risk of substance dependence."

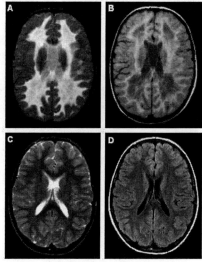

Vanishing white matter.

A similar study used brain imaging to look for **white matter** differences in chronic marijuana users compared to non-users (Silveri et al., 2011). The researchers found brain differences that suggested that cannabis use altered brain structure. One of the conclusions: "Chronic marijuana use is associated with altered **cognition** and **mood** state, altered brain metabolites, and functional and structural brain changes."

However, not all studies have found impairments in marijuana users (Jager, 2010). Also, a summary of many studies that looked for structural changes in the brain with long-term cannabis use concluded, "While changes in the hippocampus and parahippocampus were frequently identified, the findings were inconsistent across studies. The available literature also provides some evidence that regional structural changes are associated with cannabis use patterns (particularly cumulative dosage and frequency of use), as well as measures of psychopathology (e.g., measures of depressive and psychotic symptoms). Together, these structural imaging findings suggest that THC exposure does affect brain morphology, especially in medial-temporal regions" (Lorenzetti et al., 2010).

As of today, therefore, we have mixed results on whether marijuana use/overuse produces structural brain damage, although most studies show harm. The studies overall do not agree, yet most research does show some deficits in mood, brain volume, memory, and other cognitive functions with marijuana use, particularly if the use is long-term and begins in adolescence.

Marijuana **legality** has been and continues to be a hot issue. Since marijuana is currently not legal in the United States for recreational purposes, drug manufacturers have created synthetic versions that have sometimes eluded law enforcement. However, a federal law against the sale of five chemicals used in herbal blends to make **synthetic marijuana** took effect recently, and both state and federal laws now include clauses that prohibit cousin drugs, or drugs that are intended to have the same effects as a prohibited drug. Fake marijuana, which is sold in drug paraphernalia shops and on the Internet, has been marketed using several different names including **K2**, Spice, Blaze and Red X Dawn. There are many versions that use slightly different chemical formulas, too. Experts do not like the phrase **"fake marijuana"** since these drugs typically have effects and side effects that go well beyond those of cannabis and can even be lethal. Currently in South Africa a highly addictive drug is being used called **whoonga** that is a mix of marijuana, rat poison, detergent, AIDS medicines, and other ingredients. It is said that some whoonga addicts purposely get AIDS so they can receive the free medications.

A plant that has similar psychoactive effects as marijuana, in fact, a plant often touted as a legal form of marijuana, is *Salvia divinorum*, commonly known as **salvia**. The plant is native to Mexico. It is currently legal in most countries and most states in the U.S. (though, that is changing rapidly). The drug can cause hallucinations, visual effects, and dissociative experiences. It has a long history of use by **shamans** (witch doctors) among the Mazatec people of Mexico to induce spiritual visions or for healing. Loss of speech and coordination are common side effects. There has been some controversy about salvia, as some people consider it to be a significant danger, and some legislators have attempted to ban it, while others view it as a mild and uncommon psychoactive substance. Unlike most **hallucinogens** (described below), salvia does not bind to serotonin receptors. Rather, it is a partial agonist for opioids and dopamine. It is a very potent chemical with effects that are rapid and include uncontrollable laughter, illusions of movement, a feeling of twisting or merging with objects, overlapping realities, childhood memories, and visual effects.

Salvia plant.

Inhalants

Rock 'n' Roll star David Lee Roth said, "I used to have a drug problem but now I make enough money."

Some children, teens, and impoverished people seek highs from cheap, ordinary, easily obtained substances. Sometimes a high is obtained by inhaling the fumes of solvents, glue, gas, or aerosols. The most serious use of **inhalants** occurs in marginalized communities and among young people who are poor, bored, and isolated from their families and societies. For instance, sniffing fumes is a significant problem among street people in Southeast Asia and India, in parts of Africa, and in poorer communities in the United States. Some common inhalants are butane, rubber cement, paint thinner, gasoline, Erase-X correction fluid, hair spray, and contact adhesives.

The use of inhalants means inhaling volatile vapors into the nose and trachea. This is typically done by putting the volatile substance into a small container, such as a tin can or plastic bag, and holding it up to the face to inhale the fumes. **Glue sniffing** was part of the punk counterculture of the late 1970s in England and the U.S. because it complemented the rebellious image of punks. Many rock songs and movies made reference to the use of inhalants to get high. For instance, "Now I want to Sniff some Glue" is the title of a song by *The Ramones* and "Dumb" by *Nirvana* has Kurt Cobain singing "My heart is broke, but I have some glue, help me inhale, and mend it with you." Movies that refer to, or show, use of inhalants include *The Cider House Rules, Fear and Loathing in Las Vegas, Boys Don't Cry, Blue Velvet, Gummo, Airplane!,* and *Citizen Ruth.*

Inhalants have different effects depending on the substance used, but generally resemble alcohol inebriation. Heavy use can cause hallucinations and distortions of time and space. Side effects are many, including nausea, loss of motor coordination, headache, hearing loss, spasms, brain damage, slurred speech, and a glue-sniffer's rash around the mouth. Fatalities occur, too, usually from heart attack. In fact, just in Texas over a ten year period there were 144 deaths that listed inhalant abuse as the cause of death. It is extremely likely that the number of deaths from inhalants is under-reported.

Hallucinogens

A 1966 song by The Electric Prunes was titled *I Had Too Much to Dream Last Night.* Jim Morrison, lead singer of the rock band *The Doors* opined, "Drugs are a bet with the mind." He lost that bet and died at age 27. Malcolm Muggeridge, English journalist: "I will lift up mine eyes unto the pills. It is an age of pills." From surrealist artist Salvador Dali: "I don't do drugs. I am drugs." And, from the song *White Rabbit* by Jefferson Airplane: "One pill makes you larger, And one pill makes you small, And the ones that mother gives you, Don't do anything at all, Go ask Alice, when she's ten feet tall."

Certain drugs cause such severe alterations in consciousness that they are known as **hallucinogens**. These drugs produce shifts in perception that result in phenomenological experiences that are similar to illusions, hallucinations, and alterations in consciousness. Most hallucinogenic drugs, in fact, do not produce hallucinations (false perceptions), such as seeing or hearing stimuli that are not present, so the term is a bit misleading. Most of these drugs produce alterations in perception of light, color, and shapes, or changes in the perception of time.

Hallucinogens often produce a feeling of euphoria or intense well-being along with the perceptual alterations, although not always. Sometimes a "bad trip" occurs in which a user experiences terror and horrible images and sounds.

The hallucinogens are sometimes referred to as **psychedelics**. The term literally means "to make the mind/soul visible." Although the two terms, hallucinogen and psychedelic, are often used as synonyms, another more contemporary categorization divides hallucinogens into three classes: (1) **psychedelics** (or classic hallucinogens) are drugs that alter perceptions and cognition by stimulating **serotonin receptors**; (2) **dissociatives** are drugs that produce amnesia, detachment, out-of-body experience, a feeling of dreaming, disruption of identity or consciousness, and anesthesia; (3) **deliriants** (or true hallucinogens) produce full-blown hallucinations, confusion, and rage. They take their name from "**delirium**," a syndrome resulting from brain trauma that results in a severe disorganization of behavior.

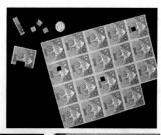

LSD (lysergic acid diethylamide), often simply called **acid**, is the most notorious and best known of the hallucinogens. It was first synthesized in 1938 by Swiss Chemist **Albert Hoffman** who accidentally ingested some and went home seeing colors and visual distortions. He said the world looked as if it was in a curved mirror, furniture took on threatening forms, and his neighbor looked like a witch with a colored mask. Later, particularly in the 1960s and 1970s, U.S. psychologist **Dr. Timothy Leary** promoted acid as a means of reaching a higher plane of consciousness and mental and spiritual significance. His phrase, "Turn on, tune in, drop out" (Leary claimed he got the phrase from communication scholar Marshall McLuhan) became a popular counterculture slogan suggesting that young people should take LSD, look inside themselves for higher levels of awareness, and become self-reliant, not dependent on the society. In contrast, rock artist Frank Zappa, leader of the band *The Mothers of Invention*, said, "We are here to turn you loose, not turn you on."

Albert Hoffman.   Timothy Leary.

LSD is an artificially produced substance (it does not exist in nature), and acts on the brain primarily by binding to certain **serotonin** receptors. This is a common physiological effect of many hallucinogenic substances (including some of the club drugs described below) – to bind with certain serotonin receptors in the brain. **Dopamine** receptors are typically activated, as well, providing a euphoric effect along with perceptual distortions and hallucinations. The precise chemical effect produced by hallucinogens is not fully known. It appears that LSD and many other hallucinogens increase the amount of serotonin, but slow the firing of serotonin neurons. Scientists have long recognized that **serotonin** is a key neurotransmitter related to psychedelic experiences, similar to what happens in the brain during **REM sleep** when a person is dreaming. Also, people with strong religious beliefs and spiritual sensations have been found to have a smaller number of one particular serotonin receptor in their brains (Wenk, 2010). So, perhaps serotonin is linked to our perceptual experiences of dreaming and similar phenomena. However, some hallucinogenic drugs do not act on serotonin receptors, so perhaps there are several brain mechanisms that lead to hallucinations.

The precise psychological effects of LSD can vary significantly from person to person and are unpredictable for any individual or situation. For example, both pleasant and unpleasant experiences may occur (called "good trips" and "bad trips"). During a **bad trip**, a person may experience the fear of going insane, paranoia, a sense of unreality, disturbing hallucinations, and distortions of body parts. Deaths have occurred from bad trips, for example, because a user jumped out a window from a tall building.

One of the most disturbing side effects of LSD is a **flashback**, in which users later experience hallucinations without the drug. These can occur weeks or months after drug use, and may be stimulated by darkness, going to sleep, stress, or driving – it's like **classical conditioning** (Pavlov's dog), in that the brain can react to a stimulus that was previously associated with a drug. Flashbacks occur suddenly, without warning, and are more common in chronic users. There have been reports of flashbacks being initiated by antidepressant medicine in teens who had been frequent LSD users (Markel et al., 1994). A study of 123 LSD users found that half of them experienced flashbacks for five years after stopping the drug, and found the most common trigger was a dark room (Abraham, 1983).

A naturally occurring substance that is very similar to LSD is found in a fungus called **ergot** that contaminates many grains and cereals. Ergotism was the cause of thousands of deaths in Europe during the Middle Ages and some experts believe ergot in rye caused some women to have strange behaviors in Salem, Massachusetts, women who were judged to be witches and were executed in 1692.

Another hallucinogen is **phencyclidine**, which is commonly referred to as **PCP** or **angel dust**. PCP is a **glutamate** antagonist and **dopamine** agonist. It is used in medicine as an anesthetic. For recreational use, it comes in powder or liquid form and can be ingested, smoked, or snorted. PCP produces hallucinations, delusions, paranoia, mania, dissociation, disorientation, and disordered thinking. More than 30 variations of PCP are available illegally on the street and they go by names such as PCPy, PCE, and TCP.

From top down:
1 - shrooms.
2- one of many DMT plants.
3 - bufotenine toad.
4 - peyote cactus.

In laboratory animals, such drugs can cause a type of brain damage known as "**Olney's lesions**." In the 1970s **PCP** was called America's number one drug problem, but its use has decreased today to the point that only about 3% of young people report having tried it.

Psilocybin mushrooms, often called **shrooms** or **magic mushrooms**, contain the hallucinogenic substance **psilocybin**, which is converted in the body to **psilocin**, a hallucinogen. In 1953 these chemicals were analyzed by Albert Hofmann (yeah, the LSD guy!), who created synthetic psilocybin and related compounds. Hofmann personally ingested a large amount of the mushrooms and reported that the experience was similar to that produced by **LSD**. Psilocybin is found in over 200 species of mushrooms, some of which have been used for many years in religious ceremonies among Indian people in Mexico. Magic mushrooms act on several **serotonin** receptors.

One of the most common **hallucinogens**, found in many species of plants and even in trace amounts in mammals including humans, is the drug known as **DMT** (dimethyltryptamine). The chemical structure of DMT is very similar to **serotonin** and it activates many of the serotonin receptors in the brain. It is a natural **psychedelic** that can produce from mild to powerful hallucinogenic experiences. Many indigenous peoples have used DMT in rituals; for instance, an Amazon Indian brew used for spiritual healing contains mainly DMT.

In fact, some of the oldest drug artifacts discovered from archeological digs are pipes carved from bones that were found in caves in the Andes Mountains of Argentina. The pipes have been dated as originating from earlier than 2000 B.C. And, guess what? The burnt residue found inside the pipes was from a plant that is rich in **DMT**. So, apparently the hallucinogenic experience has been around for a long, long time. Today there are still Amazonian natives who use DMT regularly. A DMT snuff is prepared and then blown into another person's sinuses using a long bamboo tube. Much of the art and clothing decorations of some South American native tribes are derived from the visions the Indians experience while intoxicated with DMT.

Would you believe that some people lick **toads** to get high? There is a toxic, but perhaps hallucinogenic, drug called **bufotenine** found in the excretions of some toads and also found in some plants. The chemical has a structure very similar to **DMT** and therefore is also similar to the brain chemical **serotonin**; however, this particular chemical can be deadly. Still, it is used to get high and as a stimulant. For example, Native Indians in Peru and Brazil use fluids from frogs to increase their senses, strength, and stamina during hunting. Also, excretions from the Colorado River toad have been used by people in the U.S. to get high. Now, if you see someone licking a toad, you know what is going on!

Mescaline, which was briefly mentioned above, is another naturally occurring **hallucinogenic** substance. It is found in a number of plants, particularly various species of cactus, the most famous of which is the **peyote** (*pay-OH-tee*). For over 3,000 years the Native Americans in Mexico and the Southwestern U.S. used peyote in ceremonies. The branches growing from the root of the peyote cactus were cut and dried into "buttons" which were then chewed or soaked in water to make a drink. Since the taste is bitter, sometimes peyote is ground into a powder and placed into capsules.

Like most hallucinogens, **mescaline** binds to some **serotonin** receptors; that is, mescaline is a partial agonist of serotonin. The pleasurable effect occurs because some **dopamine** is activated, also. Users typically experience visual distortions, brilliant and intense colors, geometric visual illusions, stripes, checkerboards, dots, and kaleidoscope-like visual experiences. Objects, too, can look flattened, like a Cubist painting. Side effects include racing heart, vomiting, anxiety, headache, and dizziness. The user also may become clumsy, unstable in movement, and have weak muscles.

Mescaline is an illegal substance in the United States except for its ceremonial use in some Native American Churches. The author **Aldous Huxley** wrote about his **mescaline** experience in his 1954 book, *The Doors of Perception,* from which the rock band, *The Doors*, got its name. Lead singer **Jim Morrison** was a heavy user of alcohol and drugs and died from drug use in 1971 at the age of 27.

Club Drugs

LSD is a common **club drug**, a group of drugs used by teens and young adults at dance parties such as "raves" or "trances," at bars, and at dance clubs. **Ecstasy**, a version of amphetamine, is perhaps the most common club drug. Another, **GHB** (G or liquid Ecstasy) is often manufactured in homes with recipes found on the Internet. It is a depressant that is often mixed with alcohol, and in high doses can cause coma or death. It is sometimes known as a "**date rape drug**," though several substances have earned that name. **GHB** is found in a prescription medicine, **Xyrem**, which is used in the treatment of **narcolepsy**, a sleep disorder that causes people to have "sleep attacks" in which they suddenly lose muscle tone and fall down when they laugh or feel a strong emotion. This **cataplexy** is similar to the **atonia** (muscle paralysis) characteristic of **REM sleep**. People with narcolepsy have low levels of a brain chemical called **hypocretin (orexin)**.

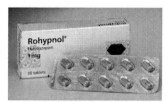

Rohypnol is also a club drug used recreationally. It is a prescription **anti-anxiety drug** similar to Valium. Taken with alcohol, rohypnol can cause severe **amnesia**, and is known as the "**forget me pill**." It is used in date rapes and sexual assaults. The manufacturer has recently added a blue dye to the drug so that when placed in a drink the liquid will turn blue. Do not drink blue liquids that are given to you! Unfortunately, most drugs used as "date rape drugs" are not easily detectable. For example, **Clonazepam** (**Klonopin**, **Rivotril** or **Rivatril**), a prescription drug used to treat panic disorder and seizures, can leave a victim in a coma-like sleep, helpless and unable to remember details of previous events.

Ketamine (K, Kitties, Ket, Vitamin K, mean green, or Special K) is an anesthetic used primarily by veterinarians. It is also experimentally used in the treatment of depression and addictions. It can be smoked, injected, or drunk. The effects of **ketamine** include high blood pressure, amnesia, depression, and impairment in attention, learning, memory, motor ability, and breathing. Ketamine is also used recreationally as a performance drug or for relaxation. It can produce **hallucinations** and a dissociative state giving the user a sense of detachment. At high doses a user may experience what is called the "**K-hole**," in which effects similar to schizophrenia occur; a condition that can be very unpleasant. Ketamine, by the way, has been found in some strains of **Ecstasy**.

"**Poppers**" is the slang term used for **amyl nitrite** when used recreationally. This is a prescription medicine that lowers blood pressure, relaxes muscles, and increases heart rate. It is used as a club drug by inhaling the vapors, often in combination with alcohol, Ecstasy, or cocaine. Sometimes amyl nitrite poppers are used to stimulate a user who is suffering withdrawal symptoms of depression and anxiety. Poppers can cause visual problems and neurological damage. If the liquid is accidentally swallowed it can be fatal.

Newer club drugs are being manufactured and introduced faster than anyone can keep up with. **Designer drugs** such as **2C-B, 2C-C, 2C-D, 2C-E**, and so on, and **2C-T-2, 2C-T-2, 2C-T-7**, and so on, and many similar concoctions are now being found in dance clubs. They are synthetic versions of a naturally occurring psychoactive substance called **phenethylamine**, a stimulant found in small amounts in a number of plants and foods. So-called **substituted amphetamines** include **methamphetamine** and **Ecstasy**. Popular in recent years is **mephedrone**, known as meph, drone, M4, or MCAT (because it is similar to **cathine** found in the **khat** plant mentioned on page 90), and sold as **plant food** or **bath salts** to elude drug laws. This designer drug is a stimulant and hallucinogen with effects similar to cocaine or Ecstasy. Common side effects include teeth grinding, poor concentration and memory, hallucinations, rapid heart beat, anxiety, paranoia, and depression. These club drugs are often used in combination with other psychoactive drugs such as GHB or alcohol. They have no medical uses. Of course, they are sometimes dangerous, even fatal, as revealed in the story that began this chapter.

As you can see, **club drugs** are used for their intoxicating effects, for relaxation, for enhanced performance, or for stimulation. They are all potentially dangerous, can cause brain damage and death. Unfortunately, many club drugs are colorless, odorless, and tasteless, and therefore can be used secretly to sedate others. Although club drugs are dangerous and harmful to the brain, apparently this fact is not known, is discounted, or is not sufficiently strong enough to deter users. **Teenager's** brains do not have well-developed **frontal lobes** and this may account to some extent for the widespread use of dangerous substances by adolescents and young adults. Maturation of the brain is not completed until the late 20s or 30 years of age. The dangers of club drugs are well-known to experts who study these substances, but this information has not had significant success in stemming the use of such drugs.

There are literally hundreds of psychedelic drugs, designer drugs, and club drugs that have been created in recent years, too many for scientists to actively study or for legislators to pass laws against. Regulating such drugs is difficult because chemical designers can tweak the drug formulas very easily and create new drugs that have much the same effect as their banned cousins.

If a particular drug is declared illegal, a drug that will produce similar psychological effects can be created by changing one or two molecules. Federal laws that attempt to ban "**cousin drugs**" (in chemistry, the term "**congener**" means substances related to each other) still cannot completely cover the vast ground of designer drug manufacturing, though that is the common approach taken today. And, unfortunately, as mentioned above, our prisons are full of people incarcerated for using illegal drugs; an expensive and devastating situation.

Treatment

In Ancient Greece when there was a problem, such as famine, disease, or flood, or if an important person was sick, then a human scapegoat was sacrificed as a religious ritual meant to remedy the problem. A slave, criminal, or disabled person was selected to be the **scapegoat**, and was known as a *pharmakos*. Variations of this term were used to refer to a wizard, and then later to poisons, perfumes, and other remedies or spell-giving potions. From these rather strange and upsetting beginnings we get the term, **pharmacology**, the scientific study of how drugs affect the brain and body.

There are over 22 million people in the United States with **substance abuse** problems, and there are estimates that as many as 100 million Americans have problems related to prescription drugs, illicit drugs, or behaviors such as gambling. Only about one-fourth receive any type of treatment for their addiction. And, here's another major problem: Over 80% of U.S. prison inmates are being held on drug-related charges. That's right: 80%! Not only is it hugely expensive and perhaps inhumane to incarcerate so many people, but in addition the vast majority of inmates do not receive any treatment for their addictions and will very likely return to using when they are released. Most addictions are chronic, and addicts experience frequent relapses. While appropriate treatments vary depending on the drug, duration of the addiction, the individual, and other circumstances, in general the most effective treatments combine medications with behavioral therapies.

Naturally, it is common to ask why addicts don't just use their **willpower** to resist drugs. Even very intelligent people believe that willpower can control the use of drugs. For instance, the person with the highest recorded IQ score, Marilyn vos Savant, said, "Avoid using cigarettes, alcohol, and drugs as an alternative to being an interesting person." Humorous and good advice, but does it help anyone?

It would be good to repeat what was said about willpower in the first chapter of this book on motivation. Willpower is a brain process like any other psychological characteristic, and is stronger in some and weaker in others. Willpower is not an effective means of breaking an addiction because the biological changes made in the pleasure pathway as a part of drug dependence normally overwhelm the ability of the frontal lobe to restrain behavior. People addicted to food, drugs, sex, or behaviors such as gambling do not have enough willpower control in their frontal lobes to inhibit the powerful desires and needs emanating from the **limbic system**. However, that is not to say that mental control of desires cannot be learned. As addicts begin to recover from the

HEROIN DEATHS IN ANOKA, DAKOTA, HENNEPIN AND RAMSEY COUNTIES IN 2008 AND 2009

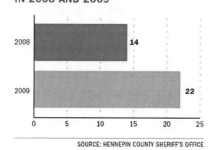

SOURCE: HENNEPIN COUNTY SHERIFF'S OFFICE

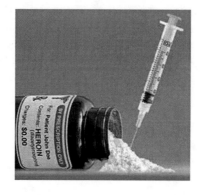

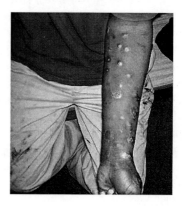

changes their brains have incurred, they will be ready for behavioral training in how to exert willpower over temptations. In the beginning of treatment, however, medical approaches are most important.

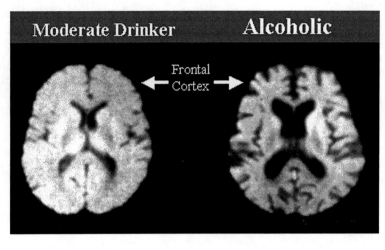

A major breakthrough in addiction treatment came in recent years with the creation of medicines that block opioid receptors. There are two such drugs: **naloxone**, which is used in emergencies to treat opiate overdose, and the similar, longer acting drug, **naltrexone**, which is used as a long-term control for opiate dependency. Both of these drugs are opioid receptor antagonists, and therefore reduce the effect of an opiate in binding at brain synapses in areas connected with pleasure and reward. The development of these drugs is a major breakthrough, though unfortunately, they are not effective for all people who have heroin or morphine addiction.

Amazingly, researchers discovered that blocking opioid receptors not only helps people with opiate addictions, but also helps reduce the craving and the pleasurable effects of **alcohol**. Therefore, some people addicted to alcohol can take naltrexone as an effective treatment. There are many such drugs, such as buprenorphine, that partially block opioid receptors and help addicts get off drugs. However, such medicines do not work on all addicts. It turns out that the nature of the opioid receptors and the type of motivation for drug abuse are both influenced by genetic factors which influence whether or not the treatment will work. That is, people with a particular genetic nature or a particular type of opioid receptor will respond favorably to these drugs, while people with different genes will not. This means that in the future diagnosis of drug addicts will need to be more specific, likely including genetic information, in order to prescribe appropriate treatments.

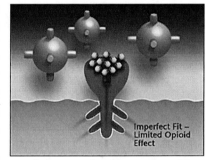

Medicines such as buprenorphine partially block opioid receptors thus preventing addictive drugs from activating the receptors.

Since all addictive drugs act on the **pleasure pathway**, often by stimulating opioid receptors, it is possible that naltrexone or similar medicines that block opioid receptors in the brain will be effective in the treatment of many different drug addictions, from cocaine to methamphetamine, not only for opiate and alcohol addictions.

Currently another drug is also used to help **opiate** addicts deal with **withdrawal** symptoms. Although chemically different from morphine and heroin, **methadone** is a synthetic (laboratory produced) opiate that acts on the brain's opioid receptors. Though methadone is sometimes used to treat chronic pain, it is more commonly used in the treatment of people who are addicted to opiates. Methadone is an agonist for opioids, binding to and activating receptors, and therefore produces some of the effects of opiates, but with fewer withdrawal symptoms. And, methadone is also an antagonist for the NMDA glutamate receptors; doing so helps to reduce the craving for morphine or heroin. When methadone is properly dosed for an individual it can help an addict reduce or even stop their dependence on opiates.

An **antioxidant** dietary supplement that naturally occurs in plants known as **ALCAR** (acetyl-l-carnitine) has been shown in laboratory mice to prevent brain damage from **alcohol** (Rump et al., 2010). Currently several drugs are used to treat alcoholism. **Antabuse** (disulfiram) is the oldest. Placed in alcohol, Antabuse causes the drinker to become nauseous and sick with severe discomfort, similar to a hangover. The idea is for the taste of alcohol to become repugnant to the user. Abstinence rates can reach as high as 50% with antabuse. **Campral** (acamprosate) is a glutamate antagonist that is used to stabilize brain chemistry thereby reducing the rate of relapse among alcoholics. An experimental drug called **Topamax** (topiramate) is also a glutamate antagonist and shows promise at reducing craving, lessening withdrawal symptoms, and helping alcohol abusers reduce the amount they drink. The **Sinclair Method** treats patients with a combination of **naltrexone** (mentioned above) and continued drinking.

Traditional methods of treating drug addiction, such as the twelve-step programs **Alcoholics Anonymous (AA)** and **Narcotics Anonymous (NA)**, have helped many people, but in general do not have very high success rates. Some estimates are around 10%. In fact, only about 5% of people who start AA continue for one year. That's a 95% drop out rate. Behavioral treatments have also had some success, but the overall success rates are lower than hoped. So, more and more scientists are turning to medications in search of more effective treatments.

The current model for treating drug addiction with **pharmaceuticals** involves first a **detoxification (detox)** process. Detox medications are used to withdraw patients from their chemical addiction, typically very quickly. Some of these medicines are substance imposters that mimic the addictive drug but without the side effects. Anti-craving medicines are also used during detox. Medical and psychological conditions that accompany addiction are also treated during detox, problems such as sleep disorders, eating disorders, pain, depression, and anxiety.

Second, contemporary addiction treatment relies on **stabilizing medicines**. An addict may have to take such medicines for a long period, even life-time. Some stabilizing medicines are specific to a particular psychoactive substance, such as naltrexone for heroin addiction. Many stabilizing medicines, however, target the neurotransmitters typically involved in addiction: dopamine, serotonin, and norepinephrine. These include antidepressant medicines. **Wellbutrin**, an antidepressant that inhibits reuptake of serotonin and norepinephrine, has been found to be useful in treating smoking addiction, for example.

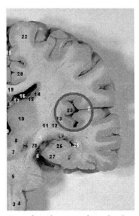

Insula shown in circle.

Scientists have recently been surprised to find that a part of the brain called the **insula** (literally = "island") is involved in drug abuse. The insula is formed by the curling and folding of the cerebral cortex inside the **temporal lobe**. The insula is an interior part of the brain, yet it is part of the cortex.

Brain imaging research has shown that this little island on the side of the head is activated when users take their drugs, and also, interestingly, the insula is active when a user is exposed to environmental stimuli or cues that are associated with their drug use. It is as if the insula helps connect the cravings with cues in the environment. Activation of the insula has been found to be connected to cocaine, alcohol, nicotine, and opiates, so this brain area seems not to be important for a specific drug, but rather is a reaction area for craving and cues.

Somewhat amazingly, it was reported that **cigarette smokers** who suffered damage to their **insulas** by strokes or brain tumors immediately lost their nicotine addiction almost entirely (Naqvi et al., 2007). Unbelievable! A related study found that inactivation of the insula in rats disrupted **amphetamine addiction** (Contreras et al., 2007). Could a treatment be based on these findings?

It is likely that the insula plays a role in remembering the pleasurable effects of a drug and anticipating them in the future, and this may make addicts feel that they need a drug. Lesions in the insula may interfere with memory and users may forget their body urges for the drug. The insula has not been a target of drug addiction research until now because scientists have been focusing on areas of the pleasure pathway. However, some experts are now saying that it is possible that treatments can be developed that act on the brain's insula.

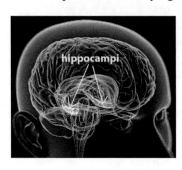

Another brain area that is receiving attention related to drug addiction is the **hippocampus**, the key learning and memory region. This curved area on the inside of the temporal lobe is one of the principal brain areas where new neurons are generated – a process called **neurogenesis**. It has previously been shown that people suffering from **depression** have reduced neurogenesis. Now, scientists are looking for similar effects of abused drugs. For instance, it has been discovered that high doses of cocaine reduce neurogenesis in the hippocampus and impair working memory (Sudai et al., 2011). It is known that antidepressant drugs can help increase the process of neurogenesis, and perhaps this offers another avenue of treatment for addictions.

Finally, the **frontal lobe** is, of course, important in controlling drug use. Alcohol, for example, is known to disrupt executive functions such as **working memory** in that brain area. It was recently discovered that training alcoholics to improve their working memories decreased their drinking (Houben, Wiers, & Jansen, 2011). So, effective treatments can be cognitive in nature.

Future Hopes

An old joke: A woman with alcohol addiction was holding an empty bottle of wine when a magic genie appeared and gave her three wishes. Her first wish was easy. She told the genie that she wanted the wine bottle to be continuously full. Presto! It was done. She drank from the bottle and it instantly filled with wine again. Then the genie asked what she wanted for her second and third wishes. "That's easy," the woman replied, "Two more of these."

Drug addiction is a chronic brain disorder. The neurobiology of addiction is beginning to be unraveled and the pace of discoveries is picking up. As brain scientists learn more about the physiological effects of addictive substances, it is likely that even more effective treatments will be developed, both pharmaceutical and behavioral. Let's hope that the drug overdose problem that was mentioned at the beginning of this chapter can be significantly abated soon.

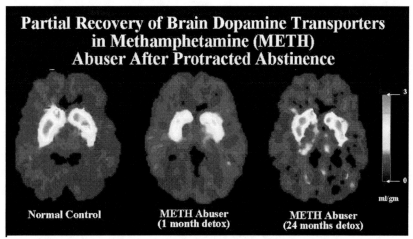

In some cases brains can partially recover from addiction after extended abstinence.

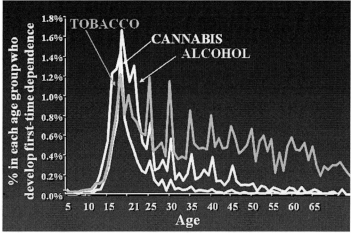

Addictions often begin quite early in life.

"So you want to be a rock 'n' roll star? Then listen now to what I say,
Just get an electric guitar, Then take some time, And learn how to play,
And with your hair swung right, And your pants too tight, It's gonna be all right.
Then it's time to go downtown, Where the agent man won't let you down.
Sell your soul to the company, Who are waiting there to sell plastic ware,
And in a week or two, If you make the charts, The girls'll tear you apart.
The price you paid for your riches and fame, Was it all a strange game?
You're a little insane, The money, the fame, the public acclaim,
Don't forget what you are, You're a rock 'n' roll star!"
– So You Want to be a Rock 'n' Roll Star by The Byrds

Chapter 5

Music

*P*erhaps you've noticed: Music is everywhere! Entertainment, bars, dance clubs, movies, weddings, funerals, sports, earphones, ballet, opera, nightclubs, restaurants, religious services, advertisements, and, well, everywhere! Anthropologists believe that all human cultures – past and present – have had music. As long as there have been people, and wherever there have been people, they have sung, danced, clapped their hands, plucked and stroked strings, threads, and wires, beat on drums of all sorts – animal skins, pieces of wood and rocks – they have banged objects together rhythmically, whistled, hummed, blown into tubes and holes in various forms of wood, glass, and metal, tapped their feet, moved to the beat, and shook their booties. Yup, music is everywhere.

What kind of music do you like? Have you heard the new album by Radiohead? Do you like to listen to Lady Gaga sing? Do you like jazz? Would you like to go to a symphony orchestra concert? Psychologists have shown that people use their **musical preferences** to communicate with others about their personalities (Rentfrow & Gosling, 2006). The researchers found that among strangers, music was the most common topic of conversation. Also, observers were able to form accurate impressions of the speakers' **personalities** based on their musical preferences.

But, what does it mean? What is music for? How did music come to be such a huge part of our world? Philosopher Friedrich Nietzsche said, "Without music, life would be a mistake." Is the human brain designed for music processing or did it just happen as part of culture and civilization? How did **music perception** in the brain evolve? Why? And, how does the brain create and process music? Music is the most curious, weird, bizarre, and downright unexplainable feature of human brains that science has attempted to understand. It doesn't seem to serve any purpose at all! What in the world is it for? It's not like eating, drinking, sex, or…well, anything else! So, then, why do we have music?

Evolution

Some experts believe that the oldest known musical instrument unearthed by archaeologists is a primitive "flute" that was found in a **Neanderthal** campsite in Slovenia in 1995 and is considered to be approximately 45,000 years old. It was made from the bone of a bear's leg and has four holes in it. It was featured on the cover of *Time* magazine and can be seen today in a museum in Slovenia. However, many experts believe the holes were made by an animal's teeth while gnawing on it and that it is just a coincidence that it looks like a primitive flute. Close examination did reveal bite marks on the bone. **Steven Mithen** (2006), a British professor of early prehistory, believes that Neanderthals did not have the cognitive ability to create a musical instrument from a bone. He believes that Neanderthals' thinking was **domain-specific** and they would

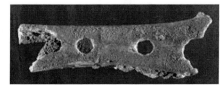

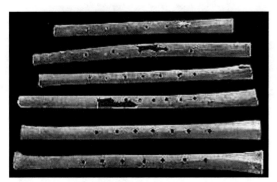

Ancient Chinese flutes.

not have been able to mentally conceive of a bone as a device of social interaction. Mithen does, however, believe that there is good evidence that Neanderthals engaged in singing and dancing, and probably tapped their feet, beat their hands, and maybe used sticks or bones to beat to the music. But he does not think they had the intellectual ability to alter items for a function entirely out of the object's domain.

While some experts aren't convinced that the Neanderthal bone was intended as a flute, some instruments (bones with holes) that are very well-preserved were clearly intended and used as flutes. One such instrument was found in Germany in 2008 and is dated at about 40,000 years old. It was made from the bone of a bird. Also, early musical instruments were found in China that are about 9,000 years old. These flutes produce a **diatonic scale** (the familiar seven-note, octave repeating musical scale you hear all the time).

Ancient written musical compositions have been found, too. The oldest written musical score is about 3,500 years old, is Sumerian (a civilization of the Ancient Near East region located in southeastern Iraq, what was known as Mesopotamia), and appears to conform to a diatonic scale. Archaeologists have found many instruments and music scores from a wide range of ancient civilizations. Does this mean that music is not a cultural convention, not an activity specific to one or two civilizations, but rather that music is an innate, universal, evolutionary feature of human brains?

An ancient flute and a modern Kaluli musician.

Okay, first, let's note (pun intended!) that music from one culture to another can be quite variable. Some cultures don't even have a word for music. And, people in Western societies might not even recognize as music some of the music created in other cultures. Whereas Western cultures emphasize the difference between consonant and dissonant sounds in music, this is not a practice in some other cultures, for example in Indonesian **gamelan** music (see Perlman, 2004, for a description of gamelan music). While music of **Western cultures** stresses pitch and melody, some African music focuses on rhythm, beat, and tempo.

In some **non-Western societies** music cannot be separated from its social purpose. Music defines social relations for some native South Africans. Music is communion with the dead for Kaluli people of Papua New Guinea. Amazingly, the peoples of some societies would not recognize as music the songs that come from our radios because the tunes are disconnected from context – social, cultural, or familial ritual. The idea of finding pleasure in listening to these sounds would be absurd and confusing to peoples of some cultures. Music, some experts contend, would be better defined not by sound qualities, but by the purposes, meanings, and social/cultural contexts of the experience. The global study of the social and cultural aspects of music and dance is called **ethnomusicology**. Music differs in profound respects in various regions around the globe. But, are there similarities to be found in the music around the world?

Music theorist **Daniel Levitin** (2008) attempts to explain the role of music in human nature by categorizing music into six purposes: songs of friendship, joy, comfort, knowledge, religion, and love. Could you think of another category of songs important for evolution? Levitin argues that music is not a distraction, but evolved as a core element of our identity as a species. Well, perhaps. Despite the variability from one culture to another, every human society has music of some sort. The great Russian author Leo Tolstoy exclaimed, "Music is the shorthand of emotion." But, why would music create emotions in the brain? What is the function of music for humans? Did the human brain evolve to perceive music for some survival purpose? That is, is music an evolutionary **adaptation**? And, is the human brain's ability to perceive music mostly innate or mostly learned?

Animals

For an answer, one might first look to **comparative anthropology**. Do lower animals perceive music the way humans do? Birds, primates, whales, and some other animals make what appear to be songs. Is that music? Well, no, probably not, at least not the way we typically think of music. Animal songs seem to be only for communication and they appear only when animals are marking territory, or signaling courtship, mating, or danger. Lower animals do not appear to use songs for pleasure or entertainment. Also, research on lower animals shows that they do not respond to small changes in pitch or other features of music in the same way that humans do (McDermott & Hauser, 2005). Even human infants respond to small changes in pitch that are not noticed by lower animals.

Coming soon to "American Idol"?

In addition, nearly all comparative research shows that lower animals do not distinguish anything like **melody**, though in some cases can recognize octaves. In one study D'Amato et al. (1988) trained monkeys to respond to a **melody** in order to get food. Later, the monkeys were presented with the same melody an octave higher or lower. Would the monkeys recognize the melody even though it was an octave different and respond to get food? No, they did not. The monkeys were responding to the specific sounds and not to the melodic pattern. They did not recognize the melody.

So, nearly all comparative research shows lower animals lacking in the ability to perceive music as humans do. However, there are exceptions, including: Birds do sing in chorus, a cockatoo was found that dances to the beat of music, gerbils were able to learn to respond differentially to very large changes in pitch (Ohl et al., 2001), and two rhesus monkeys were able to learn to recognize melodies over a change of an octave when given a task involving same/different judgments (Wright et al., 2000). In summary, though there are not a large number of studies of music perception in lower animals, with a few minor exceptions it appears that the brains of lower animals generally do not recognize music in an equivalent manner that human brains do.

Infants

What about human **infants**? Is music hard-wired into the human brain? A fair amount of research has been done on this question and the results do show good evidence of hard-wired music abilities. It appears that certain features of music are innate to a large extent, although learning and cultural experiences play a role, too, in shaping the brain's perception of music. For instance, 8-month old infants react to a transposed variation of a **melody** much the same as do adults (Plantinga & Trainor, 2005). Infants also generalize the tempo of music (Trehub & Hannon, 2006). And, here's something you've experienced: Parents all over the world sing **lullabies** to their infants, and these lullabies are similar in their characteristics and are recognizable as lullabies no matter which culture they derive from. Lullabies use higher pitch and slower tempo than other music, and do seem to reveal a true universality in music. Infants even seem to prefer lullabies to adult music (Trehub, 2000). Similarly, 4-month old infants show a preference for **consonant** music as opposed to **dissonant** music (Zentner & Kagan, 1998). So, there is evidence that at least to some extent some aspects of music may be an evolutionary adaptation programmed into the human brain.

On the other hand, there is good experimental evidence that responses to music by infants and children are not always the same as those made by adults (Lynch et al., 1990). It appears that infants are sensitive to a wide range of musical elements but then lose some of that sensitivity as they are exposed to particular kinds of music and their brains consequently adapt to their experiences. Many experts have compared this concept to how **language** develops in the human brain. Language develops easily and quickly in children under about age 6, whose brains seem open to all different language sounds. But as children develop within one language community, learning a new language becomes more difficult and the early learned patterns, such as accents, are hard to modify.

Music development seems similar to language development, too, in that infants show immediate recognition of pitch and are open to a wide range of musical qualities, but after a few years of experience they seem to become less sensitive to unfamiliar patterns of music and become more sensitive to familiar music. Music researcher **Aniruddh Patel** (2008), in particular, has argued that music and language evolved together or

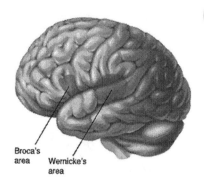

Broca's area   Wernicke's area

in close coordination in the human brain. He argues that music and speech may rely on shared brain processing of syntax and tonality. Well, it's true: Both music perception and speech perception depend to some extent on changes in pitch, syntax, and rhythm. And, music and language coexist in all cultures.

Also in support of this idea: Some brain imaging research has shown an overlap of **music perception** into the **language** areas of the brain (Levitin & Menon, 2003). Music cognition researchers McDermott and Hauser (2005) concluded from their research studies: "Evidently the exposure to music that occurs during human development renders adults insensitive to unfamiliar musical structures, paralleling the case for language acquisition." In fact, this acculturation to familiar music has been found to have an effect as early as one year of age (Lynch & Eilers, 1992). So, perhaps music perception, like language, is an **adaptation** that evolved in human culture for some survival or reproductive advantage.

Evolution Again

Naturally, (wouldn't you just know it?), not all experts agree. Cognitive scientist **Steven Pinker** in *How the Mind Works* (1997) argues that music is clearly not an evolutionary adaptation, as is language, and wonders what benefit there could be in "diverting time and energy to making plinking noises?" Though musical himself, he states that music is useless and clearly a technology that was developed and exploited for its own sake, and not an evolved human feature with a survival advantage. Pinker calls music "**auditory cheesecake**" and suggests that music is a side effect of the brain's auditory system. By the way, the **cheesecake** remark has been noticed by lots of other experts, and usually not with glee – **Steven Mithen** even has a chapter in his book, *The Singing Neanderthals* (2005), called "More Than Cheesecake?" Writing in 2007, Pinker commented about the arts in general: "They may be by-products of two other traits: motivational systems that give us pleasure… and technological know-how…" So, Pinker (and some others) sees music (and other arts) as by-products of human abilities, not as evolutionary adaptations in and of themselves.

Steven Pinker.

Well, as you might expect, not very many evolutionary psychologists and anthropologists concur with Pinker's assessment. Musicologist **Ian Cross** (2009) argues that music is deeply rooted in human biology and is important for children's cognitive development. **Aniruddh Patel** has argued that it is a false dichotomy to conclude that if something is not an evolutionary adaptation that it is a "frill." Patel writes, "Music may be a human invention, but if so, it resembles the ability to make and control fire: It is something we invented that transforms human life. Indeed, music is more remarkable than fire in some ways, because not only is it a product of our brain's mental capacities, it also has the power to change our brain."

Research Professor **Alison Wray (2008)** believes that the evolution of music is intertwined with the development of **language**; in fact, most evolutionary psychologists study music and language together because they both depend on analysis of sounds and sequences. Musicologist **Stephen Brown** (2000) holds the view that music and language both evolved from an earlier form of communication that he calls "**musilanguage**," which is an idea very similar to that of Alison Wray who uses the term "**holistic proto-language**." Well, it's almost a chicken-egg dilemma with music and language. Which came first, or did something else lead to both of them? The evolution of language certainly can be easily understood as having value for survival and reproduction. But what about the evolution of music?

A large number of ideas have been proposed to explain how music (and the other arts, as well – in fact, where there is music, there is dancing!) may have evolved as a human adaptation. In seeking an answer to what **survival value** music proffered upon early humans, anthropologists and **evolutionary psychologists** have suggested some tantalizing hypotheses. Some theorists have stressed music's connection to sociality, some to communication, some to group processes, group interaction, and resources, some to mother-infant bonding, some to general cognitive processes (classification and categorizing), some to mood regulation and emotions (fight or flight), and some to individual fitness (Barrett & Dunbar, 2007). While there is great speculation, and some nay-sayers like Pinker, it is apparent that music affects us, pervades us, and is ubiquitous. Music, obviously, is a large part of our world, whether an evolutionary adaptation or not, and an endlessly fascinating and enigmatic topic. Next, exactly what is music and how is it created and processed by the brain?

Music Perception

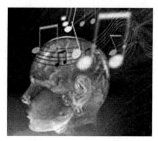

If a radio is playing a song, but no one is there to hear it, does it make music? Well, actually, no. Music is created by the brain; it does not exist in the world outside the brain. What? Yes, that's right, music is the result of **perception**. It is the brain's **interpretation** of the physical characteristics that are received via the ear and processed by numerous neural activities in the brain. It's just like color. Color isn't out there, either. Color and music exist in the mind, created by the brain's perception of physical properties in the outside world that are converted by the eyes or the ears into neural energy. Music – da da DA, dadada, da da DA – is perceived, interpreted, created by the brain. So, if a radio is playing and there is no one there, well, then there are only physical characteristics (sound waves in the air), not music. Sha-la-la-la-la.

The most common question about music and the brain is this: Where (or how) is music perceived in the human brain? The answer might surprise you: Music is perceived all over the place in the brain! There is not one, single place for music perception in the brain because music is so complex. It has melody, rhythm, pacing, notes, beat, and other characteristics. Music perception and creation is **distributed** throughout the brain.

Also, music in the brain requires many sensory and cognitive processes. We need auditory processing, detection of rhythm and pitch, and cognitive processes such as attention, classification, and memory. So, there is not just one place or one brain process, one "where" or one "how" of music in or by the brain, but rather there are multiple places and multiple ways in which music is perceived. This is because music is a complicated phenomenon with multiple elements that need to be processed and bound together in the brain. Music researcher **Daniel Levitin** (2006) summarized: "Music is distributed throughout the brain. Music listening, performance, and composition engage nearly every area of the brain that we have so far identified and involve nearly every neural subsystem." Yes, music activates so many brain areas partly because music is so complex, incorporating many separate components.

Okay then: What is music? Well, that's a tough one. Scientists and musicologists simply do not agree on an answer. That's right: There is no definition of music on which all experts can agree! Music is not just sound or noise, somehow it is something more or different. Music is something like *organized* sounds. That definition was first used by avant-garde composer **Edgar Varese** who wrote such innovative music in the early 1900s that some people did not call it music. Varese included howling, scraping, ambient rumbling, machine noises, and honking in his compositions. Of course, even experts won't agree on that definition. For example, playing one note over and over again would be organized sound, but not many people would call it music: A A A A A A A A A A A A... However, some experts in fact *would* call this repetitive note music because it has an organized pattern of presenting that one note over and over again. What do you think – music or not music?

John Cage.

All definitions of music were thrown for a loop in 1952 when avant-garde musician **John Cage** introduced his composition *4'33"*. The piece is four minutes and 33 seconds of silence! Well, not silence exactly, since as Cage sat at the piano (not playing even one note) the audience made many sounds of coughing, shuffling feet, whispering, clearing throats, and so on. That was the musical piece – the sounds the audience made. Or, was it music? Did it meet Varese's definition: organized sounds? Jazz great **Dizzie Gillespie** said, "I don't care much about music. What I like is sounds." And, the so-called King of Rock 'n' Roll **Elvis Presley** added, "I don't know anything about music. In my line you don't have to."

As you know, there is an extremely wide range of music: jazz, polkas, doo wop, marches, pop, waltzes, folk, salsa, Tibetan chants, funk, freakbeat, classical, bluegrass, the blues, sludge metal, punk, alt rock, country....well, you get the idea. Did you ever think about this: We often translate languages from one to another, but who would try to translate one style of music to another, and why? Would it be fun to translate a waltz into punk rock?

Though we can't get experts to agree on a definition of music, I think we can agree that most people know music when they hear it; or, at least *think* they know music when they hear it. Perhaps that is good enough for now. Let's move on to discuss some of the basic elements of music (organized sounds).

Pitch In

Are you ready? Now, here's what I want you to do: Sing or hum a little ditty, a little tune. Right now. Really. That's right: Sing or hum a little song. Or, part of a song. Like *Happy Birthday To You* or *Mary Had a Little Lamb* or *Twinkle, Twinkle Little Star* or *Stairway to Heaven* or *I Wanna Hold Your Hand* or, well, anything. Choose a little ditty and sing or hum it right now. Out loud. Out loud! Do it – it will help you understand what is explained below. Go ahead, sing or hum. I'll wait.

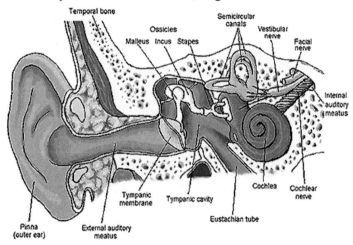

Done? Okay. Now, when you sang or hummed that little song, you were using several components of music. First, you used **pitch**, perhaps the most important element. Pitch is the brain's perception of the frequency of vibrations. Imagine your vocal chords vibrating, or a string being plucked. The string vibrates, and so does the air around it. The vibration goes to your outer ear and is then guided and directed to your **eardrum** (**tympanic membrane**) and there the exact vibration continues via three small bones (the **ossicles**) in your middle ear to an organ called the **cochlea** in the inner ear. The cochlea is shaped as a spiral, like a snail's shell. Inside the cochlea is a band of about 3,500 hair cells strung out something like the keys on a spiral piano. The hair cells are strung out along a band that varies in thickness and width called the **basilar membrane**, which is at the base of the part of the inner ear, the **organ of Corti**, that converts sound waves into electrical signals.

So, the brain is not using the *physical* properties of sound, but rather, the brain translates or converts physical sound into *neural* signals (electrical and chemical processes). Hearing is not a mechanical event, it is a *perceptual* event. The scientific study of sound perception, including speech and music, is called **psychoacoustics** (**acoustics** is the science of mechanical waves, most notably those waves important for human hearing). The inner ear and brain use biological processes to perceive sounds.

The microphone inside the ear was discovered in 1851 by Italian physiologist **Alfonso Corti**, and hence is called the **organ of Corti**. This complex sensory organ is surrounded by fluid and is protected by being packed into the hardest bone in the body. Different hair cells inside the cochlea respond to different vibrations

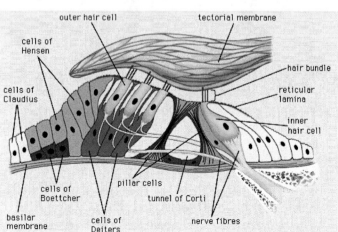

because of the varying thickness and width of the **basilar membrane**. Some cells fire more when a high frequency sound wave enters the cochlea, some fire more for a low frequency wave, and some in between. Electrical signals are created by the cells as they respond to the vibrations of sound waves, and those electrical signals are then transmitted to the brain. Where do they go?

An area of the **brainstem** first receives the signals from the inner ear, and the cells in that area of the brainstem are arranged just as in the cochlea. The importance of the brainstem was revealed by research that found **musicians** had enhanced processing for both music and speech because of musical training that affected **brainstem** activity (Musacchia et al., 2007). The researchers summarized: "Musical training is known to modify cortical organization. Here, we show that such modifications extend to subcortical sensory structures and generalize to processing of speech. Musicians had earlier and larger brainstem responses than nonmusician controls to both speech and music stimuli presented in auditory and audiovisual conditions."

Well, while most scientists believed, and maybe still believe, that the **brainstem** is merely a transition area, it appears that the area of the brainstem that receives signals from the cochlea is, in fact, actively involved in complex processing of auditory information. It is interesting that both verbal ability and music perception were enhanced by musical experience, once again showing the links between music and language in the brain. The two functions language and music have shared neural circuits. By the way, another study found different responses in the brainstem for harmonious and disharmonious sounds, suggesting that the brainstem reacts somewhat to **harmony** in music (Bridelman & Krishnan, 2009).

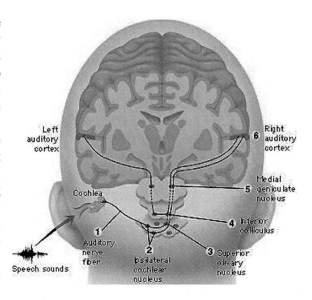

From the brainstem the electrical signals then course through various brain areas and eventually reach the cerebral cortex. The **primary auditory cortex** in the temporal lobe is the main area of interpretation of incoming sounds. At the top of the temporal lobe is a bump (**gyrus**), known as the **superior** (at the top) **temporal gyrus**. In the middle of this bump is the primary auditory cortex, also known as **Heschl's gyrus**, which is located just in front of the language area known as **Wernicke's area** at the very top of the temporal lobe. When looking at the side of a brain it is difficult to see the auditory cortex because it is hidden deep within the groove or wrinkle known as the **lateral fissure**.

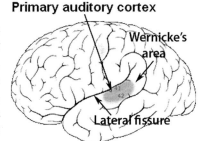

The **primary auditory cortex** is laid out in columns of cells that are a bit similar to a **piano keyboard** in that they respond to **frequency** information. Since frequency is a terribly important part of our environment (cues about sounds helped survival – a predator stepping on a stick before attacking its prey gives a subtle warning), animals and humans have evolved innate brain mechanisms for interpreting different sounds. Pitch perception has been identified in many different animals. For example, a "**pitch center**" was found in the temporal lobes of monkeys (Wang, 2005). The research measured the firing of individual neurons near the primary auditory cortex and found brain cells that respond to notes of a certain pitch regardless of what instruments are playing the notes. That is, there appear to be pitch sensitive neurons in the **temporal lobe**, particular brain cells in the cortex that respond to the note of C or G, for instance, whether played by a violin or a trumpet.

𝕻itch 𝕺ut

Hungarian composer and conductor George Szell remarked, "In music one must think with the heart and feel with the brain."

Perception of pitch is important in many ways; for instance in detecting patterns of speech that would indicate emotion, or when the speaker is asking a question (the pitch rises at the end of the sentence), and also pitch helps to cue a listener to the age or gender of a speaker. Obviously, men tend to have lower voices than women. This difference was undoubtedly important in evolutionary history. Researchers have found, for example, that women raise the pitch of their voice (making it more feminine) just before and during ovulation, thus signaling to a mate that reproduction is possible (Bryant & Haselton, 2008), and that men with lower pitched voices have more children than men with higher pitched voices (Apicella et al., 2007). It's likely that **vocal dimorphism** evolved partly due to its value in mate selection.

There is a primary auditory area on each side of the brain, left and right. Each ear sends signals to both the left and right hemispheres, but a little more is sent to the opposite (**contralateral**) hemisphere than to the same-sided (**ipsilateral**) hemisphere by each ear. The primary auditory cortex then parcels out information to nearby,

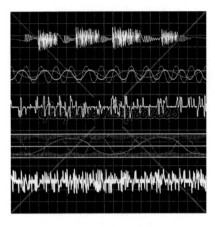

surrounding regions of the temporal lobe known as the **secondary auditory cortex**. It is here that more complex analysis occurs. The primary auditory cortex focuses on the properties of an individual sound, while the secondary auditory cortex analyzes the relationships between sounds. For example, the order of sounds or words, known as **syntax**, is processed mostly by cells just in front of the primary auditory cortex as well as in the frontal lobe.

Okay, when you sang your little ditty, you made a number of **tones**, or musical sounds, sometimes referred to as **notes**, though the term note more accurately refers to the **written** symbol for a tone. Music is made of tones. Some of the ingredients of music include the way tones vibrate, the way tones are organized into patterns, and the subjective nature of our perceptions of notes. Tones in a particular order can make a **melody**. The timing of the notes makes **rhythm**. These and other elements of music are processed in the brain to give us our perception of, and emotional reaction to, a musical piece. If you are interested in learning more about the elements of music, they are keenly described by **Philip Ball** in his book, *The Music Instinct; How Music Works and Why We Can't Live Without It* (2010).

One of the key elements the brain uses to perceive music is the vibration made by a tone. For example, in the little tune you just sang, each tone (or note) that you made had a **pitch**. That is, you sang or hummed some high tones and some low tones. The **vibrations** (waves) that you made with your voice went to your inner ear and were converted to electrical signals that went to your brain. Vibrations occur at different **frequencies** (rates of vibrating). A string (similar to your vocal cords) can vibrate very fast, or very slow, or anywhere in between (by the way, when you blow into a flute or similar instrument you are making the tube vibrate and consequently the air inside it and around it will vibrate at the same frequency).

Frequencies are measured in cycles per second, which are called **hertz (Hz)**. This unit of measurement (one Hz equals one cycle of vibration) is named after German physicist **Heinrich Hertz** who studied various kinds of sound waves. When asked what practical value there was in radio waves, Hertz famously shrugged and answered, "None." Incidentally, it's the same answer that was given by the inventor of movies when asked what practical value they had. Okay, so inventors don't know everything! Now back to vibrations: Fast frequencies (thousands of cycles per second), like that made by the squeal of a pig, are perceived by the brain as a **high pitch**. Slow vibrations (not very many cycles per second, like vibrations made by a truck roaring down the highway) are called **low pitch**.

The human ear can hear frequencies from about 20 Hz to 20,000 Hz. That's a heck of a range! Imagine a string vibrating back and forth 20,000 times in one second! Vibrations slower than 20 cycles in a second cannot be heard by humans. Ditto for vibrations faster than 20,000 cycles in a second. However, at the extremes of this range sound is mushy, unclear, and not musical in any way. For practical purposes, we normally hear frequencies from about 30 to 12,000 Hz. The frequencies that enter our ears will be perceived by the brain as various pitches. If we vibrate a string at 140 cycles per second, then your tympanic membrane (ear drum) will vibrate at 140 Hz. That vibration will be transferred to the basilar membrane where certain cells will increase their rate of firing because of this particular vibration. The electrical signals that are created will be delivered to the brain where they will be processed.

Octaves

Conductor Leopold Stokowski said, "A painter paints pictures on canvas. But musicians paint their pictures on silence."

There are seven whole notes in the **diatonic scale**, the scale you are familiar with that we most often use for music. The notes are named A, B, C, D, E, F, and G. Notes that fall between these are called **sharps** or **flats** (C sharp is the same as D flat). The eighth note makes the same vibration frequency as the first, but doubled. The note called 'A' has a frequency of 110 Hz. This standard was set by a committee in 1939. Before that, there was no standard for the exact pitches of the notes. Therefore, a flute made in England, for example, was set to a slightly different 'A' tone than a flute made in Germany. You could not be in a band with instruments made in

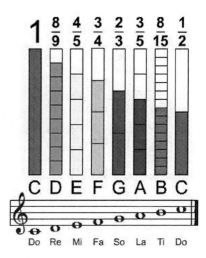

different places before 1939 because the instruments would be out of tune with each other. However, a stringed instrument such as a guitar or violin does not have this problem since the tension of a string can be adjusted to set the pitch of the string.

Today, a tone of 'A' has a frequency of 110 Hz. If we vibrate a string at 220 cycles per second, we also call that pitch 'A;' it is one **octave** higher than 110 Hz. A frequency of 330 Hz would also be a note called 'A.' And so on. Perhaps you are familiar with the term used for a particular key on a piano: "middle C." This term means the C that is in the middle of the piano; there are Cs lower and Cs higher than middle C on the piano keyboard.

When we twang a string it vibrates at more than one frequency. When these frequencies are multiples of each other, our brain hears the pitch of the lowest, base frequency. So, for example, a string set to the key of A will vibrate at 110 Hz, 220 Hz, and 330 Hz, but your brain hears the note at 110 Hz, the basic pitch we call "A." The lowest frequency is called the **fundamental**; it is what we notice, what we perceive, although trained experts can also hear the other vibrations which are known as **overtones**. The resulting sound is called **harmonic** and the brain responds by **synchronizing** the firing of cells in the auditory cortex.

There is good evidence that the ability to perceive **octaves** is present in lower animals and in human infants. The **octave**, thus, is a primary, essential ingredient of auditory perception that is dependent on fundamental brain physiology and neural processes. That is, brains are wired to perceive octaves. A young ear can hear about ten octaves, and most of us can distinguish sounds that are only one-seventeenth of a note apart.

A piano has the widest pitch range of any musical instrument, from 27.5 to 4,186 Hz. A typical adult male voice ranges from 85 to 180 Hz, and that of a typical adult female from 165 to 255 Hz. A violin has a frequency range of 196 to 3,136 Hz, and a guitar from 83 to 880 Hz. A cymbal can be as high as 15,000 Hz.

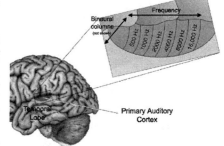

The auditory cortex of the human brain contains cells that respond to frequencies in a direct "map" called **tonotopic**. This direct mapping of pitch by the cells of the brain suggests that pitch was an important survival factor in human evolution. The mapping in the cortex is so precise that if we could monitor the firing of those cells of the auditory cortex in a person listening to a single note we could tell exactly what pitch the person is hearing. Astonishingly, a similar experiment was done using a lower brain area in a barn owl!

Researcher **Petr Janata** placed electrodes into a main area of the auditory pathway known as the **inferior colliculus** of a barn owl. This part of the midbrain is a major intersection of cells that respond to incoming auditory messages in order to analyze those sounds (the **superior colliculus**, just above, is a major brain area for integrating incoming visual signals). Now the interesting part: Janata played for the owl a song that was missing the fundamental frequencies such that each note only contained the overtones. We know that a note that normally vibrates at 110, 220, 330, and 440 Hz is heard by the brain at 110 Hz. But, amazingly, if the overtones are played missing the fundamental frequency (110 Hz), a human

brain will still hear the fundamental pitch. Brains are acutely attuned to hearing the fundamental part of a note – will fill it in when hearing the overtones. Apparently, the ability to hear the missing fundamental develops around the age of 3 or 4 months (He & Trainor, 2009). So, what did the barn owl hear? Janata connected the electrodes that were placed into the inferior colliculus of the owl to an amplifier with speakers. Now here's the astonishing part: What came out of the speakers was the song that he had played to the owl, but it was playing at the fundamental frequencies of the notes!

That means the cells in the owl's brain were firing at the same rate as the missing fundamental frequencies of the song the owl was listening to. So, just as with humans, an owl's brain fills in the missing base frequency when hearing overtones. Cool, huh?

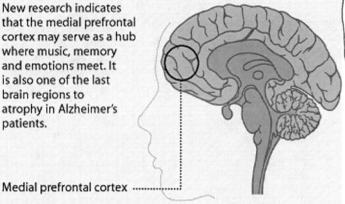

New research indicates that the medial prefrontal cortex may serve as a hub where music, memory and emotions meet. It is also one of the last brain regions to atrophy in Alzheimer's patients.

Medial prefrontal cortex ············

Janata's team, using fMRI, identified an area of the prefrontal cortex that tracks musical tones (Janata et al., 2002), and Janata also found the prefrontal cortex responds when autobiographical memories are triggered by music (Janata, 2009).

Janata hypothesizes that the **medial prefrontal cortex** is the nexus of music, emotions, and memory in the brain. That is the area that brings it all together. "What seems to happen is that a piece of familiar music serves as a soundtrack for a mental movie that starts playing in our head. It calls back memories of a particular person or place, and you might all of a sudden see that person's face in your mind's eye," Janata said. "Now we can see the association between those two things—the music and the memories."

In Harmony

Now, here's something obvious: Certain combinations of musical notes can sound pleasing to us, while other musical patterns are unpleasant to most human ears (though there is sometimes disagreement between individuals, and particularly between cultures, as you are likely aware). When two or more pitches are sung together simultaneously, we get **harmony** (from the Greek for *join together*). It is generally believed by music researchers that sound frequency (pitch) is represented in subcortical (lower) areas of the brain, but that the integration of notes into harmonics does not occur until the auditory signals reach the primary auditory area in the cortex (Bendor & Wang, 2005). However, Bidelman & Krishnan (2020) found different responses in the **brainstem** to pleasant harmonies than to unpleasant ones, and concluded, "Basic pitch relationships governing music may be rooted in low-level sensory processing and an encoding scheme that favors consonant pitch relationships may be one reason why such intervals are preferred behaviorally."

Yes, some harmonies sound better to us than others. If you play two keys of a piano at the same time you can demonstrate this phenomenon. Playing at the same time two white keys on a piano that are right next to each other makes a sound that nearly everyone finds unpleasant (**dissonant**), while playing at the same time two white keys that are separated by three white key makes a **consonant** (pleasant) sound to human ears. Any two sounds have different frequencies (vibrations) and sometimes these two frequencies mix together well (they are compatible with each other) and sometimes they do not mix well, they fight against each other. The former are processed in the brain as a pleasant harmony, while the latter are judged to be dissonant and unpleasant.

In a musical sequence, the distance between one note and the next is called an **interval**. When we listen to a piece of music, the changes in pitch from one note to another are called intervals and are based on the number of staff positions from one note to the next. The interval from C to E is a called a major third, while C to A is called a major sixth (six staff positions from C to A). **Dissonant** sounds can get people quite aroused, even upset, which shows the power of music to move us emotionally.

Amazingly, at one time the Catholic Church even banned certain musical combinations that sounded dissonant or unpleasant. Music that contained more than one part playing at a time (**polyphonic**) or musical intervals that were excessively dissonant were considered the work of the devil and were not allowed in church music. For instance, an augmented fourth or **tritone** was considered diabolical. The interval between the notes F and B is a tritone. Try playing those two notes together on your piano or on a guitar and see how dissonant they sound. Should they be banned from music? Well, personally, I kinda like tritones, but I think we should ban polkas – they're satanic!

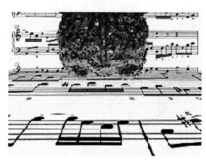

Harmony apparently plays an important role in musical preferences, at least in Western music. A recent study found that listeners rated musical chords as pleasant or unpleasant based on whether or not the chords were harmonically related (McDermott, Lehr, & Oxenham, 2010). But, the tendency was found to be stronger in listeners who had musical experience, suggesting that learning is important for musical preferences. Lead researcher Josh McDermott interpreted the results by saying, "It suggests that Westerners learn to like the sound of harmonic frequencies because of their importance in Western music. Listeners with different experience might well have different preferences. Intervals and chords that are dissonant by Western standards are fairly common in some cultures. Diversity is the rule, not the exception."

Janata and his team (2002) looked at human brains using brain imaging and discovered that the **prefrontal cortex** forms a **map** of the musical notes and keys it is hearing. That is, the harmonies of music are mapped onto the prefrontal cortex in a manner that represents the relationships between notes and keys. Different areas of the frontal lobe are activated by different keys. One brain region lights up for D major, another for A minor, and so on. Furthermore, these brain areas relate to each other in a map-like way that mimics the theoretical relationships between musical notes and keys. It seems our brains are representing harmonies in a manner that exactly mimics the nature of music.

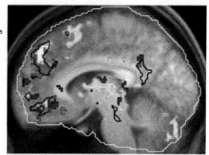

𝔓itch 𝔓erfect

Some people have memorized the **pitches** of the various **notes** of the scale and can recognize them when they hear them. They know an A when they hear it. They have memorized all of the pitches of the **diatonic scale**. Those individuals are said to have **perfect pitch**. Do you have that unique ability? Sometimes called **absolute pitch**, perfect pitch is the ability to identify or produce a pitch without any reference point.

Most musicians use a tuning fork or a fixed note from another instrument to adjust their voice or stringed instrument, but some people have memorized the standard notes in their long-term memories and can produce or recognize the pitch of a note without any assistance. Before a performance by a band or orchestra, the stringed instruments need to be tuned. The flute player will play a tone in the pitch of A, for example, and the guitar and violin players will adjust their string tensions to match the pitch of A. However, the musicians who have perfect pitch can tune their instruments earlier without hearing the A from the flute. They have memorized what an A sounds like and can adjust their instrument accordingly.

It has been estimated that about 1 out of every 10,000 people has perfect pitch. However, some studies have found that this ability is more common if measured slightly differently – if we don't ask the listener to name the note (A, E, C sharp, B flat, and so on), but rather to recognize whether they heard the exact same note earlier without naming it (Marvin & Newport, 2008). That's easier for people.

Music theorist **Elizabeth Marvin** and her colleagues (Deutsch, 2006) suggested that people who learn **tonal languages** have an advantage in developing perfect pitch. There are languages of the world in which the

meaning of a word depends to some extent on its pitch, such as Mandarin Chinese and many other Asian languages, which are known as **tonal languages**. Marvin hypothesizes that the brain's neural networks for perceiving pitch and for perceiving language were related in evolutionary development. Similarly, Saffran & Greipentrog (2001) have shown some evidence that perfect pitch is a hindrance to learning language and infants unlearn perfect pitch during language acquisition. Exposure to musical training between the ages of three and six increases the chance that perfect pitch will be maintained into adulthood (Takeuchi & Hulse, 1993).

Perfect pitch, however, is partly derived from genetic factors. For example, perfect pitch occurs in a higher percentage of people in **Asia** than in the West (Zatorre, 2003). A recent study has identified a **gene** on chromosome 8 that is more common in people of European heritage who have perfect pitch (Theusch, 2009). Most musicians do not have perfect pitch, but many have a skill called **relative pitch**; you give them a particular note and they can find all the others based on that reference point. Can you do that?

Of those of us who do not have perfect pitch or relative pitch, some of us can sing a song or two that we know very well in the exact pitch in which it was originally performed. We have the pitches of those songs stored in our memories. That ability is called **partial perfect pitch**. Perhaps you can do that. You could test it by singing one of your favorite songs and then playing it to see if your singing pitch matches the recording. Incidentally, about 5% of people sing off-key and either can't tell that they are off-key (**tone deaf**), or they simply don't care if they sing off-key (I think I've heard some of them at karaoke bars!).

Musical Elements

Spanish novelist and poet Cervantes wrote, "He who sings scares away his woes."

Now, back to the tune you sang. The tones you made not only had pitch, they also had **loudness**. The loudness of a note is determined by the height, or strength, or **intensity** of the wave it forms when vibrating. Remember, the rate of vibration (the **frequency**) determines the **pitch** of the note – high or low. But the **intensity** of the vibration determines its **loudness**.

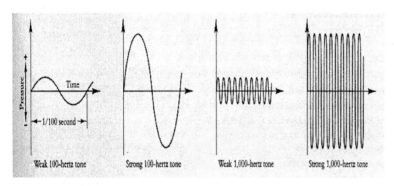

Weak 100-hertz tone   Strong 100-hertz tone   Weak 1,000-hertz tone   Strong 1,000-hertz tone

Pitch and loudness are independent features of a note. You can have a low note that is loud or quiet. You can also have a high note that is loud or quiet. Imagine tapping your finger on the table. You can tap hard or soft (loudness), but you also can tap slow or fast (pitch). The vibrations that characterize sound waves have both dimensions – frequency and intensity. It's like waves in the ocean. The waves can be hitting the beach very frequently or very slowly. But, also the waves can be very high (tall) or very short. High waves (intensity), for instance, can hit the beach often or not so often (frequency). A musical note has these two properties and our brains interpret those physical characteristics as pitch and loudness.

Each note that you sang also had a **duration**. Some notes last longer than others. This is part of music. A note can be held very briefly or for a very long time. This not the same as rhythm (beat) or tempo, two other qualities of the tune you sang. Rhythm refers to the pattern, or beat, by which the notes are arranged – for example, three long notes followed by a short one. In music terminology there is a similar concept called **meter**. Tap your palm on the table – DA, da, da....DA, da, da...DA, da, da. ONE two three, ONE two three... **Meter** refers to how often you **emphasize** a note in a pattern. Pop and rock music tend to use rhythm and meter of four beats with the first one emphasized – ONE two three four ONE two three four ONE two three four. Also, a particular rhythm and meter can be played at varying speeds. This is called **tempo**. You sang your little tune at a certain speed. You can sing *Happy Birthday* very fast, very slow, or somewhere in between. So, you see, brains need to have very complex processing abilities to detect pitch, loudness, duration of a note, rhythm, meter, and tempo. Such music perception is complicated and requires many brain areas and capacities.

Okay, back to your little ditty for a couple more important things about the **elements of music**. Now, here's something very interesting that I think you will like: Your singing of that little tune sounded entirely unique – different from anyone else who might be singing the very same tune. Consider this: A piano sounds like a piano. A flute sounds like a flute. A guitar sounds like a guitar. A trombone sounds like a trombone. And, you sound like you!

Each instrument (voice) has its own special, distinctive sound. This characteristic of music is called **timbre** (pronounced *TAM-ber*). This occurs because each instrument has a unique combination of frequencies that it creates. A piano playing a tone of C sounds different than a flute playing the same note of C even though they are the same loudness. This is because the pattern of vibrations is slightly different from one instrument (voice) to another. A sound wave is not pure. It consists of many different vibrations combined together. Each instrument and each voice has its own distinctive pattern.

Certain timbres are preferred over others by different people. You may prefer the sound of a piano to that of a trombone, for instance. Someone else may like the sound of a banjo. Again, this demonstrates that music affects us emotionally and can even trigger responses in our brain's pleasure pathway.

The fact that certain timbres are preferred famously got **Bob Dylan** into trouble. While Dylan had previously always played acoustic guitar, in 1965 at the Newport Folk Festival he performed for the first time with an electric guitar. Many people in the audience were aghast and angry! Many booed and some walked out on Dylan's performance later complaining that the electric guitar was not

true to folk music, it was an abomination. **Timbre** had lost some fans for **Bob Dylan**. Although an electric guitar can play the same notes as an acoustic guitar, the sound made, of course, is not the same, not the same at all. Which do you prefer?

It's fascinating that a large part of timbre is indicated by the sounds that are made by an instrument just before making a note. Those non-musical sounds that occur just prior to the note – the starting up sounds of scratches, plucks, bowing noises, bangs – are known as **transients**. The human brain is especially keen at detecting and recognizing these distinctive sounds. Evolution likely provided us with this ability in order that we can detect danger immediately by the start-up sounds (transients) before the actual trauma befalls us. The sound of a creature stepping on a stick nearby will be recognized by our brains even before the total sound reaches our ears. The result is that a brain can easily recognize a saxophone or a viola, a bass drum or mother's voice, a tuba or a triangle, or a ocarina or a cello just from the transients each one makes. Many experiments have been performed asking people to identify what musical instruments are playing on a recording after the experimenters have removed the transients. That is, the very first parts of the sounds are removed from the recordings prior to listeners hearing them. Remarkably, listeners have a great deal of difficulty naming the instruments when those nonmusical start-up sounds have been removed. A banjo can sound very much the same as a bassoon in such a case.

Now, **melody**: If you sing the *Twinkle, Twinkle, Little Star* and then sing the *Alphabet* song (ABCDEFG, HIJ…) you will notice that they both use the same pattern of tones, the same ups and downs of pitches. They have the same melody. A melody consists of pitch intervals and rhythm and is repeated within a song or musical piece. It is what we notice, what we sing along with in a song. Notice that you can start the melody at any pitch. It is the ups and downs – the pattern – that matters in recognizing a melody, not the absolute pitches of the notes. The overall

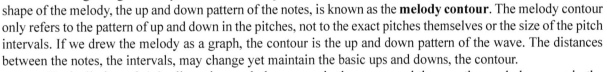

shape of the melody, the up and down pattern of the notes, is known as the **melody contour**. The melody contour only refers to the pattern of up and down in the pitches, not to the exact pitches themselves or the size of the pitch intervals. If we drew the melody as a graph, the contour is the up and down pattern of the wave. The distances between the notes, the intervals, may change yet maintain the basic ups and downs, the contour.

Typically in rock 'n' roll music a melody appears in the verses and then another melody occurs in the chorus. In classical music the melody is sometimes not as obvious, but serves as a recurring theme. Lots of music uses a short pattern that repeats over and over in a musical piece which is known as a **motif**. If the motif refers to a certain idea, person, or place, then the term **leitmotif** is used, particularly in operas. On TV shows and cartoons a leitmotif is often used to identify a particular character. On one episode of the TV series *Family Guy* the father, Peter Griffin, got his own cartoonish tune that followed him everywhere he went; a funny parody of the leitmotif idea.

As mentioned above, there are numerous studies of human **infants** to determine which **musical elements** they can identify. Research so far has shown that infants clearly can perceive complex combinations of sounds, can recognize melodies even when at different, modified pitches, particularly if they are diatonic scales, can perceive even small changes in pitch and patterns of pitch, and can recognize rhythm and tempo (for example, see Trehub & Hannon, 2006; Mithen, 2006; and McDermott, 2009).

Normal human brains obviously are capable of complex processing of sounds, probably even before birth. Human brains seem to be pre-wired to process musical notes and melodies. Also, when we listen to a concert, a recording, or a piece of music, the sounds come into our ears as a jumble of frequencies with **reverberations** (the echoes created by the environmental space), overtones, and other complications and nuances. However, our brains are able to make sense of the complex mix of frequencies and perceive individual tones having timbre, rhythm, and other musical qualities. As a result, we hear an organized musical piece.

Music of the Hemispheres

Many **neuroscientists** are attempting to find exactly where music is processed in the human brain. The research results, so far, have been disappointing. There are three reasons for this. First, as briefly described above, music is complex with many different components, and also intersects with memory, vision, emotions, and other brain processes. Second, for the most part, music processing is **distributed** throughout the brain and is not centrally located in a small, specific area. Music processing involves many brain areas, so pathways or neural networks are more common than localized areas for analyzing a musical piece. Third, there quite often are contradictions in the research findings. For example, people sometimes have damage to specific brain areas and as a result demonstrate a musical effect, such as increased or decreased interest in music. However, when these very brain areas are studied in normal subjects, they do not indicate a musical localization in the brain. Curious!

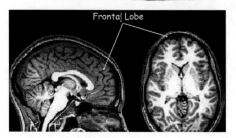

So, the result of these three problems is that it is generally not possible to point to a specific area of the brain as the music area. However, there are some exceptions.

When brain scientists look at how the left and right **hemispheres** of the cerebrum respond to music, they find that typically for most people the right hemisphere shows more activity than the left hemisphere. As a result, newspaper and magazine articles have assigned music to the cerebrum's **right hemisphere**. And, well, yes, there is a good deal of evidence that this is a plausible generalization; but, it is a generalization – there are plenty of exceptions. As you know, in general, for most people, the cerebrum's **left hemisphere** is lateralized for **language**, logic, and the analysis of parts. On the other side, the **right hemisphere** has been shown to be better at perceiving patterns and **holistic** processing. A jig-saw puzzle is a major difficulty for the left hemisphere, but easy for the right hemisphere. On the other hand, expressing or understanding language, or analyzing the logic of a problem, or detecting the details of a stimulus, are extremely challenging, even impossible, for the right hemisphere, but are **left hemisphere** specialties.

Well, what about music? One view that perhaps over-simplifies yet gives a general summary of brain imaging studies is that music normally activates areas of the **right hemisphere** that are similar in location to those areas of the left hemisphere that process language – the **posterior superior temporal gyrus** and regions of the **inferior frontal gyrus**. The **right hemisphere** appears to be better at interpreting **melody contour**, the up and down pattern of a sequence of notes, while the **left hemisphere** excels at processing the **pitch intervals**, the distance between one note and another in pitch. These brain modules for music perception appear to overlap with circuits for processing **language**. Brain imaging research has found that when people vocally improvise either music or speech, their brains are active in the **frontal** and **temporal** lobes, with language showing more activation on the left. However, many of the activations were bilateral, so there was **overlap**, or sharing, of brain areas for music and language (Brown, Martinez, & Parsons, 2006a). Music researcher **Isabelle Peretz** and her colleagues have concluded that the right hemisphere excels at perceiving the holistic pattern of pitch contour while the left hemisphere is better at detailed aspects of pitch and pitch steps.

While **language** is typically processed by the left hemisphere, there are properties of language that are better processed in holistic, pattern-like ways, a specialty skill of the right hemisphere. For instance, the ability to tell if a statement is a question by hearing the pitch increase at the end of the statement, or noticing when a

Frontal Lobe

statement is offered sarcastically by the tone of voice, are not left hemisphere abilities, but are managed more easily on the right side. These and other **non-linguistic** cues of speech are called **prosody**, and are processed more in the **right hemisphere** than the language-leaning left. This, too, is true of **music**. When the brain is interpreting the whole patterns of music, such as melody, then the right hemisphere is most active. The contour of a melody, distinguishing pitch, and appreciating harmony are right hemisphere specialties. However, if we analyze music, if we name music, if we use our right hand, or if we concentrate on the written notation of music, then the left hemisphere has an advantage.

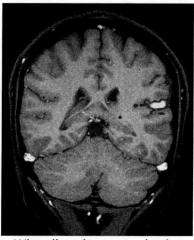

Interestingly, as **musicians** learn more and more about music and begin to name musical elements, and to think linguistically and analytically about music, they begin to shift some music perception from the right hemisphere to the left. So, **musicians** are more likely to use their **left hemispheres** when processing music than are non-musicians whose right hemispheres are most active when singing or hearing songs. By the way, **children** show less **lateralization** of music perception than do adults – that is, children are more likely to use both hemispheres when processing music rather than isolating particular kinds of music perception to one side of the cerebrum. When singing, most people show more activation of

When listening to music, the brain shows activity in the auditory area of the temporal lobe.

the right primary auditory area (Perry et al., 1996). This finding may be related to a singing person hearing their own voice and deriving the pitch of the notes in order to make adjustments to the vocal motor control. Musicians

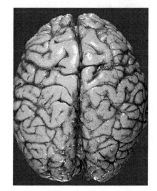

with **perfect pitch** show a left asymmetry (Schlaug et al., 1995) and larger brain volume on the **left** (Zatorre et al., 1998).

Left hemispheres generally are better at dealing with **analysis**, and so it is with perception of music. When multiple sounds are being processed, the left hemisphere focuses on sequences, or the succession of sounds. Thus, the **left temporal lobe** is important in the perception of the **rhythm** of a musical piece. The brain does not act like a tape-recorder, nor does it focus only on individual inputs. Somehow, the secondary auditory cortex of the **left temporal lobe** is able to process the **sequence** of notes that occur in music and give us a sense of the rhythm to which we are shaking our booties. The **right hemisphere** does not focus on sequences of sounds, but rather figures out the **relations** between sounds that are simultaneous. For example, Zatorre (1985) found that the **right temporal lobe** was critical for perception of **melody contour**. Brechmann & Scheich (2005) found that the **right hemisphere** is more active when detecting **pitch**, but the **left hemisphere** is more involved when judging **duration** of a musical note. The auditory cortex apparently does not concentrate on, or process, individual notes in and of themselves. Each note is taken as part of a pattern, and is processed with regard to what came before or simultaneously.

More Left and Right

Many cases of people who developed a sudden interest and desire for music occurred following **damage** to the **left hemisphere**. It is as if the left side of the cerebrum was holding back, inhibiting, putting the brakes on the musical right side, and when the left was damaged, the right was able to flourish. For example, patients with **frontotemporal dementia**, a disorder that wreaks havoc on the frontal and temporal lobes, often spontaneously develop interest and skill in the arts and music (Miller et al., 2000). Brain imaging shows that their left hemispheres are dysfunctional.

Further, some studies have shown that if researchers inhibit the left hemisphere using electricity or magnetism, then special abilities of the right hemisphere may appear (Snyder, 2009). On this same theme, it has been known for many years that electrical stimulation of the **right** auditory cortex can result in vivid **music perception** (Penfield & Perot, 1963). Patients undergoing brain surgery who are stimulated in the **right temporal lobe** report hearing very specific and clear musical passages. Also, there are many instances of people who have suffered damage to their left hemispheres but continued to perceive music.

Maurice Ravel.

One of the best examples is Russian classical music composer **Vissarion Shebalin** who had a stroke in his **left hemisphere** that left him unable to speak or understand language, yet he continued to compose music. His colleague **Dmitri Shostakovitch** said his music was just as good as before his brain damage (Luria et al, 1965). Some brain scientists believe that a similar fate befell the French composer **Maurice Ravel**, well-known for his repetitive orchestral work called *Bolero*. In 1928, when *Bolero* was written, Ravel was experiencing a number of health problems that neurologists believe were the result of the early stages of **frontotemporal dementia**. Ravel's language and verbal abilities gradually became impaired and he was unable to write music, but still Ravel was expert at perceiving music and detecting small mistakes in musical pieces. He died in 1937 following exploratory brain surgery. So, again in these case studies we see that language and music may overlap in the brain, yet they appear in many cases to be separate systems.

The left and right hemispheres typically are not symmetrical. In most people, the left hemisphere is larger. This is primarily due to the brain's language areas which normally reside on the left. There is one area of the brain where the asymmetry is the greatest. It is an area in the temporal lobe just at the rear of the auditory processing area. It is called the **planum temporale**. This brain area is involved with both language (part of Wernicke's area) and music. About 65% of people have a planum temporale that is more developed in the left hemisphere than in the right. Only about 10% have right side asymmetry. In some, the left planum temporale is five times larger than the right; it is the most asymmetrical region of the cerebral cortex. This asymmetry has been identified in fetuses, suggesting a genetic factor.

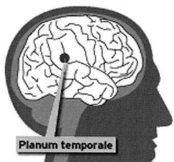

Planum temporale

Now, for something interesting: Many studies have identified the planum temporale as actively involved in music processing. But more than that, people with perfect pitch have been found to have greater asymmetry toward the left planum temporale than others (Schlaug et al., 1995). Remember that the left hemisphere specializes in language and may be useful for note labeling. Part of the left bias among people with perfect pitch may be due to genetic predisposition, but also recall that musicians tend to become less right-hemisphere lateralized with musical experience.

So, most research indicates a lean toward the **right hemisphere** in most people during music perception. Does this lateral bias come about as the brain develops with experience, or is it a pattern that is hard-wired during prenatal development? Well, it appears to be hard-wired based on recent research that measured brain activity in 1 to 3 day old **newborns** while they listened to excerpts of Western music and also to altered versions of those excerpts (Perani et al., 2001). The researchers reported: "In adults, specific neural systems with right-hemispheric weighting are necessary to process pitch, melody, and harmony as well as structure and meaning emerging from musical sequences. These results demonstrate that the infant brain shows a hemispheric specialization in processing music as early as the first postnatal hours. Results also indicate that the neural architecture underlying music processing in newborns is sensitive to changes in tonal key as well as to differences in consonance and dissonance."

So, only a day after birth the brain is ready for a vast amount of **music perception** and is sensitive to music predominantly in the **right hemisphere**. By the way, research has shown that **newborns** react to the

beat of music, too (Winkler et al., 2009). Other studies have shown that as the infant becomes an older child, music perception in the brain becomes narrower, more **specialized**. It appears that experience with certain kinds of music primes the brain for creating neural circuits that respond differentially to the types of music that are heard. It's a bit like **language** development in that way.

Sandra Trehub and her team have studied music perception in **infants**. A typical procedure is to use **operant conditioning** (reinforcement) to determine if an infant can perceive elements of music. The infant listens to music and is trained to turn his/her head when hearing a particular stimulus. To reinforce the behavior, the infant gets to see an interesting event, such as a mechanized toy that is activated at that moment (Trehub, 2000). So, for example, the infant listens to a piece of music and when a note sounds different than it did in a previous listening, the infant signals recognition by a turn of the head. This behavior is reinforced by seeing a toy bear dance. Okay, using this procedure researchers were able to determine that infants between 8 and 11 months of age could detect **melodies** and were even able to notice a change of only one note within a melody. As mentioned above, infants indeed do seem to have a built-in music processor, though experience will modulate and shape their music perception.

In another experiment with infants (Balaban, Anderson, & Wisniewski, 1998) the researchers played both a familiar melody and then later an altered version of that melody to each ear of 8 - 9 month old infants. Remember that the left ear sends more signals to the brain's right hemisphere, while the right ear sends more signals to the left hemisphere. The original melody was changed in two ways. First, in **contour**. That is, one of the notes in the melody that went up in pitch from the previous note was changed to a note that went down – the contour of the melody changed. The infants noticed this best with their right hemispheres.

Second, the melody was changed in pitch **interval**. That is, one of the notes was changed to a higher pitch, but it was already higher than the previous note, so the contour was not changed – the melody still went up in pitch at that moment. The babies noticed this change in the pitch interval better with their left hemispheres. Similar results have been found in other studies, even with adults. It seems that the right hemisphere is better at processing the up and down pattern of the melody while the left hemisphere is concentrating more on the specific pitch changes.

7he Musical Brain

Much-admired musician Ray Charles said, "I was born with music inside me. It was a necessity for me – like food or water." And, from John Mayer: "Hopefully people can see my music is tethered to my brain."

Music is **distributed** throughout the brain. When listening to music, or singing, or composing music, many different areas and brain circuits are activated. Music is truly an integrated brain task. Music involves so many different psychological, emotional, and cognitive functions that we should not expect the brain to have one module dedicated to it. Music draws on many brain areas that have evolved functions such as language, emotion, categorizing, pitch, timing, and finding relationships among (or analyzing) various components. Scientists have used brain imaging techniques to attempt to tease apart the brain's modules and circuits that are involved in music perception.

Like language, music can be thought of as having **syntax** (put the words in the right order in a sentence versus put the notes in the right order

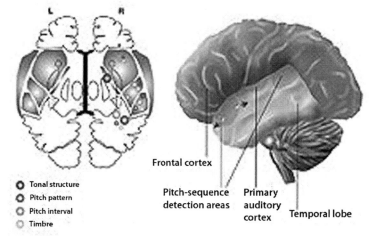

in a melody) and **semantics** (the meaning of a sentence or musical passage). Studies using EEG (measuring the electrical activity of brain cells that are firing) have found that **musical syntax** is localized in the **frontal lobes** of both hemispheres in areas that overlap with the brain's areas for processing language syntax, such as Broca's area (Koelsch, 2009). When we connect music with meaning, the EEG shows activity in the back of the temporal lobes on both sides, near the area for language reception called Wernicke's area. The music and language processing circuits in the brain appear to be independent from each other to some extent, though they apparently use overlapping regions or pathways to some extent. Keeping track of changes in **tone** is another matter. As mentioned above, **Petr Janata** and his team (2002) identified an area of the **prefrontal cortex** that tracks activation in tonal space. Different areas of brain cells were found to be responsive to different musical keys. However, the topography of that brain area changed and rearranged itself from one scanning session to another. This is the area of the frontal lobe that Janata believes brings together cognition, emotion, and memory.

In one of the more fascinating studies of the brain on music, Lindenberger et al. (2009) took EEG recordings and found that pairs of guitarists playing a jazz-fusion melody together had **synchronized** brain waves. Not just their music, but *their brains* were swinging together! The synchronization was greatest in the frontal lobes, but also occurred in the temporal and parietal lobes. I guess musicians who play together are not only tuning their musical instruments, they're also tuning their brains!

Also fascinating: We all know that music connects with us emotionally. This is one area in which a performer can beat a **computer**! In this research (Koelsch et al., 2008) non-musicians listened to music while the scientists measured their brains' electrical responses. As you might guess, the brains made obvious emotional responses to unexpected chords and changes in key. So, it seems that even brains not trained as musicians are innately programmed to react to music's "grammar." Now the really cool part: The researchers had the subjects listen to the same music played by a computer. Guess what – the emotional response of the brain was less than when reacting to music played by a human performer! Something about the expressiveness of the musical technique was picked up by the brain and reacted to more emotionally than to the rather rigid, predictable computer version. So, all you musicians out there: Don't worry about computers taking your jobs, yet!

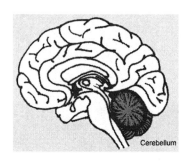

Cerebellum

The brain's **cerebellum** (the little brain) attached to the back of the brainstem below the cortex has also been found to play a critical role in music perception. As you may recall, the cerebellum has been studied most for its role in processing the coordination of muscle **movements**. Neural circuits in the cerebellum help us to control and guide our body movements as we engage in coordinated actions. Now, if you think about music for a moment, or listen to a catchy song, you might start tapping your foot or your hand, or even start dancing, and (EUREKA!) a light bulb may go on inside your head just above the cerebellum when you hit on the obvious notion that both coordinated body movements and music involve timing, beat, rhythm, bounce, cadence, or swing. Poet Ezra Pound said, "Music rots when it gets too far from the dance."

Neural activity occurs in the cerebellum when people listen to music, but amazingly not when they listen to noise (Levitin, 2006). Music gets us moving, but noise does not. Also, the cerebellum is more active when people are listening to music that they *like* than when listening to music they don't like. Of course you know that – you bounce around more when hearing music you enjoy.

When **dancing**, the cerebellum is involved, but so are many other brain areas. It appears that dance is the result of an interacting network of brain areas including the cerebellum, parietal lobe (spatial navigation), and limbic system areas (Brown, Martinez, & Parsons, 2006b). An old Polish Proverb says, "The man who can't dance thinks the band is no good." The association between music and dance is so close that some cultures make little distinction between the two. For instance, there is no distinction between the words for music and dance in the language of some peoples of Nigeria. Also, there is no distinction between dance and song in Lesotho. And, in sub-Saharan Africa any sounds that can't be danced to are not considered to be music.

So, the **cerebellum** appears to be a player in processing the **beat** of music, but it probably is involved in even more. Lawrence Parsons (2003) and his team carried out extensive **PET scans** of subjects listening to music and found that when the right

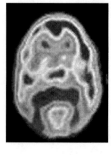

temporal lobe was active, so too was the left cerebellum. Similarly, though not as robust, when the left temporal lobe was active, there was activity in the right cerebellum. Some scientists now believe the cerebellum is involved with cognition and emotions (it has many connections with the amygdala and the frontal lobe, areas known to be active when processing emotions and cognition) and this could help account for why music often moves us.

Researchers Schmahmann and Caplan (2006) wrote: "There is increasing recognition that the cerebellum contributes to cognitive processing and emotional control in addition to its role in motor coordination." But the cerebellum appears to have company in keeping track of the rhythm, meter, and **tempo** of music. Differential activity has been found in the hippocampus, basal ganglia, and auditory areas when listening to a waltz versus a march (Fujioka, Zendel, & Ross, 2010). The researchers concluded, "The close interaction of auditory, motor, and limbic systems suggests a distributed network for metric organization in temporal processing and its relevance for musical behavior."

Speaking of liking certain kinds of music, what kind of music do you like? Does certain music give you pleasure? Do certain beats, rhythms, or melodies send chills down your spine? Some scientists have sought the connection between music and pleasure. As you might remember, the **pleasure pathway** in the brain (also called the **mesolimbic pathway**) extends from the brainstem through the limbic system and into the frontal lobe. One of the hotspots of this pleasure circuit is a pea-shaped region called the **nucleus accumbens** which uses the brain chemical dopamine to signal the release of brain opioids (similar to opium – pleasurable!). So, you might wonder, does music, or certain kinds of music, stimulate this pleasure pathway in the brain? And the answer is…. YES!

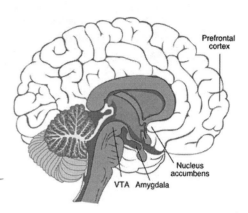

nucleus accumbens

Researchers used PET scans to watch brains light up when listeners heard music that they identified as producing intense **emotions** in them (Blood & Zatorre, 2001). The same regions of the **pleasure pathway** that are activated by food, sex, and drugs also lit up when "chilling" music was perceived. This must be the sex, drugs, & rock 'n' roll brain area! And, while the nucleus accumbens and other regions of the mesolimbic area are activated by emotional music, the basal ganglia and cerebellum are also active, apparently coordinating the processing of rhythm and meter with the musical melody being enjoyed. So, we rock to the music we like!

The **cerebellum's** connection with brain areas related to **emotion** and with the **pleasure pathway** has been emphasized by some music researchers. For example, **Daniel Levitin**, Professor of Psychology and Music at McGill University, Montreal, writes in his book *This is Your Brain on Music* (2006): "As the music unfolds, the brain constantly updates its estimates of when new beats will occur, and takes satisfaction in matching a mental beat with a real-in-the-world one, and takes delight when a skillful musician violates that expectation in an interesting way – a sort of musical joke that we are all in on. Music breathes, speeds up, and slows down just as the real world does, and our cerebellum finds pleasure in adjusting itself to staying synchronized." Levitin also says that the **motor areas** of the brain react in synch to the tempo of music as if music is a metaphor for body movement. The brain's motor areas fire as if running when the music's tempo is very fast, for instance.

So, we can now identify a rough sequence of brain activations when a person listens to music: First, the inner ear signals the brainstem to organize the information, particularly with regard to pitch and rhythm. Second, the information is shared with the cerebellum, basal ganglia, and emotional parts of the frontal lobe and limbic system. Third, the cerebellum communicates with other brain regions to help process timing and rhythm. Fourth, the auditory cortex in the temporal lobe processes pitch, melody, harmony, and tonal relationship information. Fifth, the frontal lobes are involved in analyzing musical syntax and structure and expectations (helping with emotions, too). And sixth, the mesolimbic pathway provides a sense of pleasure for particular pieces of music. Other brain regions are involved, too, in the complex coordination of music perception that is widely distributed throughout the brain.

Though scientists have had some limited success in identifying localized brain areas for **music perception**, for the most part the musical brain remains a stubborn and puzzling challenge. Research findings often contradict one another, and individual and group differences in music processing seem more the norm than the exception: Infants respond somewhat differently from adults, musicians from non-musicians, Asians from Westerners, one language from another, those with music experience differently than those without, and genetic differences have been found, too. Researcher **Isabelle Peretz** noted that the most consistent finding is that the **right superior temporal gyrus** and **right frontal lobe** are responsible for processing pitch contour. However, she added, finding a similar pattern of brain organization for music in all humans remains elusive (Peretz & Coltheart, 2003).

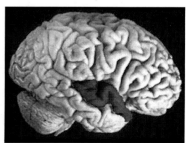

The right superior temporal gyrus.

So, although some **localization** has been revealed, music appears to be mostly a **distributed** process in the brain. The results may remind you of how plastic the brain is. Neural circuits are wired and re-wired with various, myriad circumstances. Also, let's not forget that brain areas and brain processes do not easily translate into words of English or mental concepts that we have created to categorize and explain the world. The brain is a chemical and electrical organ that does its jobs via a vast network of connections. Music, delightfully, is one of the results.

Music Preferences

By the way, what kind of music do we like? Of course, that depends greatly on individual differences, cultural styles, and what we are used to and what we expect. However, one rule that has been discovered by psychologists is similar to the **Yerkes-Dodson law** described in an earlier chapter. That law says performance is related to arousal in a curved graph. Too little arousal or too much arousal leads to poor performance. A medium amount of arousal is best for highest performance.

Now, it's similar with **music preference** and **musical complexity**. Too little complexity is boring, but too much complexity is overwhelming. A medium amount of complexity is preferred. People tend to prefer music that they are familiar with, but perhaps a little, wee bit more complex. The average adult prefers music that is just a bit more complex than nursery songs, the music they became familiar with in childhood. However, once people become familiar with music that is a bit more complex, then they can stretch their preferences. Some classical music that we enjoy today, such as **Igor Stravinsky's** *Rite of Spring*, was booed and much disapproved when first heard in 1913. Listeners said it was not music! Today, we enjoy *Rite of Spring* without any brain/cognitive effort. It is easy to assimilate. A brain needs to be exposed to something that is radically new for quite a while in order to develop a means of organizing it and perceiving it (understanding it). Getting used to complex music makes you ready for more complex music. But only in very small steps over long periods of time. Complexity, generally, is not preferred.

Commercial music and movies do not dare stray too far from the simple and familiar. A new movie, for instance, must be similar enough to previous movies that people are familiar with in order for their brains to take it in. But, not exactly similar, or it will be boring. Music is the same. It takes time for a brain to get used to stimuli that are terribly different from what is familiar. For instance, the most popular songs by *The Beatles* are the simplest of their compositions. More complex songs by Lennon and McCartney are praised by experts but not preferred by the mass of listeners. Brains learn to expect certain patterns. A pop/rock song uses beat, verses, chorus, and a bridge in a predictable way. For example, in almost all popular songs, you can normally tell what note will come next. Also, songs usually include indicators to let the listener know what is coming – a snare drum fill, an extended chord, a drum roll, a guitar riff, and so on, indicate to the listener that a change in the pattern is coming.

However, too much simplicity or repetition will become boring. One way that music can grab your attention is by adding tiny alterations to what listeners expect. *The Beatles*, for example, would sometimes throw in a bar with a different time signature. You'll find it in *All You Need is Love* and *Here Comes the Sun*. Brains are pleased when expectations are met – you like it when you hear that final note you've been expecting in a song – but if a piece of music is too predictable, it no longer excites the pleasure pathway. A tiny change can be interesting. Big changes, though, take time to assimilate. This is a problem, naturally, for experimental and avant-garde composers who want to make big changes in music. Listeners will take a while to adjust.

If you are seeking music that is similar in **style** to other music you like, there are now websites that will help you. **Pandora Radio** has the **Music Genome Project** that attempts to classify music using 400 markers. Every song in the data bank has been analyzed by musicians and technicians. On the other hand there is **Playola**, a laboratory research endeavor that is attempting to create an "intelligent machine listener" that will categorize sounds into styles or descriptions that are useful for people.

Music Disorders

Filmmaker Billy Wilder talking about a composer whose music he didn't like: "He has Van Gogh's ear for music."

Famed neurologist **Oliver Sacks** has entertained and informed many a reader with his engaging humanistic and poetic prose. Sacks primarily relays stories of people who have experienced unusual mental and psychological phenomena following injury or damage to the brain. The stories are enthralling and hypnotic, at times almost unbelievable, but also help us better understand the nature of the complex organ between our ears and how it provides the enthralling thing we call music.

In his recent book, *Musicophilia: Tales of Music and the Brain* (2007), Sacks describes case after case of people who have suddenly experienced increased interest in music following brain injury or dysfunction, and others who have various manifestations of musical disorders or musical propensities. This disposition toward music is termed *musicophilia* (love of music) by Sacks, and his book is an attempt to enlighten neuroscience as well as fascinate its readers.

Sacks, for example, tells the case of a patient he calls Mrs. C who had **musical hallucinations** (sometimes called **endomusia**). She heard songs playing with deafening intensity after taking a medicine that was given to treat her hearing loss. Sacks points out that brain imaging studies show that musical hallucinations are activated

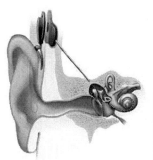
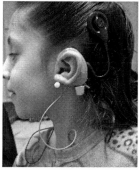

by the same parts of the brain that are active when hearing real music – the frontal and temporal lobes, basal ganglia, and cerebellum. Mrs. C was given a **cochlear implant**, a device with electrodes surgically implanted into the cochlea of the inner ear, to correct her hearing loss. Once the implant was activated, her hearing improved remarkably and her music hallucinations disappeared. Mrs. C was quite happy about her improved hearing, but later lamented that she could no longer enjoy music. It turns out that the implant did not have the sensitivity required to respond to the multiple pitch changes in music. But, fortunately, her music hallucinations had stopped.

Some neurologists have suggested that musical hallucinations are associated with epilepsy, a disorder of the electrical firing of brain cells that often affects the temporal lobe (Engmann & Reuter, 2009). One other interesting thing about Mrs. C when she was experiencing musical hallucinations: She often experienced a tune or part of a tune going through her mind over and over again repetitively. She could not shake it. This is what scientists call an **earworm**. I'm sure you've experienced it. You get a certain melody caught in your head playing over and over and you cannot get it out! The tune is stuck in your mind like an obsession. Often it's a tune you don't even care for! It's maddening! Musician Carlos Santana observed, "Some songs are just like tattoos for your brain – you hear them and they are affixed to you."

The term **earworm** is derived from a German work, *Ohrwurm*, which is used to refer to a song or tune that is very catchy. Oliver Sacks has suggested the term "involuntary musical imagery" for this phenomenon. Nearly everyone experiences earworms, and men and women report them equally, though for women they last longer and seem to be bother them more. People with **obsessive-compulsive disorder** (typically referred to as **OCD**) commonly report having earworms regularly, and the medicines used to treat OCD (serotonin reuptake inhibitors) tend to reduce the frequency of these catchy brain melodies. Researchers using brain imaging of volunteers who listened to music that was missing pieces of the melody found that the auditory cortex in the listeners' brains filled in the missing gaps as if the notes were all there. Apparently, the brain continues a well-known tune even in absence of some of its parts. The volunteers said they heard the missing notes as part of the tune (Kraemer et al., 2005). Perhaps earworms are the brains attempt to fill in a missing tune, to complete the tune over and over.

There are a number of music-specific disorders that neurologists have identified and categorized (Zatorre & McGill, 2005). The disorders typically involve the music elements mentioned above: Pitch, rhythm, timbre, memory, and emotion. Perhaps the most commonly known music-specific disorder is the inability to recognize musical notes. The public typically calls this **tone deafness**, but scientists usually refer to this disorder as **amusia**. A person with amusia finds it nearly impossible to recognize even simple tunes. *Congenital amusia* results from genetic causes, while *acquired amusia* is the result of specific injury or malfunction to brain areas related to pitch analysis. Some scientists consider congenital amusia to be a type of learning disability that affects musical perception. To highlight the difference between the music brain and the language brain, an amusic individual can speak perfectly fine, but is unable to sing.

At one time some scientists argued that tone deafness was a myth. But music researchers **Isabelle Peretz** and her team at the University of Montreal advertised for volunteers who believed that they had been unable to perceive music since birth and found at least 22 people who clearly had congenital amusia (Peretz, 2001). The study concluded that this condition results from a defect in the ability to perceive pitch. Nearly all cases of acquired amusia are due to stroke or other damage to areas of the auditory cortex or frontal lobe. One study found reduced activity in the **arcuate fasciculus** (the fiber that connects the language areas, **Broca's** and **Wernicke's**) in people who are tone deaf (Loui, et al., 2009). Hyde et al. (2007) found a thicker cortex in the auditory area of the right hemispheres of patients with amusia suggesting malformation or improper migration of neurons that may have compromised the connections with the frontal lobe.

By the way, the Montreal researchers also advertised for people who could not keep rhythm or beat to music and found one person, **Mathieu**, who apparently is **beat deaf**. Mathieu can keep time with a metronome, but when music is played he cannot move to the rhythm, so his problem with timing relates only to music. Also, when he watches other people dance he cannot tell if they are moving to the beat of the music or not. This is being touted as the first case of **beat deafness**, but in response many other people have commented that they feel the same way as Mathieu about music.

Similar to tone deafness or amusia is **music agnosia**. The term "**agnosia**" literally means to "not know." The term is used in conjunction with a number of different neurological disorders. For instance, in *visual agnosia* a person cannot recognize objects when seen; in *prosopagnosia*, a person does not recognize familiar faces; in *time agnosia* a person cannot recognize passage of time or duration of events; and, in *color agnosia* an individual cannot recognize colors. These types of agnosia, and many other variations, are the result of dysfunctions in very specific brain areas.

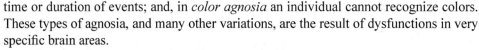

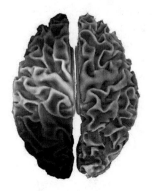

The person with music agnosia may be unable to recognize pitch, rhythm, melody, harmony, chords, or familiar songs, and will be unable to judge tonality, and reproduce musical phrases (Satoh, 2007). In *music agnosia* the brain damage may be in the left or right hemisphere depending on which functions of music are dysfunctional. Music researcher **Isabelle Peretz** (1993) has argued that agnosia may result from a dysfunction either in melody or in memory. Right hemisphere damage tends to interfere with melody, while left hemisphere dysfunction result in loss of memory for music. In both cases the person demonstrates a type of music agnosia. Peretz's team reported two cases of music agnosia in patients with lesions in the right superior temporal gyrus and in the right insula (Ayotte et al., 2000).

Music Savants

"It was a fair audience that gathered at the Lansing last night to listen to **Blind Tom**. Certainly the man was worth hearing, at least once. Probably there has never been seen on the stage a stranger figure or one more uncanny. He is a human phonograph, a sort of animated memory, with sound producing powers."

The quote comes from the Willa Cather Electronic Archive (Willa Cather was an award-winning American author) at the University of Nebraska and refers to a young black man named Thomas Wiggins. Tom was born in 1849 in Georgia. His parents were slaves and were sold to a lawyer named General James Bethune in 1850. Tom was blind and autistic. Like many children with autism, Tom's language was impaired and he engaged in what is called **echolalia** – repeating what he heard in a kind of echo. Tom's extraordinary skill, however, was in echoing music. From the age of 3, Tom loved beating on anything with a musical rhythm, and particularly loved the piano. At the age of 8 Tom was licensed to a showman who presented him as a kind of freak who could transform from a beast into an artist.

THE BALLAD OF
BLIND TOM
SLAVE PIANIST
AMERICA'S LOST MUSICAL GENIUS

Tom studied piano and showed unbelievable musical talent – he could repeat any musical piece he heard, note for note, but would typically add his own flourishes and alterations, and his behavior was eccentric and hyperactive. Billed as Blind Tom Wiggins, Tom toured the country giving concerts, which were bizarre in many regards. Author Willa Cather commented about one: "It was a strange sight to see him walk out on stage with his own lips—another man's words—introduce himself and talk quietly about his own idiocy. There was insanity, a grotesque horribleness about it that was interestingly unpleasant. One laughs at the man's queer actions, and yet, after all, the sight is not laughable. It brings us too near to the things that we sane people do not like to think of." A movie about Blind Tom was made in 1981. Blind Tom is perhaps the most famous and quintessential example of what is called a **music savant**.

Matt Savage.

Savant syndrome is a very rare condition in which a person who is developmentally or intellectually disabled has extreme talent or expertise in one specific area (Treffert, 2010). About half of savants have **autism**. **Matt Savage**, born in 1992, is an American music savant who was diagnosed on the autism spectrum. He learned to read at 18 months and taught himself how to read music at age 6. After studying classical piano, Matt turned to jazz and has toured the world and appeared on many TV shows.

Leslie Lemke, also autistic, was born with such severe birth defects that doctors needed to remove his eyes. He was disabled for years, being force fed, and did not show any progress until age 7, yet by age 16, without any musical training Leslie began playing complicated classical pieces on the piano. Blind and autistic with limited verbal skills, pianist Derek Paravicini is called "the human iPod." He has an extraordinary repertoire of thousands of songs he plays from memory. And, in one more case, Rex Lewis-Clark, an autistic child, at age 11 could hear a Mozart piece and play it back perfectly, yet he cannot navigate around his own home. Okay, those are just a few examples of music savants.

Leslie Lemke.

Psychologist **Leon Miller** (1989) has written a book about music savants in which he describes 13 cases and argues against the idea that these savants are merely exceptional human tape recorders. Much of the book describes the author's encounters with a young music savant named Eddie who had multiple disabilities, but showed fanatical interest in, and skill at, playing piano. Eddie could improvise nearly any musical piece he heard, and showed interest in practically nothing but the piano. On his 7th birthday, for instance, Eddie did not respond to the gifts he received until the author and others present picked up the puppets and stuffed animals and sang songs with them. The only present that Eddie got excited about by sight was a long knit scarf that had a picture of the piano keyboard on it.

In summary, Miller notes that the common features of the **music savants** he studied were: 1) They all had perfect pitch. In fact, Miller and other experts believe that perfect pitch may be a requirement for the music savant syndrome. By the way, absolute pitch is common in autism, too; 2) Most of the savants were echolalic. This means the children did not have good understanding of words having meanings, but were sensitive to the sounds and sequences of speech and could accurately mimic speech; 3) Nearly all the music savants were male. This male bias is found in autism and many other developmental disorders, too; 4) The children did not imitate music note for note, but rather displayed musical understanding and improvisation. They are not just copying machines, but can display genuine musical creativity in their versions of musical pieces.

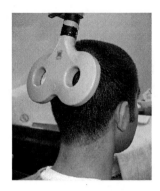

Now, here's something pretty wild to think about: Vision researcher **Allan Snyder** believes that savant abilities are latent in nearly everyone. Yes, that's right, he thinks that we all have savant-like abilities inside of us that are being inhibited. Snyder has tested his theory in a number of ways; for example, he uses **transcranial magnetic stimulation (TMS)** (a non-invasive technique that involves holding a very powerful magnet next to a person's head) to inhibit the left hemispheres of volunteers supposedly to free up the special skills in music and the arts of the right hemisphere (Snyder, 2009). In a 2004 paper, Snyder and his colleagues wrote, "...savant-like skills reside in everyone, but only individuals with a rare form of brain damage, like autistic savants, gain privileged access to these skills... such nonconscious skills might be accessed artificially by temporarily shutting off those parts of the brain implicated in the savant syndrome by using 'slow' magnetic brain stimulation over the left fronto-temporal lobe.

Consistent with this hypothesis, it was found that transcranial magnetic stimulation (TMS), known to suppress cortical activity, improved 'literal' savant-like abilities, like drawing skills and proof reading in healthy individuals. So, it is becoming clear from magnetic brain stimulation (TMS) studies, as well as from the phenomenon of acquired savants, that by turning off part of the brain, it is possible to access processes, information and even 'skills' which are not normally consciously accessible and that this process can be switched off and on." Well, that's quite an assertion. This idea likely resides more in the domain of science fiction than in science. Most experts are rightly skeptical about Snyder's idea, though we can't deny it is interesting!

One more curious fact related to music savants: There is a condition called **Williams syndrome** in which a person is missing some genes from chromosome 7 due to a biological error. Children with Williams syndrome have many common symptoms: they are overly friendly, seemingly happy, mentally disabled, have heart defects, have facial characteristics that give them an "elfin" appearance, they are often left handed and left eye dominant, are very verbal, and (get ready, here it comes, drum roll please)...they love music! Oh, and, wouldn't you know, they often have **perfect pitch**, too.

Despite low IQ scores, these children show great memory for songs, an excellent sense of rhythm, and an ear that allows them to differentiate sounds remarkably well. Research on children with Williams syndrome has determined that neurons in the primary auditory cortex

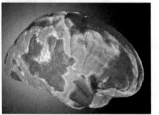

appear to be larger and more loosely packed than seen in normal individuals (Galaburda et al., 2006). Researchers also discovered that people with Williams syndrome have a larger **planum temporale** (the back part of the superior temporal gyrus) and that it is structured differently (Eckert et al., 2006). These differences in brain structure and in the size of the cells and their density in the auditory area may contribute to greater connectiveness in the brain region that processes auditory information, and may be the underlying biological cause of the children's superiority in auditory processing and language, and in their inordinate love of music.

Effects of Music

Of course you do not need a gene disorder to love music! How about you – do you enjoy listening to music? Yes? Well, what effect does it have on you? Perhaps some music relaxes you, and some other tunes agitate you. In fact, researchers have found that music does cause the release of certain brain **neurotransmitter** chemicals, and as mentioned above, can stimulate the brain's pleasure pathway. Also, since brains are remarkably plastic, exposure to music can result in changes in brain volume and neural circuits. In one study, children from 4 to 6 years of age who had received music lessons for one year showed significant changes in their brains (measured by brain imaging technology) compared to a control group who had no musical training (Fujioka et al., 2006).

Because music can produce helpful changes in the brain, some attempts have been made to use **music therapy** for a number of disorders. For instance, patients with neurological dysfunctions including visual neglect were found to have enhanced

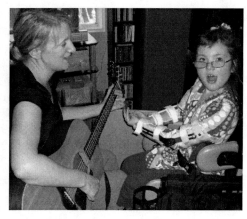

visual awareness while listening to their preferred music (Soto et al., 2009). Brain imaging showed increased activity in the frontal cortex while the patients listened to music they liked. Similarly, researchers found that recovery from Broca's aphasia was improved using a music therapy technique known as **Melodic Intonation Therapy (MIT)**. In this procedure, patients sing words instead of trying to speak them, and they simultaneously tap their left hands to the music (Schlaug et al., 2008). Patients with aphasia typically are better at singing than speaking. Scientists currently believe that language and music are dissociated in the brain because one circuit for spoken words traverses through the left hemisphere, while a separate neural circuit for sung words uses either the right hemisphere, or more likely, both left and right (Bohland & Guenther, 2006). It appears that MIT is beneficial because activation of the singing circuit while tapping the left hand (right hemisphere control) helps aphasic patients better develop new speaking brain pathways.

Music is used therapeutically, not just recreationally, in the treatment of traumatic brain injury and numerous psychological and medical disorders. Music is used in the treatment of cancer to reduce pain, anxiety, and nausea associated with chemotherapy. It does appear to have a meditative or relaxing effect. In one instance, when patients on ventilators listened to classical music, their breathing rates and blood pressures were lowered (Korhan, Khorshid, & Uyar, 2011).

At a 2006 symposium at Stanford's Center for Computer Research in Music and Acoustics, scientists suggested that since rhythmic music can alter a listener's brain waves, music therapy could be used in the treatment of

neurological conditions, attention deficit disorder, and depression. **Tinnitus** (ringing in the ears) was relieved in eight volunteers who listened to some of their preferred music that had been altered by the researchers who removed notes that were at the same pitch as the ringing noise the patients experienced (Okamoto et al., 2010). The researchers believe that when the listeners were deprived of musical notes at the problem frequency, their brains also learned not to "hear" the tinnitus ringing.

What about **music training** – can it change the brain? Yes, and it looks like the changes can be helpful not only for perceiving music, but for interpreting emotional elements of speech. Researchers measured electrical activity in the brainstem and found that musicians had enhanced and more efficient responses to emotionally-laden sound (Strait, 2009).

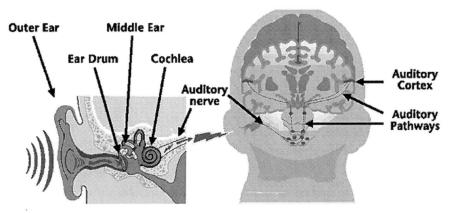

A patient plays his violin during brain surgery so doctors can find the exact place to put an electrode meant to stop the patent's hand tremors.

Also, it was discovered that children who had music lessons for more than 15 months showed higher scores on a number of cognitive tests, including some advancement over a control group in scores on mathematical reasoning (Hyde et al., 2009). Furthermore, another study found that children with intense music training scored higher on map-reading and other visual/geometry skills (Spelke, 2008). The author concluded, "If an infant hears music, the melodic processing may lead to new forms of visual processing. This may form the basis for the relationship between math and music later on."

Prominent brain researcher **Michael Posner** is an enthusiastic promoter of the idea that arts education in general can be beneficial because of the tremendous brain plasticity in children. He suggested that training

in the arts can strengthen brain regions linked to attention, self-control, and general intelligence. When children were given training designed to improve attention, Posner said, "Not only did attention improve, but also generalized parts of intelligence related to fluid intelligence and IQ increased" (Mauk, 2009).

Music seems to affect not only our auditory sense, but our other senses and our **emotions**, too. For instance, researchers have found that people who listen to happy music later rate smiling faces as happier and sad faces as sadder than do people who did not listen to the music (Logeswaran & Bhattacharya, 2009). Music can make us feel happy or sad and then we will rate others as happier or sadder than would someone who did not hear the music. Unlike noise, clatter, or even simple speech, music makes us *feel*. An old quote says, "Music is what feelings sound like."

Finally, mention should be made of the "**Mozart effect**." This is the popular idea that listening to classical music, in particular the music of Mozart, can improve intelligence. The impetus for this notion came from a 1993 study which reported that people who listened to Mozart, as opposed to those who heard repetitive relaxation music or others who experienced silence, had higher scores on a test of spatial-temporal reasoning (Rauscher et al., 1993). The researchers did not claim that general intelligence was improved, or that the effect lasted for longer than the testing session. However, the public's attention was captured and the idea spread that listening to classical music makes you smarter. The governor of Georgia, Zell Miller, even declared in 1998 that the state would provide every child with a tape or CD of classical music. And, the Florida legislature required that state-funded education for children under 6 be required to play classical music every day.

Scientists, however, were skeptical since they were familiar with an effect known as **enjoyment arousal**. You see, it turns out that people who enjoy an activity become aroused and will consequently perform better on certain tasks performed immediately after arousal. For example, people who heard an enjoyable passage from a Stephen King novel did better on a task that involved paper cutting and folding (Steele, 2006). Now, that is not to say that listening to music cannot improve performance on a task. In fact, it can. But, it doesn't have to be Mozart's music. Any music that provides arousal and is enjoyable

will produce performance increases in spatial perception (Thompson, Schellenberg, & Husain, 2001).

In addition, there is plenty of evidence that music exposure over many years can have very beneficial effects on listeners. Experts now believe that music lessons may in fact make lasting changes in the brain that enhance general learning. It has been proposed that music training can increase attention span, enhance working memory, improve concentration, and even help one learn a foreign language ("Hearing the music" in *Scientific American*, 2010). Music composer and singer Billy Joel apparently agrees: "I think music in itself is healing. It's an explosive expression of humanity. It's something we are all touched by."

Lead singer of U2, Bono, added, "Music can change the world because it can change people." Fabulous guitarist Jimi Hendrix, too, believed in the power of music: "Music doesn't lie. If there is something to be changed in this world, then it can only happen through music." Sometimes music is powerful: Poet, music manager, and political activist John Sinclair was released from prison two days after **John Lennon** sang a protest song about him in 1971. Of course, another Lennon song, *Give Peace a Chance*, was an anthem at Vietnam War protests of the past and continues to be sung by protest groups today.

People definitely believe in the power of music. Ancient Chinese mystic philosopher Lao Tzu wrote, "Music in the soul can be heard by the universe." And, **Beethoven** said, "Music is a higher revelation than all wisdom and philosophy."

So, go ahead, listen to music. Listen to music that you enjoy, and even explore and go beyond the music that you know and are familiar with. Learn more about music, and you'll probably enjoy it more. Pick up a musical instrument and learn how to play. Sing. Hum. Dance. Tap your feet. Shake your booty. Enjoy some "cheesecake!" And, yes, perhaps by doing so, you will train your brain!

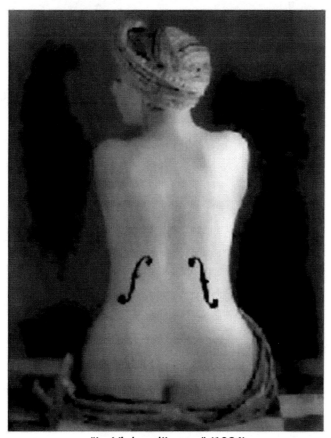

"Le Violon d'Ingres" (1924)
A fascinating photograph that cleverly combines
sex and music by avant-garde artist Man Ray.

"Feelings. Nothing more than feelings. Trying to forget my feelings of love."
– Feelings by Morris Albert

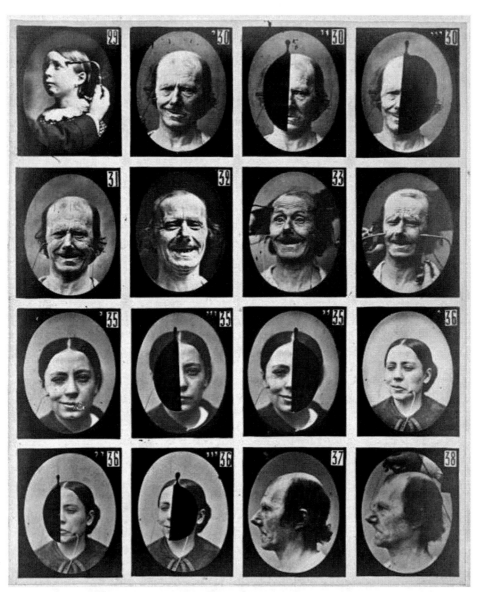

Duchenne faces.

"Young emotions are mixed emotions, For it's a world where love and confusion reign."
– Young Emotions by Ricky Nelson

6

Chapter 6

Emotions

*A*s you know, emotions are crucially important in our lives. Who would want to live without them – to be a mannequin or a computer without any feelings? Emotions surround and engulf our phenomenological experience: We love, we hate, we get angry, afraid, and surprised, we feel delighted, sad, embarrassed, and sometimes we are disgusted. Emotions are typically triggered by some experience or happenstance such as seeing a snake, winning the lottery, being stared at by others after making a faux pas at a social gathering, hearing a chilling piece of music, experiencing the death of a close relative, seeing a maggot-infested, decaying piece of meat, opening the door to a surprise birthday party, meeting a long-lost friend, discovering you were betrayed, or encountering a pleasant event. Yes, emotions get triggered by objects and events.

But, of course, emotions are created by, and connected to, biological events in our brains and in our bodies. While some early Greek philosophers taught that emotion derives from the heart and some ancient Romans thought the seat of emotions was in the liver, today we know that the controlling mechanisms of emotion lie in the brain. It is from the brain that the bodily physiology is stirred and the muscles are tensed or relaxed. Emotion is a brain and body mechanism that involves neural networks, physiological reactions, and body and facial movements. Our emotion systems have been fine-tuned over many years of evolution into intricate brain and body reactions to various circumstances, objects, and events that prepare us for action in those situations.

Definitions

While everyone seems to know what emotions are, it turns out that scientists have a fairly hard time defining them. The main problem is that emotions involve so many different aspects – feelings, body reactions, thinking, memory, interpretations, facial expressions, mood, motivation, and just the mere subjective nature that seems to pervade an emotional experience. It's a bit like explaining color to a color-blind person. How would you explain emotions to a robot, for instance? Emotions are tremendously complicated, and though we might all know what they are, we have a very difficult time untangling their numerous components and defining them.

Scientists tend to think of an **emotion** as a natural manner in which the brain and body respond to a situation that requires action. An emotion is a complex psychological and body reaction to an external influence, or sometimes a reaction to a memory or to the imagination of an object or event. The word emotion comes from the Latin *emovere*. The word has two parts: *movere* means to move (from which we get the English term "motivation"), and the prefix *e-* means "out." So, the origination of the terms suggests that a "**motivation**" comes from within, from inside of a person and makes the person move, while an "**emotion**" is movement that is pulled out of a person by circumstances. You feel hungry because of something inside of you, but you feel afraid when you see a snake, for example.

Latin

Dec 14

Feeling, by the way, is only one component of emotion, and some scientists make a very clear distinction between emotions and feelings. For most people and even for some psychologists, emotion and feeling are terms that are used interchangeably, or at least, are used nearly synonymously. Most of us consider emotions and feelings to be the same thing. But for neuroscientists who study the brain's systems that move us, this is not a common notion. For scientists, emotions and feelings are different concepts that need to be separated for a clear understanding of how our brains and bodies work. As an example, neuroscientists often consider love and hate to be feelings, not emotions. And, consider this: we *feel* aroused, hungry, thirsty, horny, nervous, cold, or upset. But those are not considered to be emotions.

For better or worse, scientists do not include all **feelings** as emotions. Some of the above are even considered motivations, such as hunger. Is hunger a feeling or a motivation, or both? It appears there is a somewhat confusing overlap in the use of the terms *feelings*,

motivations, and *emotions*. In fact, emotions are so complicated that there are many scientific concepts and theories that differ from one another even on such a seemingly basic issue as what to include or not include as an emotion! We cannot even agree on the definition of an emotion! Perhaps this can serve as a notice of the oft-forgotten fact that brains and bodies have anatomical and physiological functions that are not always amenable to description in simple words, and are not often easily divided into clear categories using the concepts we create in our language. Brains are biological organs performing electrical and chemical processes that do not cleanly fit into sentences in English!

Still, those scientists who spend their careers studying and thinking about emotions make a fairly distinct differentiation between emotions and feelings. For instance, the famous neuroscientist **Antonio Damasio** has written a number of books in which he describes his theory that emotions are connected to brain programming that represents the body. Damasio stresses the complex mechanisms in the brain that are necessarily tied to **body representations** when we have an emotional reaction. For Damasio, and for most other neuroscientists as well, an emotion is the physiological circuitry of the brain and body, a natural pattern of chemical and neural responses that plays a regulatory role and gives an organism an advantage in maintaining life. Emotions are engaged automatically, are biologically determined and carried out by a fairly restricted ensemble of brain areas and networks that connect with face and body proper. Emotions have the biological function of preparing an organism's body for a reaction to a situation. Emotions are the brain's (and body's) rather narrow and automatic reactions to events that require an action in order to increase the chances of survival (see Damasio, 1994, 1999, 2003, & 2010).

A **feeling**, on the other hand, is a subjective mental state that may or may not follow from an emotion. Feelings are created by brains that possess the ability to process and perceive the state of the body and that can also perceive thoughts and modes of thinking related to emotions. A very simple animal may have an emotion in the sense that it can react to dangerous situations, for example, by regulating its body and moving its muscles, but that animal may not have a complicated enough brain to produce a corresponding mental representation of its body nor have thoughts related to the experience. We may well say that the animal has an emotion, but not a feeling or consciousness of the emotion. **Emotion** refers to the brain and body processes that prepare an organism for responding to a situation. These brain and body processes are

automatic, innate, natural reactions that have been honed over long periods of evolution and they give the organism a survival advantage. **Feelings**, on the other hand, are created by brains that are even more evolved and have the capacity to represent processes occurring in the body.

Feelings are closely linked with awareness or **consciousness**. We can become aware of our brain's representation of our body processes. We can be aware of feelings. However, Damasio argues that there is a clear difference between a feeling and knowing that you have a feeling. That is, Damasio argues that a feeling is a certain state of brain circuitry that you may or not be aware of. You can have a feeling but not know it!

For example: Have you ever been in a situation where you suddenly realized you were nervous? Damasio says the feeling of nervousness likely was in your brain before you knew about it. It is possible to be happy or sad without knowing it. One woman told her psychiatrist she was not depressed, but after taking medication realized she had been. Feelings can be *un*conscious. That is a weird idea because the way we normally use the word "feeling" implies an awareness of the feeling. Normally when we say we have a feeling we mean we have the knowledge of a feeling.

Well, perhaps Damasio is right. Perhaps it is a mistake to let our normal concepts and terminology guide our understanding of psychology! Think of it this way: **Feelings are the brain's way of creating a mental or psychological notation or representation of an emotional reaction by using certain brain areas and networks.** Then, we can become aware of the feeling and even think about it. For instance: You see a snake, your brain and body react in a prescribed manner (that's the emotion), and then a bit later you may have a feeling of fear (your brain creates a representation of what is going on in your body), and then perhaps you become aware of the feeling of fear, an awareness that is partly your brain's conscious mental state resulting from your body's biological processes, but also partly influenced by your brain's ability to think about the event and connect it to memories. Your brain recognizes the danger and signals your body to react (emotion), your brain registers the reactions happening in your body (feeling), and then you become aware of the feeling and think about it (cognition). Does that make sense?

By the way, psychologists often use the term **affect** (from the Latin term meaning "to afflict or to touch" – from which we get terms such as affection) as a synonym for emotion. For example, the study of the biological aspects of brain and body with regard to emotions is commonly known as **affective neuroscience**. This chapter is about affective neuroscience! Also, sometimes in psychology the term affect is used in contrast to **cognition**, the act of thinking, perceiving, and remembering. However, while that is a common distinction made in psychology, it is a somewhat false distinction since the concept of emotion (affect) indeed does have a cognitive component. For instance, we can control our emotions to some extent by thinking. That is, emotions depend on, and are influenced by, cognition to some extent. So, cognition and affect are not entirely separate. Another example: In the study of mental illnesses, what are now known as "mood disorders" were once called "affective disorders," and the term "affective" is commonly used today to refer to emotional conditions. Mood is considered to be an affective state, for instance. So, in your journey through the discipline of psychology you will often encounter the term "affect" in place of emotion.

One of the foremost scientists who has spent a career studying affective neuroscience is **Joseph LeDoux**. His book, *The Emotional Brain* (1996), details his attempts to understand the neural systems underlying emotion, particularly his studies of the **amygdala** and its role in learned fears. For LeDoux, similarly as for Damasio, emotions are hard-wired brain and body processes that evolved to aid survival. LeDoux views the emotional system as similar across species. But, just as does Damasio, LeDoux separates feelings from emotions. LeDoux's research concentrates on brain systems that generate emotional reactions. He proposes that science does not need to look at the higher brain systems, such as cognition, thinking, and consciousness, and their role in emotions, though they may be part of a broader picture. LeDoux explained, "One can study how emotions are processed in the brain without reference to more complicated feelings. Emotional feelings result when we become consciously aware that an emotion system of the brain is active. Emotions evolved not as conscious feelings, but as brain states and bodily responses. The brain states and bodily responses are the fundamental facts of an emotion, and the conscious feelings are the frill that have added icing to the emotional cake."

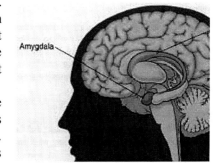

Amygdala

Okay, let's accept for now that emotions and feelings are separate experiences, and that science can study just the innate brain and body systems that determine emotional reactions without study of feelings and consciousness. But, then, we might next wonder: Just what are the different types of emotions that are wired into the brain?

IS my amygdala enlarged

Categories

What are the categories of emotions that organisms experience? What types of emotions are there, and what is their range? It has been common in psychology to divide emotions into two groups: the **basic** or **primary emotions**, and the **secondary** or **complex emotions**. In the past, the most commonly listed primary emotions were these six: happiness, sadness, anger, fear, surprise, and disgust. From this theoretical approach the secondary or social emotions were considered to result from combinations or blendings of these six primary emotions. For example, contempt could be thought of as a combination of anger and disgust, remorse could be considered a combination of disgust and sadness, and disappointment could be thought of as a combination of sadness and surprise. This approach was not based on brain research, but on behavioral observations of emotions and feelings.

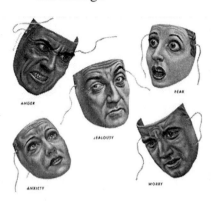

Amazingly, some contemporary psychologists have questioned whether there even are, in fact, any primary emotions at all (Barrett, 2006). Perhaps emotions don't neatly fit into a typology, or categorizing, system. Barrett, for example, cites research showing that emotions do not have clear boundaries that were carved by nature. She argues that psychological research on emotions is wrong to assume that emotions such as anger and disgust are given to us by nature and thereby exist separate from our perceptions of them. She argues that research does not support the view that each emotion produces distinctive changes in the body. Neuroscientists strongly disagree with her on this issue.

Other contemporary psychologists have argued that research on emotions has concentrated too heavily on certain affective states such as fear, happiness, and sadness, and that we have ignored the so-called **knowledge emotions**, such as interest (curiosity), confusion, surprise, and awe (Silvia, 2008). Just what is the range of emotions? In fact, if we go back in history we find that evolution theorist **Charles Darwin** described a very broad range of emotions including "abstracted meditation, perplexed reflection, and stupefied amazement" (Darwin, 1872). More recently, emotion researcher **Carroll Izard** (2007) has proposed a new paradigm of emotions that marks emotion as a major organizing factor in consciousness and as an influence on mind and behavior. Izard also has argued that **facial expressions** are an important barometer of emotions, but believes that they can vary in form and intensity. He has speculated about the evolutionary development of emotions and theorized that emotions affect personality and life outcomes by influencing how people think, behave, and interact with others (Izard, 1971).

Emotions vary in what is called "**valence**," that is, whether the emotional experience is pleasant or unpleasant. So, anger and fear, for example, are said to have negative valence, while happiness has positive valence. Sometimes an object or an event is said to have positive or negative valence, too, indicating our desire

to approach it because it produces pleasure, or our tendency to avoid it because it is aversive. Valence has been a subjective dimension so far in psychology, one that requires asking a person if they experience pleasure or not, but perhaps brain science can change that by finding brain activity that indicates valence.

When psychologists attempt to categorize emotions by valence there is some trouble because some emotions (surprise, for example) don't fit into that scheme. A **surprise** might be pleasant, but it also could be unpleasant. The **facial expression** for surprise is well known to you, I'm sure: Raised eyebrows with wrinkled forehead (the most distinctive sign of surprise), wide open eyes, stretched skin between the eyes and eyebrows, and a dropped jaw (the amount of drop indicates the intensity of the surprise), and sometimes a wide open mouth. Sound familiar? The facial expression for surprise is sudden and then is quickly over, only lasting a split second. Watch the face

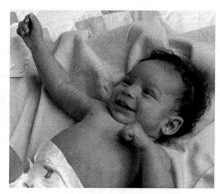

after the surprise expression has ended (after a split second) for the **valence** expression. That is when you will find out if the surprise was a pleasant one or an unhappy one. A face may show delight, fear, sadness, or confusion after the initial surprise expression.

The emotion of surprise seems so automatic and universal, but where does it come from? Do newborn **infants** experience emotions? Or, do emotions develop as a part of socialization? Like the nature-nurture question, this dichotomy is a bit unfair, since all human qualities are an interdependent, interacting, blending of both forces. That is, our psychological characteristics result from an intricate inter-mingling of the forces of heredity and experience. However, feelings of pleasure and pain seem evident in newborns, as does a startle or fear reaction (to a loud noise, a fall, or other stimuli).

Also, people in all **cultures** show similar emotions and reactions, including facial expressions. Such behavioral responses are evident in human infants and in lower animals. So, the capacity for emotion and the range of emotions seem mostly determined as part of our evolutionary heritage. But the nuances and particulars of emotions are obviously learned. An angry person might act aggressively, talk it out, or merely pout, depending on his or her cultural and personal experiences. Culture plays a modulating and shaping role on the innate, evolutionary basis of our emotional lives. Both nature and nurture contribute in an interacting manner.

Physiology

Mark Twain remarked, "Any emotion, if it is sincere, is involuntary."

Our bodies react to emotional experiences in many ways, including the release of various hormones and changes in our cardiovascular systems. These physiological events prepare the body for action, as in the **fight or flight response** to fear. Interestingly, these physiological changes are useful in the short run, but can be harmful in the long run. For example, the hormones released during emotional distress help us by providing energy and strength, but ultimately can damage body organs, including brain cells (Sapolsky, 1996). So, a life of constant **stress** could, in fact, kill you! Watch out for too many emotions!

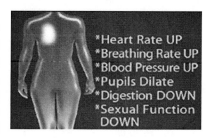

Most people assume that physiological events in the body are caused by the awareness or feeling of an emotion. However, over one hundred years ago American psychologist **William James** and Dutch psychologist **Carl Lange** separately proposed that this common view is exactly backwards. How do we identify an emotion? The **James-Lange theory** said that the physiological events of the body come first and that they give rise to the emotion. That is, one experiences an emotion because of awareness of the body's reactions. The James-Lange theory is playfully summarized by the statement: "I am running, therefore I must be afraid!" One fascinating fact in support of this theory is that people often do feel happier when they force a smile. Try it! This is called the **facial feedback hypothesis**. It appears that feedback from the muscles in your face influences your brain to feel happier (Izard, 1971). **Damasio's** modern approach to the neuroscience of emotions is very similar to the James-Lange conception. Damasio places the body reaction first in the emotional cascade. However, there are other views, too.

Years ago, researchers **Walter Cannon** and **Phillip Bard** showed what they believed was good evidence that the James-Lange theory cannot be completely correct. They showed that physiological responses are too slow; that emotions occur faster than body reactions. Cannon and Bard believed that a certain area of the brain, not the body's physiological responses, was the central factor in emotion. The **Cannon-Bard theory** said that the brain produces both the emotion and the body events at about the same time. Cannon and Bard also could not find clear physiological differences between the different emotions, so reasoned that the body could not be telling the brain what emotion was being experienced. However, contemporary researchers believe that they have uncovered clear distinctions in the physiology of emotions (e.g., Ekman et al., 1983). Still, the debate between these two theories continued for years, and to some extent, continues today.

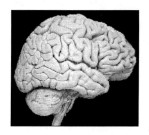

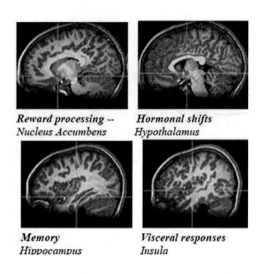

Reward processing --
Nucleus Accumbens

Hormonal shifts
Hypothalamus

Memory
Hippocampus

Visceral responses
Insula

However, subsequent research has indicated that both of these early theories of emotion have some truth to them, but that they also are incomplete. Physiological events do appear to be different for different emotions, and do apparently provide cues for emotions, as James and Lange argued. But, the brain is the main determiner of emotion, as Cannon and Bard pointed out.

In fact, modern researchers believe the evidence is excellent that there are different brain pathways and patterns of activity for the basic emotions. Unfortunately, it's difficult to embrace either of the two early theories entirely since they both exclude certain important features of emotions, such as the cognitive processes that accompany, and even help shape, an emotion. Arousal of the body's physiology can often be interpreted in different ways depending on the situation. An emotion, it turns out, is a complicated tangle of many interacting events – in the mind, in the body, and in the way the feeling is expressed.

Cognition

Emotions are often associated with the thinking and interpreting that one does during an emotional experience, such as, "That guy's a jerk," "This is a scary situation," or "What a fun place this is!" How do we determine which emotion we are experiencing in a situation? In unclear situations, cognition, or mental interpretation, becomes an important part of creating or influencing an emotion. **Cognition** refers to mental processes such as attention, language, thinking, memory, making judgments, planning, and problem solving. One clear example of how emotion can influence cognition is **flashbulb memory**. When we experience an event that is very emotional, a surge of adrenalin and other hormones influences brain cells to make the memory circuits stronger. It's like the memory sticks in our minds. But, how does cognition influence emotion?

A famous experiment in 1962 by Stanley Schachter and Jerome Singer showed how subjects could be influenced to **interpret** their emotions a certain way. The subjects were given injections of adrenalin. This aroused their autonomic nervous system physiology. The subjects were then placed in a room where a stranger (an actor) was acting either happy or angry. Now, in this situation, the subjects felt their bodies becoming aroused, that is, they felt the effects of the adrenalin, but they didn't know why they were aroused since they had been told that the injection they were given was a vitamin (a control group was told the truth). The researchers found that the subjects who did not have an interpretation for their arousal (had not been told that they had been given adrenalin) felt either happy or angry depending on how the stranger was acting. Apparently the subjects interpreted their body arousal as either happiness or anger depending on the situation. The subjects in the control group did not have the same interpretation since they knew why their bodies were aroused. The idea that cognition is important in influencing our emotions is today often called the **Schachter-Singer theory**. These two psychologists theorized that an emotional experience needs an interpretation. When we feel our body being aroused, we automatically attempt to give it a label, to process it cognitively, and the cues in the situation help us make that interpretation.

In an earlier experiment, Schachter (1959) had found that people who were frightened wanted to be with other people in the same situation, apparently to make comparisons in order to cognitively determine precisely what to think and how to act in the light of the frightening situation. Subjects were told that they would be receiving electric shocks as part of an experiment. They were told they would have to wait while the equipment was set up. They were then given the choice of waiting alone, waiting with others in the same experiment, or waiting with others in a different experiment. Compared to a control group, these subjects overwhelmingly chose to wait with others in the same boat. Schachter said that misery not only loves company, but misery loves miserable company!

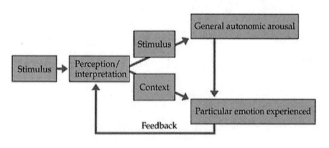

Stimulus → Perception/ interpretation → Stimulus → General autonomic arousal

Context

Particular emotion experienced

Feedback

Psychologists believe that emotions sometimes need to be analyzed cognitively. In other words, in order to better determine what you are feeling, or what you should think about it, or how you should act, especially if we you are in an ambiguous, unclear situation, you very well might observe those around you, those who are in a similar situation, in order to get some ideas. This is part of what is called **social comparison theory**, the notion that our thoughts, and our feelings, and our actions often come about through comparing ourselves with others. How should we feel, think, or act when it is not obvious? Look around at others to get some clues!

When people are **aroused** they may look around at the circumstances or the surrounding people to determine just what emotion they are feeling, or for an explanation for their arousal. We may come to identify our

aroused state as a particular emotion depending on the situation. For example, researchers found that if a hiker encountered an attractive woman while on a swaying bridge (an arousing situation) he was more likely to find her attractive and to later call her for a date than if he encountered her on a hiking trail (not a very arousing situation) (Dutton & Aron, 1974). Seeing a woman while in an aroused state apparently made men more likely to believe that it was the woman who caused their arousal. Whoa, I guess if you want someone to like you, you should meet him or her in a situation that causes arousal! Invite your date to go on a roller coaster! But, wait – that won't work because the situation is not ambiguous enough – it will be clear to your date that his/her arousal is caused by the roller coaster. Okay, better make it a less obvious situation, like standing near a waterfall. Have you got some ideas about your next date?

Most people think that emotions are separate from intellect, or that emotions get in the way of **intelligence** and rational, logical thinking. Consider, for example, the character of Mr. Spock on the TV series and movies called *Star Trek*. Mr. Spock supposedly maintains a high intellect and logical thinking by not allowing his emotions to interfere with his reasoning process. Most people accept this idea – that emotions are a hindrance to clear reasoning. Even renowned scientist **Carl Sagan** warned about emotions getting in the way of good thinking. He wrote: "Where we have strong emotions, we're liable to fool ourselves." Similarly, American author and critic Marya Mannes opined, "The sign of an intelligent people is their ability to control their emotions by the application of reason." It appears that this is a common notion – the idea that emotions are a burden, a detriment, to clear, rational, logical reasoning.

Now, current research suggests that this idea is quite wrong. Studies have found, for instance, that patients who have **brain damage** that makes them unable to feel certain emotions also suffer from **cognitive impairments**, particularly in making judgments (Damasio, 1999).

Also, researchers have discovered that when people are making decisions, the emotional areas of their brains are active (Shibata, 2001). Apparently emotions help us to direct our thinking, thereby helping us to make better decisions and to reason more correctly. So, emotions and cognitive processes perhaps are linked in a give and take manner; perhaps reasoning has no clear direction without emotions and is hampered without a guide. The great painter **Vincent Van Gogh** wrote, "The little emotions are the great captains of our lives and we obey them without realizing it."

The scientists who study the interplay of emotions and decision making often conclude that emotions rule decisions almost completely. Damasio points out that people who lack emotions because of brain injuries

have difficulty making any decisions at all. They just cannot make up their minds! Mr. Spock of *Star Trek* and other Vulcans would be lost, in reality, if they totally suppressed their emotions. Economists for decades have based their theories on the assumption that human **decision-making** is a rational, logical process. But brain science is now showing that nearly all decisions are driven by emotions. People are overwhelmingly irrational. One look at people's political choices makes that pretty clear to any observer. Brains did not evolve to be rational, logical machines. That's why we have computers! Brains are exquisitely designed for certain properties, and emotion is clearly one of them. Perhaps we should do as advised by painter and teacher Robert Henri who wrote: "Cherish your own emotions and never undervalue them."

Evolution

But, why do we even have emotions? Where did they come from? Perhaps it is obvious to most people today: Emotions evolved because they helped organisms adapt and survive. However, interest in the evolution of emotions is fairly new. As you might guess, the first mention of emotions from the perspective of evolutionary theory came from **Charles Darwin**. In his 1872 book, *The Expression of the Emotions in Man and Animals,* Darwin speculated that emotions grew from natural selection and therefore had counterparts in humans and lower animals. For his book, Darwin had researched emotions by studying the facial expressions, postures, and behaviors of both humans and animals, known as **affect display** – the facial, vocal, or gestural displays that are characteristic of emotions and that serve a communication purpose. Emotions not only are associated with physiological events within the body proper, but also with muscle movements. This component of emotion includes facial expressions and nonverbal body movements that are made during emotional experiences, such as a smile, raised eyebrows, furrowed brow, wide-open mouth, stooped shoulders, or a hand slapped on the forehead.

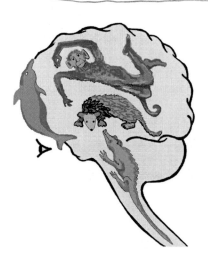

Modern **evolutionary psychologists** believe that different emotions evolved at different times over vast periods of time in our ancient history. Each emotion was fine-tuned over the course of natural selection to become a finely detailed circuitry and orchestration of brain and body systems. Very primal emotions, such as fear, evolved first to help animals survive by avoiding dangerous conditions. Social emotions, such as embarrassment, guilt, or gratitude, evolved later to help groups communicate with each other and understand their communal situations. The most complicated emotions, such as ambivalence, came last as brains became more complicated and capable of large-scale memory and cognitive operations.

Evolution provided men and women with slightly different brains that could react to situations that were advantageous to each sex. Research has shown, for example, that men are slightly faster at recognizing anger on another man's face than are women. But women are slightly quicker at detecting happy, sad, surprised, or disgusted facial expressions (Williams and Mattingley, 2006). The authors explained that from an evolutionary perspective the potential for physical threat from a male is greater than that from a female. A perceptual system that prioritizes detection of angry male faces that directly signal potential threat was therefore likely to be advantageous.

Likewise, the thinking brain's ability to modulate or influence emotions also is considered to be a more recent evolutionary development. Although we live in a mostly urban, technological, crowded world, scientists believe that most human emotions are best adapted to the life our ancestors lived as nomadic foraging bands. No wonder it's so hard to function in a high-tech society!

Contemporary research has found that **sleep** is important in recalibrating some negative emotions. Perhaps you've noticed that as the day wears on your reactions to fear and anger increase in intensity. It appears that evolution has made us more reactive to threat during night-time hours. But, an episode of REM sleep sets us back to a higher reactivity to happy stimuli. In a recent experiment, participants who viewed angry or

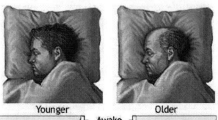

fearful faces showed increased reactivity across the day. However, if the participants took a nap that included **REM sleep**, their reaction to fear and anger decreased, and their recognition and ratings of happy, positive emotions increased (Gujar et al., 2011). Sleep, and in particular REM sleep, may be an important factor in regulating emotional homeostasis.

One important observation that Darwin made was that even people born blind display the same facial expressions, body movements, and body positions as anyone else when exhibiting emotions. Darwin concluded that **affect display** seems to be innate and universal and therefore emotions are a natural, characteristic feature of humans and lower animals.

Interestingly, some of the photos used by Darwin came from the research of French physician **Guillaume Duchenne** who electrically stimulated facial muscles to determine which were responsible for emotional expressions. Photographs of the faces were published in the 1862 book *Mécanisme de la Physionomie Humaine*. In this wonderful book, Duchenne noted two types of smiles, one he considered to be a genuine, innate smile that involved raised corners of the mouth and raised cheeks forming wrinkles at the corners of the eyes (so-called "crow's feet"), and a second smile that he considered to be fake, a smile that only involved raised corners of the mouth without involving the muscles of the eyes. The first, the genuine smile, is today referred to as a **Duchenne smile.**

Smiling

Acerbic quipster Oscar Wilde commented, "Some cause happiness wherever they go; others whenever they go," while absurdist comic Groucho Marx offered, "If you find it hard to laugh at yourself, I would be happy to do it for you."

A smile normally depicts **happiness**, pleasure, amusement, or good humor. Though, of course, among humans smiles are often faked. Typically, a fake or artificial smile does not involve the same facial muscle ingredients as a real smile. The so-called **Duchenne smile** includes flexing of the muscles around the corners of the mouth (as does a phony smile), but also flexing of the muscles around the eyes. Many researchers believe that the Duchenne smile represents spontaneous, genuine smiling and believe that it is difficult or impossible to artificially create the eye muscle movements that are part of the Duchenne smile. Incidentally, an artificial smile is called a **Pan-Am smile** because flight attendants on Pan American Airlines were well-known for habitually flashing a fake smile to each air passenger. Andy Rooney said that if you smile when no one else is around, you must really mean it.

The **facial feedback hypothesis** (mentioned above) suggests that the act of smiling can make people feel happier. Support for this idea came from a study in which people were shown how to make a Duchenne smile. Amazingly, they did report feeling happier when smiling (Ekman et al, 1990). Another study showed that people who received **botox** injections that made certain facial muscles unable to move did not show as much activation in emotion brain regions when imitating angry faces as they had before their injections (Hennenlotter et al., 2009). Perhaps our brain does get some feedback from the muscle movements of our face. Perhaps you should smile more, maybe you'll be happier!

Okay, if genuine smiling is a sign of **happiness** and pleasure, then might it be possible that people who smile more have certain advantages in life outcomes? Yes, it does appear to be so: Research has found that people who are happier have more stable personalities, more stable marriages, and better cognitive and interpersonal skills, and the degree of smile intensity in childhood and college photos was found to be correlated with **life satisfaction** (Hertenstein et al., 2009). Perhaps the amount of smiling and the intensity of smiling are inversely related to the amount of **stress** in life. Maybe people who smile more have less stress. **Robert Sapolsky** and others have shown that **stress** can shorten **life span**. But, could the intensity of smiling possibly be related to life span?

The answer apparently is yes! Abel and Kruger (2009) rated the amount of smile intensity found in the faces of 230 baseball players from the *Baseball Register*. The researchers controlled for other factors that might be related to life span, such as body mass index, career length, marital status, college attendance, and year of birth. A statistical analysis of the data did find that smile intensity was related to life-span longevity. For example, players who showed Duchenne smiles in their photographs were half as likely to die in any year compared with players who did not smile in their photos. Whoa! Maybe we'd better start smiling more! Or, is this a chicken-egg problem? Maybe we need something to smile about! And, remember the old saying: *A smile confuses an approaching frown.*

There's a new sub-division of psychology that studies what are called positive emotions, such as happiness, contentment, and fulfillment. This sub-field is called **positive psychology**. Positive psychology is a recent branch of psychology that attempts to make life more fulfilling for people by applying scientific research to help increase positive emotions in individuals and societies. Neuroscientists contribute to positive psychology by attempting to find the neural underpinnings of emotions, and by identifying methods by which emotions and feelings can be influenced. Neuroscientific research may not only help people who have diagnosable disorders, it may also contribute to helping us build better, higher quality societies in which people can find contentment and fulfillment.

Most people would say that the opposite of happiness is **sadness**. This, however, is not exactly right. Happiness and sadness are both emotions, and they both have obvious facial displays associated with them, yes, that's true. But, lack of happiness is not the same as sadness, nor is lack of sadness the same as happiness. In fact, a person can have a mixed feeling, a bittersweet moment when one is a little happy and a little bit sad. Haven't you had a moment like that?

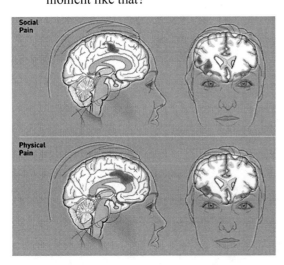

Social Pain

Physical Pain

Likewise, **sadness** and depression are not the same brain states either. **Depression** is a very broad state that involves mood, disturbances in eating, sleeping, and thinking, and several behavioral disturbances. Brain imaging research has shown a clear distinction between sadness and depression. Contrary to a popular notion, depression is not the same as extreme sadness. Both, however, are related to the neurological processes associated with physical pain. Brain images show that depression, grieving, and other **social pains** activate the same brain areas that are activated when a person is suffering from **physical pain**. When a depressed or grieving person says that he/she is in pain, there is definitely a biological truth to their complaint (Eisenberger et al, 2003).

The neuroscience of **sadness** is very complicated. For instance, an analysis of twenty-two brain imaging studies of sadness reported a total of seventy different brain regions were involved (Freed & Mann, 2007). Seventy regions – wow – yes, sadness is complicated and widely distributed in the brain. Sadness involves thoughts, memories, feelings, other emotions such as disgust, pain, and visual and auditory memories. The brain regions that were most often noted as involved in sadness were the basal ganglia, anterior cingulate cortex, cerebellum, ventral prefrontal cortex, and the insula. Most of these areas are discussed below because of their participation in a number of different emotions. By the way, research on happiness has shown just as wide a distribution in the brain as for sadness. Apparently, these emotions are so important that our brain has evolved numerous mechanisms for processing, analyzing, and modulating them and their many components.

*U*niversals

The idea that emotions and affect display are **universal** was not always widely accepted by scientists. For instance, in the middle of the twentieth century anthropologists Margaret Mead, Gregory Bateson, and Jean Biggs argued that emotions and emotional expressions are predominantly learned within one's **culture**; that cultural differences in emotion were common. Evidence to support this view can be found in an article by

Mesquita & Frijda (1992). This view, obviously, was contrary to Charles Darwin's view that facial expressions of emotions are innate and shaped by evolution. In the 1970s the pendulum began to swing back toward viewing emotions as innate and universal across animal species and human cultures. Most of this change was due to the research and writings of psychologist **Paul Ekman**.

In 1967 Paul Ekman traveled to New Guinea to study and observe the isolated Fore people. Ekman wanted to know how the Fore people would respond to faces that showed typical expressions of emotions as well as how their faces expressed emotions. In support of what Darwin had proposed, Ekman found the facial expressions for basic emotions were the same amongst this isolated group as seen in peoples of other cultures (Ekman, 1972).

Ekman's research has been called groundbreaking because it reversed the tide and helped usher in an interest in how evolution has contributed to shaping human behavior.

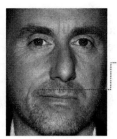

contempt

① lip corner tightened and raised on only one side of face

Right: anger, fear, disgust, surprise, joy, sadness.

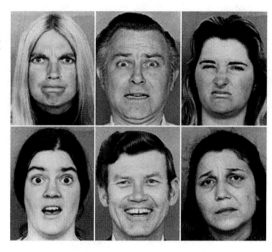

Today it is widely accepted by scientists that people in all cultures of the world are remarkably consistent in their **facial expressions** of emotions, and in their ability to judge other people's emotional states by seeing facial expressions. While there are some minor variations in body language and posture from one culture to another, it is amazing how similarly people react to emotional experiences.

Ekman originally identified five universal emotions – anger, fear, sadness, happiness (joy), and disgust – but more recent evidence has added the two emotions of surprise and contempt, though some cultural differences have been found in the expression of those two. So, in summary, though there are some minor wrinkles in the data, it appears that there are seven **universal emotions** wired by evolution into the human race: happiness (joy), sadness, anger, fear, disgust, surprise, and contempt (facial expressions for each are shown above).

Let's Face It

Let's try it: Notice someone's face (or your own face in a mirror) when thinking about 1) an awful, hideous odor (did you wrinkle your nose?); 2) a foul tasting food (did you make the "yech" expression with your mouth?); 3) a big surprise (did you open your mouth and raise your eyebrows?); 4) a scary figure (did you widen your eyes and flare your nostrils?). It appears that humans have universal ways of signaling their emotions with their faces; expressions that are similar in lower animals, too. Studies found that *fearful* expressions expand the sensory areas of the face, taking in more information, while *disgusted* expressions do the opposite, resulting in closing off or contracting the sensory areas (pinch your nose) thus reducing incoming information (Susskind et al., 2008).

CREEPY   BORED   MAD

SHOCKED   CHILLIN

So, apparently circuits in our brains allow us to look at someone's face and know what emotion that person is experiencing based on the expression (mostly eyes and mouth) they are making. It's easy to imagine that this was an important skill for survival of our ancient ancestors, and one can understand how it exists in the modern brain. But, how does the brain do this? One might think that our brain learns to associate our own facial expression with an emotion and then transfer it to the faces of others. This is likely not true, however, since people with **Moebius syndrome**, a rare disorder that causes paralysis of the face, can still recognize emotions in others based on facial expressions (MacDonald, 2003). Therefore, these responses are likely hard-wired, innate properties of brain and body circuitry – both the facial expressions that are characteristic of emotions, and the brain's ability to recognize what emotion is being displayed.

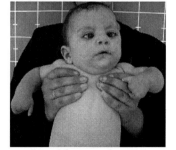

Moebius syndrome.

Ekman popularized the observation made by Darwin and Duchenne that facial expressions are a clear and distinctive sign of specific emotions. Further, the American psychologist **Carroll Izard** has made significant contributions to what is sometimes called **Discrete Emotions Theory** – the idea that there are universal, recognizable, innate emotions. Izard and his colleagues have argued that the basic emotions in humans emerge in the first few months of life and that facial expressions of emotions provide babies with cues about which emotion a person is experiencing (Izard et al., 1995; Izard & Abe, 2004).

Brain imaging studies of people looking at emotional faces has discovered neural activity in many brain areas, but particularly in the **amygdala** and **prefrontal cortex** (Sabatinelli et al., 2011). Research that measures how much facial expression occurs during emotional reactions suggests that women, on average, show more facial activity than do men. However, this finding does not hold when measuring people with schizophrenia, who show less facial expression in general (Simons et al, 2010). Furthermore, depressed people are worse at recognizing emotions except for sadness, and people with traumatic brain injuries are significantly impaired at facial recognition of emotions (Williams & Wood, 2010).

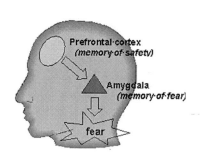

ℒie 𝒟etection

Paul Ekman expanded his research of emotion by studying the precise muscle movements made by the face when experiencing an emotion (Ekman & Friesen, 1978). Ekman believes that tiny facial movements that he calls **microexpressions** are innate, universal, and unconscious. He argues that these microexpressions cannot be controlled and therefore are clear signs of the emotion being experienced by a person. Ekman and his colleagues

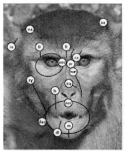 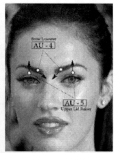
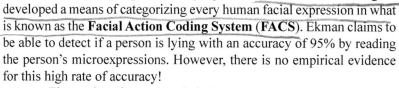

developed a means of categorizing every human facial expression in what is known as the **Facial Action Coding System (FACS)**. Ekman claims to be able to detect if a person is lying with an accuracy of 95% by reading the person's microexpressions. However, there is no empirical evidence for this high rate of accuracy!

Ekman does, however, admit that there is no one single indicator of deception. Ekman's research and theories did result in a TV show, though, which is called *Lie to Me*. Ekman maintains a website on which he corrects errors that occur in the show. For example, in one episode a character touched his nose while talking and the experts in the series concluded that the character was lying because of the characteristic nose-rub when being deceptive. Ekman rightly pointed out that touching the nose is not an indicator of lying, that the nose-rub when nervous is a myth. The show *Lie to Me* has gone so far to include video footage of Paul Ekman walking through the jungles in his visit to remote cultures. However, in the TV series the video is modified by replacing Ekman's face with the face of the TV actor star of the series.

  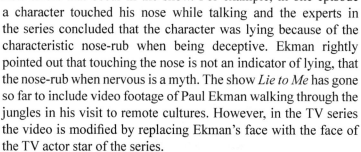

Fear
Upper eyelids raised

Disgust
Nose wrinkled

Anger
Jaw thrust forward

While Ekman's claims about lie-detection are exaggerated, his views about the universality of emotion and nonverbal affect displays have been roundly accepted. It appears that at least primary emotions have an evolutionary basis and are automatic, innately-programmed brain systems. Would it be possible, then, to detect when people are lying using a system similar to that of FACS? People who are trained to use FACS to "read" the emotions of others are very confident in their ability to detect lies. However, it appears that their confidence is overrated. Research has found that the very best human lie detectors have an accuracy rate of about 60% (Navarro, 2008).

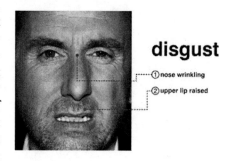

disgust
- ① nose wrinkling
- ② upper lip raised

There are questioning techniques that can increase the chances of detecting a liar. For example, **lying** takes more **cognitive** power than telling the truth. Therefore, asking people to manipulate information cognitively will be a much slower, more difficult process for a person telling a lie. For instance, ask a person to tell a story backwards or out of order. A truth-teller will have little difficulty with this; but a liar may stumble. Innocent people are more likely to answer quickly, while a liar needs time to fabricate. Another technique is called **guilty knowledge**. A person who has robbed a bank knows what the bank teller looks like, whereas an innocent person who had never been in the bank will not know the teller's appearance. Asking such questions can trip up a liar.

The best-known lie detection device is the **polygraph**, commonly known as a **lie detector**. It is often shown or used on TV shows. This is a machine that measures a number of physiological responses, such as pulse, blood pressure, breathing, and skin conductivity (the **GSR** or **galvanic skin response** is a measure of the electrical conductivity of the skin due to sweating), under the assumption that a person who is lying will show an automatic, unconscious increase in such physiological indices. In fact, the polygraph is more an arousal detector than a lie detector. Polygraphs are notoriously unreliable to the point that their results are not permitted in court cases. Psychologists have estimated the

validity of the polygraph at about 60%, though it is hard to get an accurate indication of validity since the polygraph is mostly used as an interrogation device. There are numerous examples of spies who have passed the lie detector test.

There are many reasons such a technique will fail. Some innocent people show emotional responses, for instance, when asked suspicious questions. On the other hand, some guilty people do not get nervous. Also, some criminals learn tricks to fool the polygraph. Distorting the baseline is an example. Put a thumb tack in your shoe and step on it each time you answer truthfully. The baseline will show a high level of arousal and lies will show the same autonomic nervous system response. Despite their low validity, polygraphs are still used quite frequently, and the U.S. military is even developing a hand-held polygraph to use in the field. Also, **voice stress analysis** is a lie-detection method similar to the polygraph. The idea is that people telling a lie will have micro-tremors in their voice. This technique also has low validity.

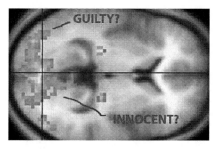

But why measure physiology, why not go right to the source – the brain! In fact, several companies are now using **brain imaging** to detect lies. Though this technique shows some promise of having high validity, currently there is not good data on exactly what brain activity is associated with lying. Some results indicate that frontal lobe activation is more common when fabricating a tale, but looking for brain regions that are active during lying may not be successful. Another use of brain imaging might be more valid: This idea is to combine the guilty knowledge protocol with brain images. For instance, if a person's visual cortex becomes active when asked what a bank teller looks like, it might be an indication that the bank teller was seen by the person. That is, it is possible that brain activity in certain regions may indicate memories of certain events that were only possible in a guilty person.

One attempt at this is called **brain fingerprinting** (Farwell & Smith, 2001). This procedure uses the **EEG** to measure brain waves and is partly based on the finding that brain waves increase in intensity about 300 milliseconds (1000th of a second) after exposure to a meaningful stimulus. This is known as a **P300 response** (P means a positive deflection in voltage). A P300 is one example of an **event related potential (ERP)**, a change in the electrical firing of brain cells in response to an event. There are many such ERPs, some that are negative, such as a N400 that occurs when a person sees an unexpected word in a sentence. In this case brain waves deflect negatively in voltage about 4/10 of a second after experiencing the stimulus.

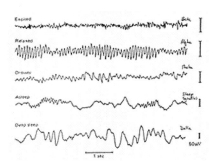
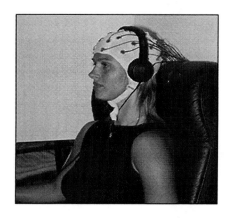
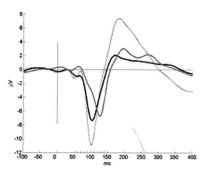

In the case of the P300 (or P3), when you see or hear something **meaningful** to you, your brain waves intensify (increase in voltage), particularly in the parietal lobe, about one-third of a second later. So, for instance, a suspect can be shown a variety of possible murder weapons. Only the police and the guilty party know which weapon was used. However, if the suspect shows a **P300 response** to the correct weapon, that indicates knowledge of it. Interesting, no?

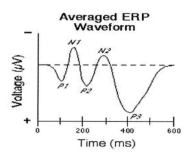

Emotion Abnormalities

One of the major flaws of current lie detection techniques that rely on bodily changes is that there are people who do not react physiologically to lies. They are known as **psychopaths**, and have the psychiatric diagnosis of **antisocial personality disorder** (**APD**). It is said that psychopaths have no conscience. That is an exaggeration, but on the right track. Psychopaths show a lack of empathy, display amoral conduct, and have an outwardly normal, even friendly, appearance. The polygraph does not detect lies told by psychopaths because they do not show physiological reactivity to stress, nervousness, or fear. Even a stimulus that signals an aversive event does not generate a fight-flight reaction in people with APD.

Ted Bundy, psychopath and serial murderer.

Psychopathy (*sigh-KOP-ah-thee*) occurs in about 4% of the population, and the vast majority are men. Psychopaths might be thought of as compulsive criminals, liars, cheaters, and fakes, and appear not to feel shame, guilt, or remorse for their actions. They seem to lack an ability to care about the feelings of others and therefore have an ability and affinity to con people. Shallow affect is common and genuine emotions are rare, brief, glib, and egocentric. While a psychopath may sometimes exhibit a superficial charm, the overall tendency is to use manipulation, violence, and sex to control others and satisfy their own needs. Criminal psychologist **Robert Hare** developed the **Hare Psychopathy Checklist** as a diagnostic tool.

Psychiatrists and many psychologists believe the term psychopath has been co-opted by Hollywood and is no longer a useful term. They prefer APD, which is defined as a pervasive pattern of disregard for, and violation of, the rights of others that begins in childhood or early adolescence and continues into adulthood. Criminality, lying, lack of remorse, impulsivity, aggressiveness, irresponsibility, and reckless disregard for the safety of self or others are common symptoms. Psychopaths quickly become angry and irritable, show aggression, and are sensitive to shame and humiliation. However, they do not show normal social emotions, such as sympathy, empathy, and gratitude, which may be part of the reason they can easily inflict suffering on others without concern.

In fact, the physiology of psychopathic behavior has been extensively studied, particularly the role of the **frontal lobe**. Medical researcher **Adrian Raine** and his colleagues (Raine, 2000; Gao & Raine, 2010) have spent years studying criminals with APD and murderers. The research indicates a clear pattern of reduced activity in the frontal lobes, reduced gray matter volume in the frontal lobes, and reduced autonomic activity. It was noted that greater deficits were present in murderers who came from non-deprived backgrounds than in those from deprived backgrounds indicating that criminality can stem from brain abnormalities that arise from impoverished or abusive backgrounds, but also from brain disorders caused by genetic or other factors separate from upbringing. Also, some research has shown that an abnormal physiological reaction in children as young as 3 years old is associated with criminal behavior in adulthood (Gao & Raine, 2010).

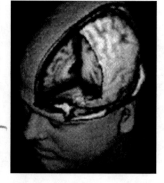

Abnormalities in the **frontal lobe** were also found in people with **APD** in other research (Narayan et al, 2007). The frontal lobes are the brain areas responsible for higher thinking, planning, moral reasoning, and control of emotions. Hare (1999) notes many studies that show that people with APD lack physiological responses common to **fear**. A study by Raine (1990) found that low levels of **arousal** in adolescents helped predict later criminal behavior in adulthood. Low autonomic activity was found in 9-10 year-old boys who had psychopathic traits (Isen et al., 2010). Other research has shown abnormalities in the connecting white matter between the frontal lobe and the amygdala, also.

Damasio's team studied two adults who had experienced **lesions** to their **frontal lobes** before the age of 16 months. Both adults showed characteristics similar to APD including severely impaired social behavior, defective autonomic responses to punishment, and defective moral reasoning (Anderson et al., 1999). Buckholtz et al. (2011) found that the dopamine reward system, including the **nucleus accumbens**, is **hypersensitive** in people with psychopathic traits including impulsivity and antisocial behavior. The researchers found increased activity in the mesolimbic pathway that uses dopamine and is associated with pleasure and drug addiction in people with APD symptoms. The researchers speculated that a heightened response in the **reward pathway** could make people less fearful about the consequences of their behaviors. So, there is plenty of evidence that psychopathy is represented by various brain anomalies.

Pleasure Reward Pathway

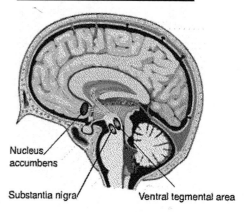

Another apparent disorder of the brain's emotional system is called **alexithymia**. This term refers to a personality trait in which people have difficulty identifying and describing emotions, and have problems distinguishing between emotional feelings and body sensations. The term literally means "without words for emotions." Alexithymia has been found in about 6% of the general population and is associated with particular psychological disorders such as autism, Asperger's syndrome, eating disorders, depression, and substance abuse. Neuroscience studies of this personality trait have detected deficiencies in the **right hemisphere** (which

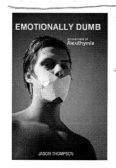

tends to be more actively involved with emotions), and in the transfer of information from the right hemisphere to the left (more language-oriented) hemisphere, likely due to a smaller corpus callosum, which can result from childhood abuse (Hoppe & Bogen, 1977).

Another study found that alexithymia may be related to dysfunction in the **anterior cingulate cortex** (Lane et al., 1997). And finally, a study of more than 8,000 Danish pairs of twins found that while genetic factors were significant, non-shared environmental factors also contributed to alexithymia (Jørgensen et al., 2007).

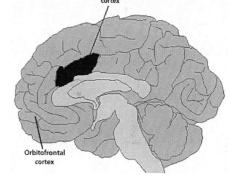

Antonio Damasio has written about patients who, after damage to their frontal lobes, appeared unable to experience emotions (Damasio, 1999). For instance, Damasio describes a man named **Elliot** who had surgery to remove a tumor from an area of his brain just behind his eyes (the **orbitofrontal cortex**). Subsequently, though Elliot showed normal intellect, he was unable to make decisions. How could this have come about? Damasio observed that Elliot no longer showed any evidence of an emotional reaction. When tested by Damasio, Elliot did not show physiological reactions nor did he report emotional

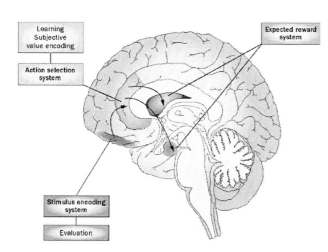

arousal when shown emotional stimuli, such as a severed limb, a gun, or a house on fire. Elliot's palms never got sweaty no matter how upsetting the stimulus.

Damasio concluded that not only is the **frontal lobe** a critical player in the brain's emotional network, but that emotions are important components of **decision making**. Without emotions to guide us, our decisions will hang pointless and without value. The evolution of the cerebral cortex, and particularly the frontal lobe, did not make us exacting rational, thinking machines, but rather made us even more dependent on our emotional brain. The philosopher David Hume may have been right when he said, "Reasoning is the slave of the passions."

🧡he €motional 🐉rain

Okay, here's a simple way to illustrate the brain and learn about brain anatomy: Hold your hand up, bend your thumb into your palm, and then close down your fingers curling them tightly around your thumb, and bend your wrist forward. The fist you have now made represents your brain. Your thumb is your limbic system, including the **amygdala** and **hypothalamus**. The area just above your wrist is the brainstem, and at its top is the **ventral tegmental area**. Next, about where the tips of your fingers touch your thumb is the **nucleus accumbens**. These areas – amygdala, hypothalamus, brainstem, ventral tegmental area, and nucleus accumbens – are all intimately related to motivation, emotion, pleasure and desire.

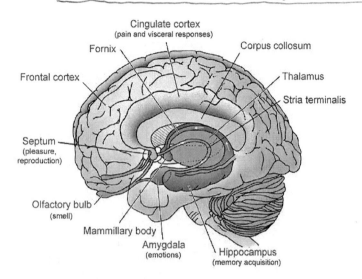

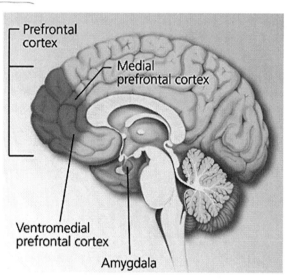

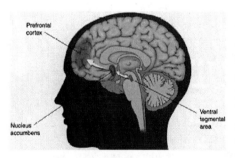

Now continue to look at your fist: Your palm and the front surface of your fingers represent the **cingulate cortex**. The very front part of that area, located just in front of your thumbnail is the **anterior cingulate cortex** (*anterior* means to the front). This brain region is also a very important source of brain connections for emotions. Your curved fingers in the front of your fist represent the frontal lobe of the brain; the front-most part is called the **prefrontal cortex** and the lower part, from the tips of your fingers to the first knuckle is known as the **ventromedial prefrontal cortex**. Notice that this area of the frontal lobe (the finger tips) curls around to meet up with the limbic system (your thumb). This is how the thinking, frontal lobe connects with the lower, subcortical areas such as the amygdala so that emotions have some cognitive control. The very front part of your fingers, about where your middle knuckles are protruding out, the part of brain that would be right behind the eyes, is called the **orbitofrontal cortex**. Now, you can see by this arrangement that the frontal lobes are an integral part of the emotional brain because they have close connections to the limbic system and surrounding areas.

Wouldn't it be nice to point at a certain brain area and be able to say that there is where a certain emotion resides? No, unfortunately, the emotions do not reside in specific compartments in the brain. Rather, emotions are wired into **circuits** that traverse several of the brain areas represented by your fist. Contemporary research in neuroscience has supported the evolutionary view that there are independent neural systems in the brain each handling a specific basic emotion (Wicker, 2003). However, emotions are a bit like music as it was described in the last chapter – many brain areas interact with each other to create the neural networks that subserve our emotional experiences.

Yes, each of the universal emotions appears to have its own separate pattern of brain activity, but the various brain regions that are involved **overlap** each other in the activations for different emotions. That is, neuroscientists have shown evidence that each of the primary emotions has its own innate brain circuitry and physiological pattern of activity in the body, but several brain areas repeat their roles for different emotions, so we find overlap in how emotions are represented in the brain. Next, here is a listing of some of the major anatomical brain regions that play a significant role in the emotional life of the brain:

1. Amygdala

The **amygdala** is a nucleus in the middle of the temporal lobe, just in front of the hippocampus. There is one in each hemisphere, two amygdalae. The name comes from the Greek word for "almond," which describes the shape of this brain area. Each amygdala has about a dozen sub-divisions and makes connections with many other brain regions including the hypothalamus, the facial nerves, and the brainstem. The amygdala's connection to the face was demonstrated by Damasio and his team who reported the case of a woman who suffered rare

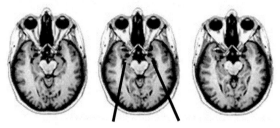

damage to both her amygdalae. The patient, known as **SM**, was unable to recognize **fear** from facial expressions (Adolphs et al., 2005). This inability, apparently, was due to her lack of fixation on the eyes, the part of the face that most depicts the expression of fear. When SM was explicitly instructed to notice the eyes, her recognition of the fear expression was normal. Testing patients with bilateral (both sides) amygdala damage also showed that these people had severe reduction in eye contact during social conversations and showed an increase in gaze at the mouth (Spezio et al., 2007).

Three views of damaged amygdalae in SM.

By the way, SM has been observed and written about extensively. She has been dubbed "The woman who felt no fear." Her lack of fear has led her into some precarious situations. She wanders into dangerous venues without any qualms. As a result, she has been held up, physically attacked, nearly killed in an act of domestic violence, and threatened with death. When passing through a "haunted house" on Halloween, she showed no fear of the grotesque monsters or dark hallways. She reacted with smiles and curiosity. Though she claims to hate snakes, when SM was confronted with one she only showed interest, no fear. She even attempted to touch a tarantula and had to be stopped to prevent her from being bitten.

The observation about SM's inability to recognize fear gave rise to speculation that the amygdala may be important for detecting **relevant social stimuli** visually and then directing attention to that visual area. Such an idea was tested on five people who had lesions to their amygdalae. The five subjects watched a screen that presented visual stimuli such as arrows, eyes, and faces that were made of lines. The subjects pressed the space bar on a computer in response to the visual stimuli. Based on their findings, the researchers concluded, "The results suggest that the social valence of a stimulus is critical for **amygdala** involvement in visual processing. The results also support the implicated role of the amygdala in detecting and analyzing relevant social stimuli, and orienting attention accordingly" (Akiyama et al., 2007).

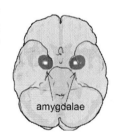

amygdalae

So, yes, the amygdala does appear to play a role in helping people detect what is relevant, what we should pay attention to, in our visual world. This means socially relevant stimuli, such as the eyes of a person who is afraid! These research findings are important because they stimulate scientific ideas about the neuroscience of disorders such as **autism**, **Asperger's syndrome**, and other disorders that involve problems in detecting **social cues**. People with autistic spectrum disorders typically have difficulty interacting socially with others and with communication. Often, people with autistic disorders treat others as if they are objects, seemingly unable to conceptualize other people as individuals with minds with whom they can interact. The autistic child seems to not notice the relevant social stimuli, particularly in a person's face. The amygdala, since it is implicated in detecting social stimuli such as facial expressions, may indeed be a player in such disorders. Researchers are now studying autistic children to look for amygdala dysfunctions.

The amygdala has been studied the most by neuroscientist **Joseph LeDoux,** who even sings and plays guitar in a rock 'n' roll band called *The Amygdaloids*, consisting entirely of scientists who write and perform songs peppered with ideas about the brain, the mind, and mental disorders.

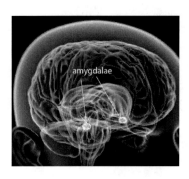

In the 1970s and 1980s LeDoux began his research based on his interest in the **classical conditioning** of fears and how that type of learning was represented in the brain. Classical conditioning is the process that was studied by **Ivan Pavlov**. In Pavlov's most famous example he conditioned dogs to salivate to the sound of a bell. The same process occurs when you learn to be afraid of something. LeDoux did not believe that brain imaging technology was the best way to find what he wanted; he said that using brain imaging to find out about the brain was like studying New York State to find out about New York City. Instead, LeDoux favored animal research so that he could study individual brain cells and circuits. Eventually, his exacting research was able to follow the learned conditioning of fear within the brains of laboratory rats. He found that the circuit for learned fear is centered in the amygdala.

LeDoux trained rats by associating the sound of a tone with a mild electric shock. The rats quickly learned to "freeze" when they heard the tone. They were classically conditioned to have a learned fear response. LeDoux then used a tracer chemical that stains neurons in order to follow the neural signal through the neurons in the rat's brain. He found the signal went from the ear to the thalamus and then to the amygdala. When this circuit was cut in a rat's brain, the animal could no longer be conditioned to fear a tone. LeDoux also found that the amygdala reacts to predators. When rats are threatened they make a high pitched scream. Other rats who hear this scream have instant amygdala activation, what LeDoux considers an emotional fear response that signals the body for action.

From his studies LeDoux concluded that the brain has two pathways for processing and reacting to dangerous stimuli. One pathway is fast and automatic – it passes through the amygdala and sets in motion the **fight or flight response** (perhaps it should be: *freeze*, then fight or flight?), that LeDoux calls the "**low road.**" In this quick brain reaction, the body changes – heart rate, respiration, and blood pressure increase, pupils dilate, and digestion slows. The amygdala senses expressions on faces in a few thousandths of a second. This is the response that polygraphs attempt to capture. It is fast and **unconscious.**

The second pathway, that LeDoux dubs the "**high road,**" involves the thinking part of the brain. Information about the dangerous stimulus is passed to the higher cerebral cortex where brain regions act more slowly at analyzing and understanding the situation, perhaps putting the brakes on, or modulating, the fight or flight response. This is where feeling is created, too. Emotion and feeling are separate in LeDoux's explanation. **Emotions** involve the **low road**, while **feelings** require **cognition** (thinking) which is part of the **high road.** According to LeDoux, emotions and cognitions are separate, but interacting, mental functions that are represented by separate, but interacting, brain systems.

Interestingly, the **amygdala** connections (the low road) are stronger than those from the **cortex** (**the high road**), so an emotion, once activated, is difficult to shut down. It is hard to control emotions. So, here is an example: You are driving in your car and then suddenly, unexpectedly, you are cut off by a fast moving vehicle. Your first response is visceral – a gut reaction that is quick and automatic. Your eyes widen, your foot hits the brake, and you gasp for breath (low road). Then, a bit later, you think about it. You analyze the situation. You pull yourself together. You might realize that it is best to forget it and go about your business (high road), although you will still feel the surge of adrenalin in your chest!

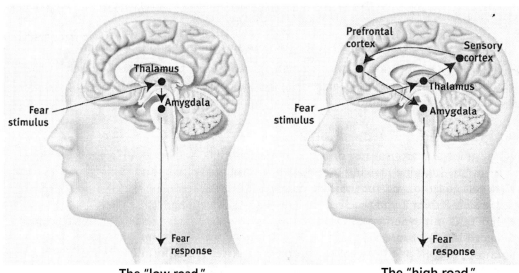

The "low road."   The "high road."

2. Frontal Lobe

A somewhat common therapy for mental patients from the 1930s to 1950s was a **lobotomy**, a surgical procedure that cut neural circuits in a person's **frontal lobe** of the brain. Most patients after receiving a lobotomy showed considerable lack of motivation and emotion. They became **passive**, which was considered an improvement, even a cure, in their illness. Lobotomies, thankfully, are a thing of the past. But, they remind us of the frontal lobe's importance for our emotions and thinking.

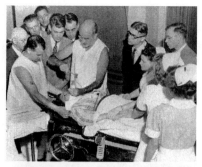

Similarly, Damasio's patient named Elliot, described above, tragically demonstrates the importance of the frontal lobe on emotions. The **orbitofrontal cortex**, just behind the eyes, is the part of the brain that was damaged in this case. The orbitofrontal cortex is believed to be involved with **decision making** and connecting emotional brain activity to the stream of thought in **consciousness**. Damage to the orbitofrontal cortex can reduce the ability to determine the value of choices. Patients with damage to this area from strokes or tumors have perfectly normal language and intelligence, but make horrible personal choices. Cells in this area in the monkey brain have been recorded while the monkey is making choices between different foods and the cells encode the value of the choices (Padoa-Schioppa & Assad, 2008). So, these seem to be the brain cells that track the value of objects. Neurons in your orbitofrontal cortex are keeping track of the reward (pleasurable) value of various objects and events in your experience! Cool, huh?

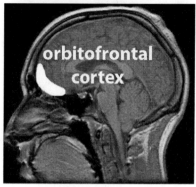

Similarly, the **ventromedial prefrontal cortex** (lower, middle) has been found to be active in **decision making**, and even in the process of taking into account the pleasurable aspects of a situation to help make a decision, as is found in the orbitofrontal area. For example, the authors of a recent study concluded: "We show that the orbitofrontal and ventromedial prefrontal cortices compute expected value, reward outcome, and experienced pleasure for different stimuli. Attractor networks in the ventromedial prefrontal area then implement decision processes that transform value signals into a choice between the values, thereby guiding action" (Grabenhorst & Rolls, 2011). There is some evidence that these brain areas are thinner in psychopaths.

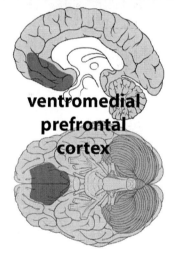

One idea about how this works is that the prefrontal brain areas are receiving signals about emotions from **subcortical** (below the cortex) areas, such as the amygdala, and then integrating these signals into a network that includes pleasure, reward, goals, and cognitive processing in order to make decisions. The orbitofrontal area apparently acts unconsciously as it accesses other brain areas, including memories, and makes us choose a certain food or a certain sexual partner or an action. People with damage to this brain region find it impossible to make a decision. The frontal lobe does not protect us from our emotions so that we can reason better, but just the opposite, it takes emotions into the formula as a major factor in making a decision.

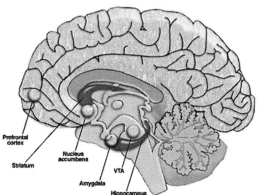

Antonio Damasio has proposed an idea called the **somatic marker hypothesis** (Damasio, 1994). His view is that when we have experienced unpleasant events in the past, our bodies' reactions have been marked, or remembered, in our brains. When we experience a similar situation in the future, our frontal lobes recall the previous somatic markers and we avoid the situation. Our frontal lobes remember the body states that we learned in the past and make decisions to avoid such situations in the future. Damasio argues that this is why psychopaths and others who have frontal lobe dysfunctions do not show strong autonomic nervous system activation to unpleasant stimuli and they do not seem to learn from punishment or from mistakes. People who are intelligent and verbal can be social monsters!

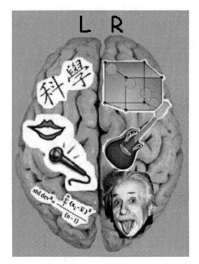

But, emotional processing in the frontal lobes seems to be **lateralized** (more in one hemisphere than the other). A number of studies have shown differences between the right and left hemispheres in processing emotions in the frontal lobes. The most common conclusion is that the **left** hemisphere is biased toward processing **pleasant** emotions while the **right** hemisphere is biased toward emotions with **negative** valence. The evidence was summarized as follows: "The left forebrain is associated predominantly with parasympathetic activity, and thus with nourishment, safety, positive affect, approach (appetitive) behavior, and group-oriented (affiliative) emotions, while the right forebrain is associated predominantly with sympathetic activity, and thus with arousal, danger, negative affect, withdrawal (aversive) behavior, and individual-oriented (survival) emotions" (Craig, 2005).

So, in general it appears that the **left** side of the brain is more involved in processing **pleasant** emotions, while the **right** side leans more toward **unpleasant** emotions. The left hemisphere likely contributes to positive emotions primarily through its role in inhibiting negative emotions that are processed in the amygdala. Professor of psychology and psychiatry **Richard Davidson** explained: "We have found that the left prefrontal cortex participates with other structures in a circuit that may be important for certain types of positive emotion. Activation patterns in the right prefrontal cortex, by contrast, are more associated with certain types of negative affect accompanied by increased vigilance to threat-related cues, a symptom that often occurs with certain types of anxiety. Our new imaging work suggests that the **left** prefrontal cortex may be important in **inhibiting** activity in the **amygdala** and dampening response to negative events, and particularly in shutting off the negative response quickly once it has been activated."

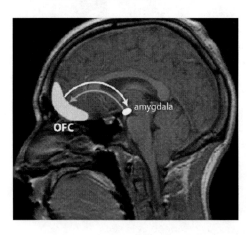

Davidson also emphasized the role of the left orbitofrontal cortex and nearby brain regions in controlling **impulsive violent behavior**. His research team found evidence that exposure to **stress** early in life can lead to alterations in the **orbitofrontal cortex** (Hanson et al., 2010). Genes, too, were found to contribute. The research of Davidson and others clearly suggests that frontal lobe dysfunction, particularly in the left hemisphere, whether the result of poor environmental history, heredity, disease, or trauma, can lead to problems with aggression, psychopathy, anxiety, and depression. But, there's even more about left and right:

While both cerebral hemispheres contribute to emotion, research has shown that generally the **right hemisphere** is more involved than the left in **emotional expression** and **emotion detection**. For example, Alves et al. (2009) concluded: "Main results tend to support the right hemisphere hypothesis, which predicts a better performance of the right hemisphere to perceive emotions." And, Bourne (2010) reported, "All emotions showed significant lateralization to the right hemisphere, however, differences in strength of lateralization within the right hemisphere were found." Also, for people who experience brain trauma, damage to the right prefrontal cortex impairs emotions much more than does damage to the left hemisphere. So, we might say that the **right hemisphere** is more **dominant**, has more control, or is more important for processing and perceiving emotions than is the left.

Antonio Damasio and his team stimulated individual neurons in the right prefrontal cortex of a patient with **epilepsy** who was undergoing brain surgery. They found that those neurons in the front of the **right hemisphere** began firing almost immediately when the patient was shown pictures of very unpleasant images, such as a severed limb or a burning house (Kawasaki, 2001). The researchers noted that the cells were reacting so rapidly to the stimulus that it implied an emotional system separate from cognitive appraisal, as if the right prefrontal cortex was wired by evolution to react to dangerous situations. It is likely that this brain area is intimately connected to the regions of the **amygdala** involved in fear learning. So, there appears to be an unconscious, automatic brain network for reacting with fear to dangerous stimuli that involves cells in the right frontal lobe with connections to the amygdala.

And, here's even more about **lateralization**: The facial expressions that accompany emotions are more intense and more expressive on the left side of the face, which is controlled predominantly by the brain's right hemisphere, than on the right side of the face. Even **chimpanzees** and other primates show this asymmetry (Lane & Nadel, 2000). Apparently evolution has wired us to show greater expression of emotion on the left sides of our faces than on the right sides. Remember, though, the left side of the face is controlled more by the right hemisphere of the brain. Neuroscientists conclude that this means that the **right hemisphere** is more **expressive** about emotions than is the left.

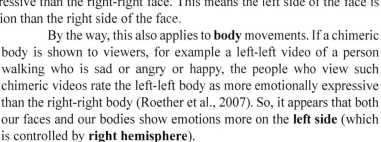

One of the ways lateralization is studied is by using mirror-image chimeric faces. A **chimeric face** is a face in which the left and right halves have been combined from two different faces. In this research, the chimeric face is made by replacing one half of a face not with a different face, but with the mirror image of the other side of the same face. So, a viewer will see a face that has, in essence, two left sides or two right sides.

Suppose we take a photo of your face when you are smiling. We then cut the photo in half vertically. We then make a mirror image of the left side of your face and attach it to the real left side in a chimeric photo. A viewer is now looking at a left-left photo of your face. We can also make a right-right chimera, of course. In such cases, viewers rate the left-left chimeric face as more emotionally expressive than the right-right face. This means the left side of the face is better at expressing emotion than the right side of the face.

By the way, this also applies to **body** movements. If a chimeric body is shown to viewers, for example a left-left video of a person walking who is sad or angry or happy, the people who view such chimeric videos rate the left-left body as more emotionally expressive than the right-right body (Roether et al., 2007). So, it appears that both our faces and our bodies show emotions more on the **left side** (which is controlled by **right hemisphere**).

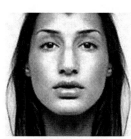

Top: chimeric face, left-left.
Bottom: angry face.

Interestingly, there apparently is one exception to this: The emotion of **anger** is expressed more on the **right** side of the face than on the left. Remember, different emotions have slightly different brain networks supporting them. **Anger** evolved to have a brain network that is expressed more on the **right** side of the face. Here's how neuroscientists explain this: When someone is looking at you, the right side of his/her face is on your left. That means that the right side of his/her face is processed more in your right hemisphere (objects seen on the left are visually represented first in the right hemisphere). If a person displays anger in his/her face, the expression will be greater on the right side of his/her face, and viewers will process it more quickly in their right hemispheres, which are better at processing emotions. That makes for a quicker response to an angry face! Evolution has given us a brain and facial expression system that allows us the quickest possible reaction to anger. Now, don't get angry if you didn't get that – just read it again!

Now, before we bestow total certitude on the **lateralization** of emotion in the brain, consider that not all research has found the right-left differences mentioned above. For instance, a meta-analysis of 65 brain imaging studies did not find evidence of lateralization of emotion except to some extent in men (Wager et al., 2003). The researchers concluded that, "The lateralization of emotional activity is more complex and region-specific than predicted by previous theories of emotion and the brain." So, once again we are reminded that brains are complex and there are many individual and group differences that make generalizations a bit of a problem.

3. Insula

The location of a brain area known as the **insular cortex**, or more commonly, the **insula**, is difficult to describe. The **cerebral cortex** is the outer layer of cells of the cerebrum, the top, wrinkled part of the human brain. Some of the wrinkles or grooves (**sulci**) are very deep. One such **sulcus** on the side of the brain is called the **lateral fissure**, and it bends and curls deep inside, bending within the interior of the temporal lobe. It is deep in this area of the cerebral cortex where we find the insula, a word that means "island." This is a little island in the brain, tucked into the side of the head, folded below the surface. The outer brain region of the cerebral cortex that lies to the outside of the insula, that shields it, just on the surface of the cortex, just overlapping the area where temporal, frontal, and parietal lobes meet, is known as the **operculum** (which means "lid"). So, the little island has a lid over it!

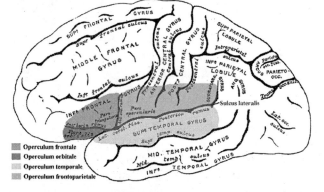

The insula has connections to the olfactory (smell) and gustatory (taste) sensory systems, and is part of the main cortical area for processing taste sensations. The insula works together with other cells in the operculum to give us our sense of **taste**. Cells in these areas respond to sweet, salty, sour, and bitter, for example. The insula also receives neural signals from visual pathways, and cells in the insula have been found to respond to the sight of faces. The back (posterior) portion of the insula receives neural signals from the body and is important in processing pain and body sensations. Some auditory connections are found in the insula, also.

So, then, what does the insula have to do with emotions? The connections listed above may give you a hint! It turns out that the insula is the main cortical area for processing the emotion of **disgust**. Disgust refers to things that are revolting. It is the emotion we feel when we react to things that are gory, unclean, distasteful, putrid, infected, or just plain icky! How often have you said, "That's disgusting," and made the typical face with nose pinched and corners of mouth turned down as if to keep the offending object out of our smell or taste? Of course, we can be disgusted by certain tastes and odors; in fact, that is probably the first evolutionary development for the emotion of disgust, to detect harmful food.

Operculum frontale
Operculum orbitale
Operculum temporale
Operculum frontoparietale

Offensive odors and tastes stimulate cells in the insulas of monkeys, too. Just as with other basic emotions, comparative psychology shows that emotions we see in humans are also seen in other animals. Taste and smell, however, are not the only triggers for the emotion of disgust. For instance, we can be disgusted by visual images, as well, and, of course, we can easily tell from facial expressions when other people are disgusted. That, apparently, is one major role of the insula – to influence and to detect in others the emotion of disgust.

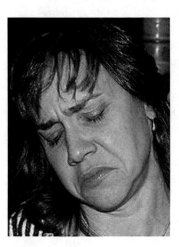

Psychologists have also found a relationship between taste disgust and **moral judgment**. Have you ever made a moral statement that a person's behavior was disgusting? Well, psychologists have found that if people taste a bitter beverage that produces a feeling of disgust, those people then later make more harsh moral judgments compared to people who tasted a sweet beverage. That is, people exposed to disgust via taste later show moral disgust when rating situations of human transgressions;. Furthermore, this effect was found to be particularly strong among people who held conservative political views (Eskine et al., 2011). Liberal thinkers were not affected in their moral judgments as much by tasting a disgusting substance. Earlier research had shown that conservatives are more easily disgusted than liberals (Inbar et al., 2010) and that disgust is related to negative attitudes toward "outgroups" such as homosexuals (Terrizzi et al., 2010). So, disgust is an emotion that stretches beyond just the simple taste of a substance! It is becoming apparent that moral judgments are not based solely on rational thinking – emotions matter!

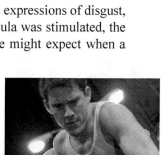

There's more: When participants were shown pictures that produced fear or disgust, brain imaging showed activity in the amygdala, prefrontal cortex, and the visual area of the brain. However, only the pictures that stimulated **disgust** were associated with brain activity in the **insula** (Stark et al., 2007). Activation in the insula was also found when participants smelled an obnoxious odor or when they saw another person make a face that depicted disgust (Wicker et al., 2003). Patients who had suffered **lesions** in their anterior (front part) insula were unable to **recognize disgust** in the facial expressions of others and also showed deficits in their ability to experience the emotion of disgust (Adolphs, 2003). Also, electrical stimulation of the insula during brain surgery triggered nausea in patients (Calder et al., 2000).

Amazingly, in another case, researchers implanted electrodes in various brain regions in patients undergoing brain surgery (Krolak-Salmon et al., 2003). The electrodes that were in a particular region of the insula showed strong activation when the patients viewed facial expressions of disgust, but did not show a response to facial expressions of other emotions. Also, when the insula was stimulated, the patients reported unpleasant sensations in the throat, mouth, lips, and nose, just as one might expect when a person feels disgusted.

By the way, the feeling of **hate**, too, involves activity in the **insula** (Zeki & Romaya, 2008). But hate includes several other brain regions, too, including areas of the cerebral cortex that are involved in motor planning, areas that can generate **aggressive behavior**. Hence, with feelings of hate, it's as if the brain is preparing aggressive actions against the hated person. Interestingly, the amount of brain activity in these various areas is directly related to the amount of hate that a person reports. This means the subjective feeling of hate can be measured objectively, a fact that may be important in criminal cases or other situations.

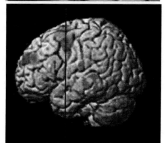

Specialized brain circuits for the emotions of **disgust** and **fear** likely evolved because these two emotions helped early humans avoid dangerous situations and harmful substances. These emotions – fear and disgust – are strongly wired into the brain, and when they are combined, that is, when we experience both fear and disgust in the presence of an object or event, the result produces an extremely memorable emotional effect. That is why movies, TV shows, and video games that present situations that include both of these emotions – situations that we find revolting, that are both **fearful** and **disgusting** – are so powerful. Such presentations rivet our attention and stimulate strong, memorable responses in our brains. We can't look away, even though we are afraid and disgusted. A bit like a traffic accident! The experience sticks vividly in our minds for a long time afterwards.

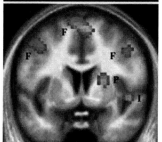

Hate includes activity in the motor area, preparing a person for action.

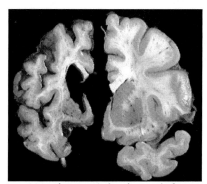

Huntington's brain on left compared to normal brain.

There are two categories of psychological disorders in which disgust is involved: First, in dementias such as **Parkinson's disease** and **Huntington's disease**, damage to the insula impairs the ability of patients to experience feelings of disgust or to recognize facial expressions depicting disgust (Suzuki et al., 2006; Calder et al., 2000). Patients with damage to the insula do not respond to icky smells and tastes with a feeling of disgust, nor do they make facial expressions representing disgust, nor are they able to recognize when others are feeling disgusted.

Second, in the syndrome known as **obsessive-compulsive disorder** (**OCD**), patients appear to have over-activation of their insulas. Too much activation of the disgust area of the insula makes people wary and disturbed by quite normal stimuli and events. Brain imaging studies using fMRI showed there was significantly greater activation of cells in the right insulas of people with OCD as compared with control subjects (Shapira et al., 2003). That is, people with OCD have insulas that respond more actively. This finding helps explain the fear of contamination that is common in people diagnosed with OCD.

4. Anterior Cingulate Cortex

Next, make a fist again with the thumb inside. The outer layer of your hand and fingers is the brain's cerebral cortex. But, the inner part of your hand, your palm, and the inner side of your fingers represents the cingulate cortex. The front part of this brain area, the part that your thumbnail is touching, is called the **anterior cingulate cortex (ACC)**. This brain area has connections with many different brain regions. For instance, the top part of the ACC (called "**dorsal**") is wired to the frontal lobe and the cortical motor areas of the brain. However,

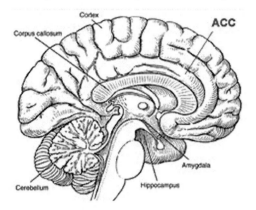

the lower part of the ACC (called "**ventral**") is linked with subcortical regions such as the hypothalamus, amygdala, nucleus accumbens, and insula. So, you can see that the dorsal part of the ACC is involved with distributing information about body movement, while the ventral part of the ACC contributes to emotions and motivations. **Embarrassment** is one of the feelings associated with activity in the very front of the ACC on the right side (Sturm et al., 2011). Embarrassment is a **social emotion** that requires cognition. As such, social feelings, like guilt, remorse, morality, and embarrassment involve several areas of the frontal lobe.

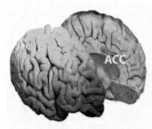

The **anterior cingulate cortex** has been called an interface between emotion and cognition (Allman et al., 2006). As such, one of its roles is to assist areas of the frontal lobes in the regulation of emotional expression. A recent study found that the volume of the ACC was related to a person's ability to use cognitive reappraisal in **controlling emotions** (Giuliani et al., 2011). A larger ACC meant a better ability to think about emotional situations and to control emotions. Similarly, an fMRI study found that the ACC helps inhibit the amygdala and thereby to control negative emotions, like **fear** (Etkin et al., 2006). The researchers described the ACC as resolving conflict between emotional and cognitive processing. They pointed out that people with post-traumatic stress disorder and those with depression often show lowered activity in the ACC during emotional processing. In **depression**, lower activity in the ACC is a predictor of poor response to antidepressant therapy.

The anterior cingulate cortex is a large and complicated brain area, so naturally it contributes to many emotions and emotion-related phenomena. The ACC has been shown to be involved with the emotion of **contempt**, for example. Contempt is an emotion very similar to disgust and involves some overlap of brain regions with disgust. However, Ekman has shown that the facial expression for contempt is not exactly the same as for disgust, and hence contempt is included as distinct among the universal emotions. Moreover, researchers using fMRI found different activations in several brain areas, including the amygdala, for contempt compared to disgust (Sambataro et al., 2006). **Contempt** refers to feelings of superiority and looking down on someone else. It is a more **social emotion** than is disgust, which can be stimulated by an object, an odor, or a taste. Contempt is directed at other people.

The ACC is involved in a number of emotion-related functions such as decision making, reward anticipation, and even **empathy** (caring about other people). Probably the most studied role of the ACC is **error detection**. This brain area shows increased activity when a subject must attend to a task that involves close monitoring, such as the **Stroop test**. Quite often used in psychological experiments that measure cognition, in the Stroop test participants are asked to name the colors of a series of words as fast as they can. But, the words are names of colors, such as RED, BLUE, YELLOW, and GREEN. The words themselves are presented in different colors. For example, BLUE is colored yellow or RED is colored green. Participants have a very difficult time naming the colors because they are thrown off by the meaning of the words. During this task, their ACCs are very active (Posner & DiGirolamo, 1998). Incidentally, participants with **attention deficit hyperactivity disorder (ADHD)** have great difficulty with the Stroop test, as do patients with **schizophrenia**, who have been shown to have dysfunctions in the ACC.

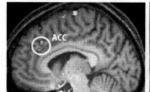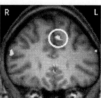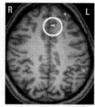

Activity in the ACC during a Stroop test indicates that the ACC helps regulate cognition.

In 2005 an amazing finding was announced: It was reported that four of six patients with **depression** had been cured by having a brain pacemaker surgically implanted into their **anterior cingulate cortices** (Mayberg et al., 2005). The brain pacemaker is an electrode that can stimulate neurons, in this case, in order to inhibit their firing. The procedure is usually called **deep-brain stimulation**. It was discovered that these depressed people had over-activity in the **ACC** region. With the pacemaker in place, some of the patients claimed immediate relief from their depression, as if a veil was lifted. Other research has confirmed that the ACC is involved in the processing and regulation of negative emotions such as depression.

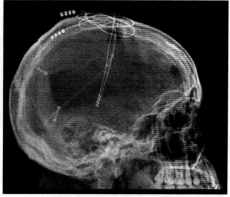

Deep-brain stimulation.

Anger, too, has been connected to this brain region, the ACC. Participants who had been insulted and asked to think about it reported feeling angry. Brain imaging showed that activity in the **anterior cingulate cortex** was correlated with such self reports (Denson et al., 2009). That is, the more anger that was reported, the more activation of the ACC.

In addition to sadness and anger, the ACC has been found to be active in the perception of **pain**, too. In particular, the connections between the ACC and the amygdala showed activity when a subject viewed sad faces (Yoshino et al., 2010). The researchers found that the feeling of pain was enhanced by sadness via activation in the ACC and amygdala. By the way, **happiness** has been found to activate some of the same brain regions, but in a distinctly different pattern (Pelletier et al., 2003). **Happy** emotional states are associated with the **pleasure pathway** in the brain, and also with activation of **frontal lobe** regions, primarily on the **left**.

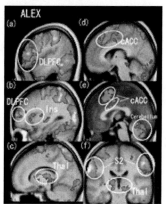

The alexithymia brain reacts differently from normal brains when viewing faces.

Final mention about the ACC will go to the finding mentioned above that dysfunction in this brain area may be related to **alexithymia**, difficulty in naming, describing, or recognizing emotions (Lane et al., 1997). Support for this notion came from a more recent study of 30 men that found dysfunction in the ACC was related to scores on a scale that measured the trait of alexithymia (Heinzel et al., 2010). This study involved brain imaging using fMRI while the subjects viewed pictures of facial expressions.

Love and More

From poet Robert Frost: "Love is an irresistible desire to be irresistibly desired." From comedian Lily Tomlin: "If love is the answer, could you please rephrase the question?" From Woody Allen: "Sex alleviates tension. Love causes it." From humorist Ambrose Bierce: "Love is a temporary insanity curable by marriage." From comedian George Burns: "Love is like a backache. It doesn't show up on X-rays, but you know it's there."

While **love** is technically not an emotion, but instead is classified as a *feeling* by neuroscientists, still, love is a brain process that engages several regions that participate in emotions and pleasure. Brain researchers have identified what they call a "**love circuit**" in the brain. The love circuit includes four brain areas: the **ventral tegmental area (VTA)**, the **nucleus accumbens**, the **ventral pallidum** and the **raphe nucleus**. The first three, the VTA, nucleus accumbens, and ventral pallidum are all parts of the brain's **pleasure (mesolimbic) pathway**, and are all involved in addictions. The raphe nucleus (raphe means "seam" – think of it as a seam along the side of the brainstem) is a cluster of cells in the **brainstem** that has the main job of distributing the brain chemical **serotonin** to the rest of the brain. The cells of the raphe nucleus also project into brain areas that inhibit the sensation of **pain**; that's a great thing for helping with feelings of pleasure!

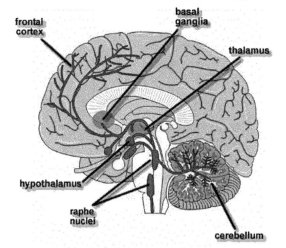

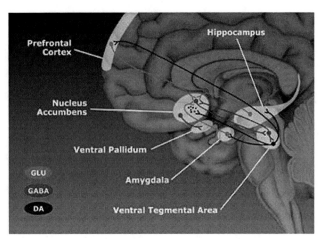

The hotspot for love appears to be the **VTA**, which is a dopamine releasing area in the brainstem. Brain imaging research has shown that the VTA lights up for people who are shown pictures of their beloveds whether they are newly in love or still in love after twenty years. Next Valentine's Day, don't send a picture of a heart to your beloved – the idea that the mind is centered in the heart is an entirely erroneous, 2000 year-old notion – instead, send a picture of the **mesolimbic pathway**, or just the **VTA**! Your beloved will not only view you as loving, but you'll be seen as unique and smart, too! Well, okay, maybe as a bit weird! Don't let that stop you. Remember the saying, "You laugh at me because I'm different, but I laugh at you because you are all the same."

A recent study examined which brain areas were associated with **romantic love** (Fisher et al., 2010). The researchers wrote, "Compared with data from happily-in-love individuals, the regional VTA activation suggests that mesolimbic reward/survival systems are involved in romantic passion regardless of whether one is happily or unhappily in love." Lead researcher Helen Fisher said she believes that love works chemically in the brain like a **drug addiction**. She said, "Romantic love is an addiction; a wonderful addiction when it is going well, a horrible one when it is going poorly. People kill for love. They die for love." And, another neuroscientist remarked, "The brokenhearted show more evidence of what I'll call craving, similar to craving the drug cocaine."

Love is sought by everyone, and can be very pleasurable, and the loss of love can really hurt. Of course, there are other feelings that are pleasurable, and still others that are painful. With physical **pleasure** and **pain**, a certain set of brain regions are activated for each. It turns out that the same sets of brain regions are activated for social pleasure and social pain, too. While activation of the ACC is typical during physical pain, the ACC is also active when we are rejected or grieving a loss. Similarly, activation of the pleasure pathway is accomplished with drugs, sex, or food, but also by social pleasures. Giving to charity, for example, was found to cause more activation of pleasure areas in the brain than did receiving an equal amount of money. Apparently the old saying is true – it is better to give than to receive!

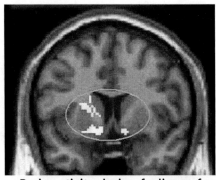

Brain activity during feelings of schadenfreude.

A recent study used fMRI to investigate feelings of envy and schadenfreude (Takahashi et al., 2009). **Envy** is a feeling of displeasure or discontent when we covet another person's belongings, position, success, or advantages. We feel envious when someone has something we want, for example. **Schadenfreude** (pronounced: *SHAH-den-froyd-uh*), on the other hand, is the feeling of pleasure or delight we feel when someone else experiences misfortune or trouble, usually someone we envy or dislike. So, to envy means to feel displeasure or unhappiness at someone else's fortunes, while schadenfreude means to feel pleasure when someone else fails or suffers.

In the brain imaging study, it was found that these two feelings, envy and schadenfreude, were associated with activations in two particular brain regions. The **anterior cingulate cortex** (**ACC**), which is involved in the emotion of contempt as described above, was found to be especially active during feelings of **envy**. However, a subcortical region, known as the **ventral striatum**, an area that includes the **nucleus accumbens**, was active during feelings of **schadenfreude**. In fact, it was discovered that social situations such as envy and schadenfreude are associated with brain activity in the exact same regions that are active during physical pain or physical pleasure. Also, the amount of envy that a person reported was directly related to the amount of activity in the ACC, just as occurs with physical pain. It's an amazing and important conclusion that apparently brains have been fine-tuned by evolution to care just as much about social situations as about physical stimuli that produce pleasure and pain. When people who are rejected socially

say that they are hurting, their brains confirm it! Psychic pain has many of the same brain activations as physical pain.

   The **ventral striatum** (including the **nucleus accumbens**) has been found to be involved in other emotions and motivations, too. For instance, it is active when you look at someone whom you find attractive (Kampe et al., 2001). This brain area is an integral part of the **pleasure pathway** and is intimately involved in **drug addictions**. The ventral striatum has connections with the VTA, the limbic system, and the frontal lobe. So, it appears that pleasurable emotions and feelings are produced by networks and activations in these multiple brain regions. It isn't from our hearts or our livers that our emotions and feelings emanate, but from the complex circuitry of our brains.

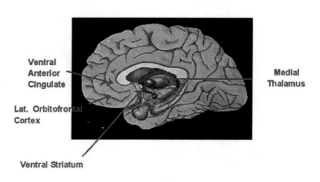

   Those who are regular viewers of the TV series called *Bones* know that the lead character, forensic anthropologist Temperance Brennan, quite often complains that love is, "Just a chemical reaction in the brain." Well, so what? So what if love is a chemical reaction in the brain? What else would it be? What would she like it to be?

   Not only love, but all of our phenomenological experiences are produced by chemical reactions in our brains. And, one more thing: She shouldn't say "just," implying that brain activity is not enough! Not enough? By now you're probably getting the very clear message that chemicals and neural networks are plenty, and sometimes even too much! To paraphrase a song by *The Beatles*: All you need is brain, Da, da, da, da, da, All you need is brain, Da, da, da, da, da, All you need is brain, brain, Brain is all you need. Brain, Brain, Brain....

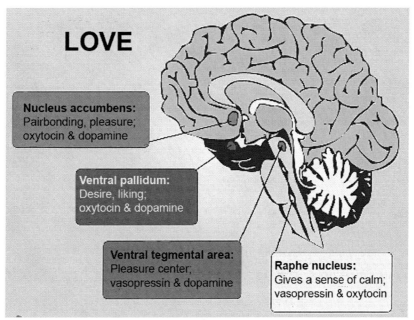

Bibliography

Abel, E. L, & Kruger, M. L. (2009). Smile intensity in photographs predicts longevity. *Psychological Science 21* (4), 542-544.

Abraham, H. D. (1983). Visual phenomenology of the LSD flashback. *Archives of General Psychiatry, 40* (8), 884-889.

Adelman, G. (1987). *Encyclopedia of Neuroscience,* 2 vols. Boston: Birkhauser.

Adolphs et al. (2003). Dissociable neural systems for recognizing emotions. *Brain Cognition, 52,* 61–69.

Adolphs, R., Gosselin, F., Buchanan, T.W., Tranel, D., Schyns, P., & Damasio, A. R. (2005). A mechanism for impaired fear recognition after amygdala damage. *Nature, 433,* 68-72.

Akiyama, T., Kato, M., Muramatsu, T., Umeda, S., Saito, F., & Kashima, H. (2007). Unilater amygdala lesions hamper attentional orienting triggered by gaze direction. *Cerebral Cortex, 17* (11), 2593-2600.

Alati, R., Mamun, A. A., Williams, G. M., O'Callaghan, M., Najman, J. M., & Bor, W. (2006). In utero alcohol exposure and prediction of alcohol disorders in early adulthood. *Archives of General Psychiatry, 63,* 1009-1016.

Alexander, B., Warner-Schmidt, J., Eriksson, T., Tamminga, C., Kaplitt, M. G. et al. (2010). Reversal of depressed behaviors in mice by p11 gene therapy in the nucleus accumbens. *Science Translational Medicine, 2* (54).

Allen, L. S. (1989). Two sexually dimorphic cell groups in the human brain. *J. Neurosci., 9,* 497-506.

Allen, L. S., & Gorski, R. A. (1991). Sexual dimorphism of the anterior commissure and massa intermedia of the human brain. *Journal of Comparative Neurology, 312,* 97-104.

Allen, L. S., & Gorski, R. A. (1992). Sexual orientation and the size of the anterior commissure in the human brain. *Proc. Natl. Acad. Sci. U.S.A,. 89*(15), 7199-202.

Allman, J. M., et al. (2006). The anterior cingulate cortex: The evolution of an interface between emotion and cognition. *Annals New York Academy of Sciences, 935,* 107-117.

Almeida, O. P., Garrido, G. J., Alfonso, H., et al. (2011). 24-month effect of smoking cessation on cognitive function and brain structure in later life. *Neuroimage, 55* (4), 1480-1489.

Alonso-Alonso, M., & Pascual-Leone, A. (2007). The right brain hypothesis for obesity. *Journal of the American Medical Association, 297* (16), 1819-1822.

Alvarenga, T. A., Andersen, M. L., Ribeiro, D. A., et al. Single exposure to cocaine or ecstasy induces DNA damage in brain and other organs of mice. *Addiction Biology, 15* (1), 96-99.

Alves, N. T., Aznar-Casanova, J. A., & Fukusima, S. S. (2009). Patterns of brain asymmetry in the perception of positive and negative facial expressions. *Laterality, 14* (3), 256-272.

American Psychiatric Association. (2000). *Diagnostic and statistical manual of mental disorders* (Revised, 4th edition). Washington, D. C.: Author.

Amunts, K. (2007). Gender-specific left-right asymmetries in human visual cortex. *J. Neurosci., 27,* 1356-1364.

Anderson, S. W., Bechara, A., Damasio, H., Tranel, D., & Damasio, A. R. (1999). Impairment of social and moral behavior related to early damage in human prefrontal cortex. *Nature Neuroscience 2,* 1032-1037.

Andreano, J. M., & Cahill, L. (2009). Sex influences in the neurobiology of learning and memory. *Learning and Memory, 16,* 248-266.

Andrews, M. M., Meda, S. A., Thomas, A., D., et al. (2011). Individuals family history positive for alcoholism show functional magnetic resonance imaging differences in reward sensitivity that are related to impulsivity factors. *Biological Psychiatry, 69* (7), 657-683.

Ankney, C.D. (1992). Sex differences in relative brain size: The mismeasure of woman, too? *Intelligence 16,* 329-336.

Apicella, C.L., Feinberg, D.R., & Marlowe F.W. (2007). Voice pitch predicts reproductive success in male hunter-gatherers. *Biology Letters, 3* (6), 682.

Arendash, G. W., & Chuanhai, C. (2010). Caffeine and coffee as therapeutics against Alzheimer's disease. *Journal of Alzheimer's Disease, 20,* 117-126.

Arnold, A. P. (2004). Sex chromosomes and brain gender. *Nature Rev. Neurosci. 5,* 701-708.

Ashtari, M., Kumra, S., Wu, J., Kane, J., Szeszko, P., & Ardekani, B. (2005). The impact of recurrent exposure to cannabis on brain development in adolescents with schizophrenia and healthy volunteers. *Radiological Society of North America.*

Ayotte, J., Peretz, I., Rousseau, I., Bard, C., & Bojanowski, M. (2000). Patterns of music agnosia associated with middle cerebral artery infarcts. *Brain, 123,* 1926-1938.

Bailer, U. F., Bailey, A., & Hurd, P. (2005). Finger length ratio (2D:4D) correlates with physical aggression in men but not in women. *Biological Psychology, 68,* 215-222.

Balaban,M. T., Anderson, L. M., & Wisniewski, A. B. (1998). Lateral asymmetries in infant melody perception. *Developmental Psychology, 34* (1), 39-48.

Ball, P. (2010). *The music instinct; how music works and why we can't live without i.* New York, N.Y.: Oxford University Press.

Bao, A-M., & Swaab, D. F. (2010). Sex differences in the brain, behavior, and neuropsychiatric disorders. *The Neuroscientist, 16*(5), 550-565.

Barrett, L., & Dunbar, R., editors. (2007). Music and cognitive evolution. In *Oxford handbook of evolutionary psychology.* New York: Oxford University Press.

Bartz, J. A., Zaki, J., Bolger, N., et al. (2010). Oxytocin selectively improves empathic accuracy. *Psychological Science, 21* (10), 1426-1428.

Baumeister, R. F. (2008). Free will in scientific psychology. *Perspectives on Psychological Science, 3,* 14-19.

Bechara, A. (2005). Decision making, impulse control and loss of willpower to resist drugs: A neurocognitive perspective. *Nature Neuroscience 8,* 1458-1463.

Becker, B., Wagner, D., Gouzoulis-Mayfrank, E., Spuentrup, E., & Daumann, J. (2010). The impact of early-onset cannabis use on functional brain correlates of working memory. *Progress in Neuro-Psychopharmacology & Biological Psychiatry, 34* (6), 837-845.

Bell, R. P., Foxe, J. J., Nierenberg, J., et al. (2011). Assessing white matter integrity as a function of abstinence duration in former cocaine-dependent individuals. *Drug & Alcohol Dependence, 114* (2/3), 159-168.

Bendor,D., & Wang, X. (2005). The neuronal representation of pitch in primate auditory cortex. *Nature, 436,* 1161-1165.

Berridge, K. C. (2009). 'Liking' and 'wanting' food rewards: Brain substrates and roles in eating disorders. *Physiology & Behavior, 97,* 537–550.

Bidelman, G. M., & Krishnan, A. (2009). Neural correlates of consonance, dissonance, and the hierarchy of musical pitch in the human brainstem. *The Journal of Neuroscience, 29* (42), 13165-13171

Blood, A. J., & Zatorre, R. J. (2001). Intensely pleasurable responses to music correlate with activity in brain regions implicated in reward and emotion. *Proceedings of the National Academy of Sciences USA, 98* 11818-11823.

Bohland, J. W., & Guenther, F. H. (2006). An fMRI investigation of syllable sequence production. *NeuroImage, 32* (2), 821-841.

Bolles, R. W. (1980). Some functionalistic thoughts about regulation. In Toates, T. W., & Halliday, T. W. (editors). *Analysis of motivational processes.* New York: Academic Press, 63–75.

Bossong, M. G., Niesink, R. J. M. (2010). Adolescent brain maturation, the endogenous cannabinoid system and the neurobiology of cannabis-induced schizophrenia. *Progress in Neurobiology, 92* (3), 370-385.

Bouret, S. G., Gorski, J. N., Patterson, C. M., Chen, S., Levin, B. E., & Simerly, R. B. (2008). Hypothalmic neural projections are permanently disrupted in diet-induced obese rats. *Cell Metabolism, 7* (2), 179-185.

Bourne, Victoria J. (2010). How are emotions lateralised in the brain? Contrasting existing hypotheses using the Chimeric Faces Test. *Cognition & Emotion, 24* (5), 903-911.

Brainard, M. S., & Knudsen, E. I. (1998). Experience affects brain development. *American Journal of Psychiatry, 155,* 8, 1000.

Brechbuhl, J., Klaey, M., & Broillet, M.-C. (2008). Grueneberg ganglion cells mediate alarm pheromone detection in mice. *Science, 321,* 1092-1095.

Brechmann, A., & Scheich, H. (2005). Hemispheric shifts of sound representation in auditory cortex with conceptual listening. *Cerebral Cortex, 15,* 578-587.

Brick, J. & Erickson, C. K. (1998). *Drugs, the brain, and behavior: The pharmacology of abuse and dependence.* New York: The Haworth Medical Press.

Brown, S. (2000). The "musilanguage" model of music evolution. In N. L. Wallin, B. Merker, & S. Brown (Eds.) *The Origins of Music* (pp. 271-300). Cambridge, MA: MIT Press.

Brown, S., Martinez, M. J., & Parsons, L. M. (2006a). Music and language side by side in the brain: A PET study of the generation of melodies and sentences. *European Journal of Neuroscience, 23,* 2791-2803.

Brown, S., Martinez, M. J., & Parsons, L. M. (2006b). The neural basis of human dance. *Cerebral Cortex 16,* 1157-1167.

Bruce, A. S., Holsen, L. M., Chambers, R. J., Savage, C. R., et al. (2010). Obese children show hyperactivation to food pictures in brain networks linked to motivation, reward and cognitive control. *International Journal of Obesity, 34* (10), 1494-1500.

Bryant, G. A., & Haselton, M. G. (2009). Vocal cues of ovulation in human females. *Biology Letters, 5* (1), 12-15.

Buckholtz, J. W., Treadway, M. T., Cowan, R. L., et al. (2010). Mesolimbic dopamine reward system hypersensitivity in individuals with psychopathic traits. *Nature Neuroscience, 13,* 419-421.

Buss, D. M. (1999). *Evolutionary psychology.* Boston: Allyn & Bacon.

Bustamante, J-C., Barros-Loscertales, A., et al. (2011). Right parietal hypoactivation in a cocaine-dependent group during a verbal working memory task. *Brain Research, 1375,* 111-119.

Byne, W. (2001). The interstitial nuclei of the human anterior hypothalamus: An investigation of variation with sex, sexual orientation, and HIV status. *Horm. Behav., 40,* 86-92.

Calder et al. (2000). Impaired recognition and experience of disgust following brain injury. *Nature Neuroscience, 3,* 1077–1088.

Caldwell, H. K., Young, W. S. III (2006). Oxytocin and vasopressin: Genetics and behavioral implications. In Lajtha A, Lim R. *Handbook of Neurochemistry and Molecular Neurobiology: Neuroactive Proteins and Peptides* (3rd ed.). Berlin: Springer. pp. 573-607.

Canli, T., Sivers, H. Whitfield, S. L., Gotlib, I. H., & Gabrieli, J. D. E. (2002). Amygdala response to happy faces as a function of extraversion. *Science*, 296, 2191.

Caspi, A., Hariri, A. R., Holmes, A., Uher, R., & Moffitt, T. E. (2010). Genetic sensitivity to the environment: The case of the serotonin transporter gene and its implications for studying complex diseases and traits. *Amer. J. of Psychiatry, 167,* 509-527.

Chaldakov, G. N., Tonchey, A. B., & Aloe, L. (2009). NGF and BDNF: From nerves to adipose tissue, from neurokines to metabokines. *Riv. Psichiatr., 44* (2), 79-87.

Chambers, J. C., Elliott, P., Zabaneh, D., et al. (2008). Common genetic variation near MC4R is associated with waist circumference and insulin resistance. *Nat. Genet., 40* (6), 716–18.

Chapman, E. (2006). Fetal testosterone and empathy: Evidence from the Empathy Quotient (EQ) and the 'Reading the mind in the eyes' test. *Soc. Neurosci., 1,* 135-148.

Chefer, V., Meis, J., Wang, G., Kuzmin,A., Bakalkin, G., & Shippenberg, T. (2011). Repeated exposure to moderate doses of ethanol augments hippocampal glutamate neurotransmission by increasing release. *Addiction Biology, 16* (2), 229-237.

Clemens, L. G. (1974). Neurohormonal control of male sexual behavior. In W. Montagna & W. A. Sadler , *Reproductive Behavior.* Oxford, England: Plenum.

Colapinto, J. (2001). *As nature made him: The boy who was raised as a girl.* Harper Perennial.

Contreras, M., Ceric, F., & Torrealba, F. (2007). Inactivation of the interoceptive insula disrupts drug craving and malaise induced by lithium. *Science, 318* (5850), 655-658.

Cooke, L. J., Chambers, L. C., Anez, E. V., Croker, H. A., Boniface, D., Yeomans, M. R., & Wardle, J. (2011). Eating for pleasure of profit: The effect of incentives on children's enjoyment of vegetables. *Psychological Science, 22* (2), 190-196.

Craig, A.D. (2005). Forebrain emotional asymmetry: A neuroanatomical basis? *Trends in Cognitive Sciences, 9* (12), 566-571.

Crair, M. C., Gillespie, D. C. & Stryker, M. P. (1998). The role of visual experience in the development of columns in cat visual cortex. *Science*, Vol. 279.

Crick, F. (1994). *The astonishing hypothesis.* New York: Charles Scribner's Sons.

Cross, I. (2009). The evolutionary nature of musical meaning. *Music and evolution*, 179-200.

Damasio, A. (1994). *Descartes' error: Emotion, reason, and the human brain.* Putnam.

Damasio, A. (1999). *The feeling of what happens: Body and emotion in the making of consciousness.* Harcourt.

Damasio, A. (2003). *Looking for Spinoza: Joy, sorrow, and the feeling brain.* Harcourt.

Damasio, A. (2010). *Self comes to mind: Constructing the conscious brain.* Pantheon.

D'Amato, M.R. (1988). A search for tonal pattern perception in cebus monkeys: Why monkeys can't hum a tune. *Music Perception, 5*, 453–480.

Darwin, C. (1859). *The origin of species.* Cambridge, MA: Harvard University Press.

Darwin, C. (2007) [1872]. *The expression of the emotions in man and animals.* New York: Filiquarian.

Dawkins, R. (1976). *The selfish gene.* Oxford: Oxford University Press.

De Jonge, F. H., Louwerse, A. L., et al. (1989). Lesions of the SDN-POA inhibit sexual behavior of male Wistar rats. *Brain Research Bulletin, 23*, 483-492.

Denson, T. F., Pederson, W. C., Ronquillo, J., & Nandy, A. S. (2009). The angry brain: Neural correlates of anger, anger rumination, and aggressive personality. *Journal of Cognitive Neuroscience, 21* (4), 734-744.

Desimone, R. (1991). Face-selective cells in the temporal cortex of monkeys. *Journal of Cognitive Neuroscience, 3*, 1-8.

Dessens, A. B. (2005). Gender dysphoria and gender change in chromosomal females with congenital adrenal hyperplasia. *Arch. Sex Behav., 34*, 389-397.

Deutsch, D., Henthorn, T., Marvin, E., & Xu, H. (2006). Absolute pitch among American and Chinese conservatory students: Prevalence differences and evidence for a speech-related critical period. *Journal of the Acoustical Society of America, 119*, 719-722.

Dewing, P., Shi, T., Horvath, S., & Vilain, E. (2003). Sexually dimorphic gene expression in mouse brain precedes gonadal differentiation. *Molecular Brain Research, 118*(1-2), 82-90.

Diamond, J. (1992). Turning a man. *Discover, 13*, 71-77.

Diamond, M. (1992). *Sexwatching: Looking into the world of sexual behaviour.* London: Prion Press, Multimedia Books, Ltd.

Diamond, M. and Karlen, A. (1980). *Sexual decisions.* Boston: Little, Brown.

Diamond, M., & Sigmundson, H. K. (1997). Sex reassignment at birth: Long-term review and clinical implications. *Archives of Pediatric and Adolescent Medicine, 151*, 298-304.

Dimond, S.J., & Beaumont, J.G. (1974). *Hemisphere function in the human brain.* New York: Wiley.

DiNapoli, L., & Capel, B. (2008). SRY and the standoff in sex determination. *Molecular Endocrinology, 22*(1), 1-9.

Dingfelder, S. F. (2007). Phantom pain and the brain. *Monitor on Psychology, Jan.*, 22-23.

Dingfelder, S. F. (2010). A second chance for the Mexican wolf. *Monitor on Psychology, 41* (10), 20-21.

Dominquez, J. M., & Hull, E. M. (2001). Stimulation of the medial amygdala enhances medial preoptic dopamine release: Implications for male rat sexual behavior. *Brain Research, 917*, 225-229.

Donaldson, M., Gault, E. J., Tan, K. W., & Dunger, D. B. (2006). Optimising management in Turner syndrome: From infancy to adult transfer. *Arch. Dis. Child, 91* (6), 513-520.

Eckert, M. A., Galaburda, A. M., et al. (2006). Anomalous sylvian fissure morphology in Williams syndrome. *NeuroImage, 33*, 39-45.

Ehrlich, S., Weiss, D., et al. (2010). Promoter specific DNA methylation and gene expression of POMC in acutely underweight and recovered patients with anorexia nervosa. *Journal of Psychiatric Research, 44* (13), 827-833.

Eisenberger, N. I., Lieberman, M. D., & Williams, K. D. (2003). Does rejection hurt? An fMRI study of social exclusion. *Science, 302* (5643), 290-292.

Ekman, P. (1972). Universals and cultural differences in facial expressions of emotion. In J. Cole (Ed.), *Nebraska Symposium on Motivation*, 1971, (Vol. 19, pp. 207-283).

Ekman, P., Davidson, R. J., & Friesen, W. V. (1990). The Duchenne smile: Emotional expression and brain physiology II. *Journal of Personality and Social Psychology, 58*, 342-353.

Ekman, P., Levenson, R. W., & Friesen, W. V. (1983). Autonomic nervous system activity distinguishes among emotions. *Science, 221* (4616), 1208-1210.

Ekman, P., & Friesen, W. V. (1978). *The Facial Action Coding System: A technique for the measurement of facial movement.* Palo Alto, CA: Consulting Psychologists Press.

Engmann, B. & Reuter, M. (2009). Spontaneous perception of melodies – hallucination or epilepsy? *Nervenheilkunde*, 217-221.

Enoch, M-A. (2011). The role of early life stress as a predictor for alcohol and drug dependence. *Psychopharmacology, 214* (1), 17-31.

Eskine, K. J., Kacinik, N. A., & Prinz, J. J. (2011). A bad taste in the mouth: Gustatory disgust influences moral judgment. *Psychological Science, 22* (3), 295-299.

Etkin, A., Egner, T., Peraza, D. M., Kandel, E. R., & Hirsch, J. (2006). Resolving emotional conflict: A role for the rostral anterior cingulate cortex in modulating activity in the amygdala. *Neuron, 51,* 1-12.

Fairburn, C. G., Cooper, Z., Doll, H. A., et al. (2009). Transdiagnostic cognitive-behavioral therapy for patients with eating disorders: A two-site trial with 60-week follow-up. *Am. J. Psychiatry, 166,* 311-319.

Farooqi, S., & O'Rahilly, S. (2006). Genetics of obesity in humans. *Endocrine Reviews, 27* (7), 710-718.

Farwell, L. A,. & Smith, S. S. (2001). Using brain MERMER testing to detect concealed knowledge despite efforts to conceal. *Journal of Forensic Sciences, 46* (1), 135-143.

Ferguson, J. N., et al. (2000). Social amnesia in mice lacking the oxytocin gene. *Nature Genetics, 25,* 284-288.

Filbey, F. M., et al. (2009). Marijuana craving in the brain. *Proceedings of the National Academy of Sciences of the United States, 106.31,* 13016.

Finlayson, G., King, N., & Blundell, J. E. (2007). Liking vs. wanting food: Importance for human appetite control and weight regulation. *Neuroscience Biobehavior Review, 31,* 987–1002.

Fisher, H. E., Brown, L. L., Aron, A., Strong, G., & Mashek, D. (2010). Reward, addiction, and emotion regulation systems associated with rejection in love. *Journal of Neurophysiology, 104,* 51-60.

Fox, N. A., Hane, A. A., & Pine, D. S. (2007). Plasticity for affective neurocircuitry. *Current Directions in Psychological Science, 16,* 1, 1-5.

Fox, P. T. (1986). Mapping human visual cortex with positron emission tomography. *Nature, 323,* 806-809.

Frank, G. K., Kaye, W. H., et al. (2005). Altered brain serotonin 5-HT1A receptor binding afterrecovery from anorexia nervosa measured by positron emission tomography and [Carbonyl11C]WAY-100635. *Archives of General Psychiatry, 62,* 1032-1041.

Frederikse ME, Lu A, Aylward E, Barta P, Pearlson G (December 1999). Sex differences in the inferior parietal lobule. *Cerebral Cortex, 9* (8), 896-901.

Freed, P. J., & Mann, J. J. (2007). Sadness and loss:Toward a neurobiopsychosocial model. *American Journal of Psychiatry, 164* (1), 28-34.

Fujioka, R., Zendel, B. R., & Ross, B. (2010). Endogenous neuromagnetic activity for mental hierarchy of timing. *The Journal of Neuroscience, 30* (9), 3458-3466.

Furst, C. (1979). *Origins of the mind: Mind-brain connections.* Englewood Cliffs, NJ: Prentice-Hall.

Gage, F. H., & Kempermann, G. (1999). New nerve cells for the adult brain. *Scientific American, 280* (5), 48.

Galaburda, A. M., Holinger, D. P., Bellugi, U., & Sherman, G. F. (2002). Williams syndrome: Neuronal size and neuronal-packing density in primary visual cortex. Arch *Neurol., 59* (9), 1461-1467.

Galletly, C., Van Hooff, M., & McFarlane, A. (2011).Psychotic symptoms in young adults exposed to childhood trauma – a 20 year follow-up study. *Schizophrenia Research, 127* (1-3), p76-82.

Gao, Y. & Raine, A. (2010). Successful and unsuccessful psychopaths: A neurobiological model. *Behavioral Sciences and the Law,* 28, 194-210.

Gass, J. T., Sinclair, C. M., Cleva, R. M., Widholm, J. J., & Olive, M. F. (2011). Alcohol-seeking behavior is associated with increased glutamate transmission in basolateral amygdala and nucleus accumbens as measured by glutamate-oxidase-coated biosensors. *Biology, 16* (2), 215-228.

Geschwind, N. (1965). Disconnexion syndrome in animals and man. *Brain, 88,* 237-294, 585-644.

Geschwind, N. (1967). Wernicke's contribution to the study of aphasia. *Cortex, 3,* 448-463.

Giuliani, N. R., Drabant, E. M., & Gross, J. J. (2011). Anterior cingulate cortex volume and emotion regulation: Is bigger better? *Biological Psychology, 86* (3), 379-382.

Goldstein, M., Peters, L., Baillie, A., McVeagh, P., Minshall, G., & Fitzjames, D. (2011). The effectiveness of a day program for the treatment of adolescent anorexia nervosa. International Journal of Eating Disorders, 44(1), 29-38.

Grabenhorst,F., & Rolls, E.T. (2011). Value, pleasure and choice in the ventral prefrontal cortex. *Trends in Cognitive Sciences,* 15 (2), 56-67.

Graham, G. E., Allanson, J. E., & Gerritsen, J. A. (2007). Sex chromosome abnormalities. In Rimoin, David L., Connor, J. M., Pyeritz, R. E., & Korf, B. R. (eds.). *Emery and Rimoin's principles and practice of medical genetics* (5th ed.). Philadelphia: Churchill Livingstone Elsevier.

Gremel, C. M., Young, E. A., & Cunningham, C. L. (2011). Blockade of opioid receptors in anterior cingulate cortex disrupts ethanol-seeking behavior in mice. *Behavioural Brain Research, 219* (2), 358-362.

Grimbos, T. (2010). Sexual orientation and the second to fourth finger length ratio: A meta-analysis in men and women. *Behav. Neurosci., 124,* 278-287.

Guerreiro, M., Castro-Caldas, A. & Martins, I. P. (1995). Aphasia following right hemisphere lesion in a woman with left hemisphere injury in childhood. *Brain and Language, 49,* 280-288.

Gujar, N., McDonald, S. A., Masaki, N., & Walker, M. P. (2011). A role for REM sleep in recalibrating the sensitivity of the human brain to specific emotions. *Cerebral Cortex, 21* (1), 115-123.

Gustavson, C. R., Garcia, J., Hankins, W. G., & Rusiniak, K. W. (1974). Coyote predation control by aversive conditioning. *Science, 3,* 581-583.

Guyton, A. C. (1981). *Textbook of medical physiology.* Philadelphia: Saunders.

Haier, R. J., Jung, R. E., Yeo, R. A., Head, K., & Alkire, M. T. (2005). The neuroanatomy of general intelligence: Sex matters. *Neuroimage, 25* (1), 320-327.

Halpern, D.F. (2007). The science of sex differences in science and mathematics. *Psychol. Sci. Public Interest, 8,* 1-51.

Halpern, C. H., Wolf, J. A., et al. (2008). Deep brain stimulation in the treatment of obesity. *Journal of Neurosurgery, 109* (4), 625-634.

Hanson, J., Chung, M., Avants, B., Shritcliff, E., Gee,J., Davidson, R. J., & Pollak, S. (2010). Early stress is associated with alterations in the orbitofrontal cortex: A tensor-based morphometry investigation of brain structure and behavioral risk. *Journal of Neuroscience, 30* (22), 7466-7472.

Harasty, J., Double, K. L., Halliday, G. M., Kril, J. J., McRitchie, D. A. (1997). Language-associated cortical regions are proportionally larger in the female brain. *Arch. Neurol. 54* (2), 171-176.

Haselton, M. G., & Gildersleeve, K. (2011). Can men detect ovulation? *Current Directions in Psychological Science, 20* (2), 87-92.

He, C., & Trainor, L. J. (2009). Finding the pitch of the missing fundamental in infants. *The Journal of Neuroscience, 29* (24), 7718-8822.

Hearing the music, honing the mind. (2010, November). *Scientific American.*

Heimer, L. & Larsson, K. (1967). Mating behavior of male rats after olfactory bulb lesions. *Physiology & Behavior, 2*(2), 207-209.

Heinzel, A., Schafer, R., et al. (2010). Increased activation of the supragenual anterior cingulate cortex during visual emotional processing in male subjects with high degrees of alexithymia: An event-related fMRI study. *Psychotherapy & Psychosomatics, 79* (6), 363-370.

Held, R. & Hein, A. (1963). Movement-produced stimulation in the development of visually guided behavior. *Journal of Comparative and Physiological Psychology, 56,* 872-876,

Hellige, J. B. (1993). *Hemispheric asymmetry: What's right and what's left.* Cambridge, MA: Harvard University Press.

Helmuth, L. (2002). Redrawing the brain's map of the body. *Science, 296,* 1587-1588.

Helmuth, L. (2003). Fear and trembling in the amygdala. *Science, 300,* 568-569.

Hennenlotter, A., Dresel, C., Castrop, F., Ceballos Baumann, A. O., Wohlschlager, A. M., & Haslinger, B. (2009). The link between facial feedback and neural activity within central circuitries of emotion - New insights from botulinum toxin-induced denervation of frown muscles. *Cerebral Cortex, 19* (3), 537-542.

Heron, M. P., Hoyert, D. L., Murphy, S. L., Xu, J. Q., Kochanek, K. D., Tejada-Vera, B. (2009). Deaths: Final data for 2006. *National Vital Statistics Reports, 57* (14), 11.

Hidehiko, T., Kato, M., Matsuura, M., Mobbs, D., Suhara, T., & Okubo, Y. (2009). When your gain is my pain and your pain is my gain: Neural correlates of envy and schadenfreude. *Science, 323* (5916), 937-939.

Hier, D. B., & Crowley, W. F., Jr. (1982). Spatial ability in androgen deficient men. *New England Journal of Medicine, 306,* 1202-1205.

Hines, M. (2004). *Brain Gender.* Oxford University Press.

Hines, M. (2010). Sex-related variation in human behavior and the brain. *Trends in Cognitive Science, 14,* 448-456.

Hines, M., et al. (1992). Cognition and the corpus callosum: Verbal fluency, visuospatial ability and language lateralization related to midsagittal surface areas of callosal subregions. *Behav. Neurosci., 106,* 3-14.

Hines, M., et al. (2002). Testosterone during pregnancy and childhood gender role behavior: A longitudinal population study. *Child Dev., 73,* 1678-1687.

Hinrichs, B. H. (1991). What got into him?: On the causes of human behavior. *Communitas, IV,* 148-153.

Hinrichs, B. H. (1997). Brain research and folk psychology. *The Humanist, 57,* 2, 26-31.

Hinrichs, B. H. (1998). Computing the mind. *The Humanist, 58,* 2, 26-30.

Hinrichs, B. H. (2007). *Mind as mosaic: The robot in the machine.* Minneapolis, Minnesota: Ellipse Publishing Co.

Hinrichs, B. H. (2009). *The science of psychology.* Minneapolis, Minnesota: Ellipse Publishing Co.

Hinrichs, B. H. (2011). *Brain slice: An introduction to psychological neuroscience.* Minneapolis, Minnesota: Ellipse Publ. Co.

Ho, A. J., Stein, J. L., Hua, X., et al. (2010). A commonly carried allele of the obesity-related FTO gene is associated with reduced brain volume in the healthy elderly. *Proceedings of the National Academy of Sciences.*

Hobson, J. A. (1994). *The chemistry of conscious states.* Boston: Little, Brown & Co.

Hofker, M. & Wijmenga, C. (2009). A supersized list of obesity genes. *Nature Genetics, 41,* 139-140.

Holland, A. J. (1988). Anorexia nervosa: Evidence for a genetic basis. *Journal of Psychosomatic Research, 32,* 561-571.

Hoppe, K. D., & Bogen, J. E. (1977). Alexithymia in twelve commissurotomized patients. *Psychotherapy and Psychosomatics, 28* (1–4)m 148-155.

Houben, K., Wiers, R. W., & Jansen, A. (2011). Getting a grip on drinking behavior: Training working memory to reduce alcohol abuse. Psychological Science, 22 (6).

Howell, L. V., Votaw, J. R., Goodman, M. M., & Lindsey, K. P. (2010). Cortical activation during cocaine use and extinction in rhesus monkeys. *Psychopharmacology, 208* (2), 191-199.

Hoyert, D. L., Heron, M., Murphy, S. L., Kung, H-C., (2006). Deaths: Final Data for 2003. *National Vital Statistics Reports, 54,* (13), 10.

Hulshoff Pol, H. E., Cohen-Kettenix, P. T., et al. (2006). Changing your sex changes your brain: Influences of testosterone and estrogen on adult human brain structure. *European Journal of Endocrinology, 155,* S106-S114.

Hyde, K. L., Lerch, J., Norton, A., Forgeard, M., Winner, E., Evans, A. C., & Schlaug, G. (2009). Musical training shapes structural brain development. *Journal of Neuroscience, 29* (10), 3019-3025.

Hyde, K. L., Lerch, J. P., Zatorre, R. J., Griffiths, T. D., Evans, A. C., & Peretz, I. (2007). Cortical thickness in congenital amusia: When less is better than more. *The Journal of Neuroscience, 27* (47), 13028-13032.

Inbar, Y., Pizarro, D. A., & Bloom, P. (2010). Conservatives are more easily disgusted than liberals. *Cognition and Emotion, 23* (4), 714-725.

Isen, J., Baker, L., Dawson, M., Raine, A., Bezdjian, S., & Lozano, D.I. (2010). Sex-specific association between psychopathic traits and electrodermal reactivity in children. *Journal of Abnormal Psychology, 119* (1), 216-225.

Israel, M., Steiger, H., Kolvakis, T., McGregor, L., & Sadikot, A. (2010). Deep brain stimulation in the subgenual cingulated cortex for an intractable eating disorder. *Biological Psychiatry, 67* (9), 53-54.

Izard, C. E. (1971). *The face of emotion.* New York: Appleton-Century-Crofts.

Izard, C. E. (2007). Levels of emotion and levels of consciousness. *Behavioral and Brain Sciences, 30* (1), 96-98.

Jacobs, P. A., Baikie, A. G., Brown, W. M., MacGregor, T. N., Maclean, N., & Harnden, D. G. (1959). Evidence for the existence of the human "super female." *Lancet, 274* (7100) 423-5.

Jager, G., Block, R. I., Luilten, M., & Rarnsey, N. F. (2010). Cannabis use and memory brain function in adolescent boys: A cross-sectional mulitcenter functional magnetic resonance imaging study. (2010). *Journal of the American Academy of Child & Adolescent Psychiatry, 49* (6), 561-572.

Janata, P. (2009). The neural architecture of music-evoked autobiographical memories. *Cerebral Cortex,* 19, 2579-2594.

Janata, P., Birk, J.L., Van Horn, J.D., Leman, M., Tillmann, B., & Bharucha, J.J. (2002). The cortical topography of tonal structures underlying Western music. *Science,* 298, 2167-2170.

Janowsky, J. S., Oviatt, S. K., & Orwoll, E. S. (1994). Testosterone influences spatial cognition in older men. *Behavioral Neuroscience, 108,* 325-332.

Jørgensen, M. M., Zachariaea, R., Skyttheb, A, & Kyvik, K. (2007). Genetic and environmental factors in alexithymia: A population-based study of 8,785 Danish twin pairs. *Psychotherapy and Psychosomatics, 76,* 369-375.

Jourdain, R. (1997). *Music, the brain, and ecstasy: How music captures our imagination.* New York: William Morrow and Company, Inc.

Kafka, M. P. (1997). Hypersexual desire in men: An operational definition and clinical implications for males with paraphilias and paraphilia related disorders. *Arch Sex Behav, 26,* 505-526.

Kampe, K. K., Frith, C. D., Dolan, R. J., & Frith, U. (2001). Reward value of attractiveness and gaze. *Nature, 413,* (6856), 589.

Kandel, E. R., Schwartz, J. H., & Jessell, T. (2000). *Principles of neural science.* Norwalk: Appleton & Lange.

Kansaku, K., Yamaura, A., & Kitazawa, S. (2000). Sex differences in lateralization revealed in the posterior language areas. *Cerebral Cortex, 10,* 866-872.

Kaye, W. H., Frank, G. K., Meltzer, C. C., Rhodes, L., et al. (2001). Altered serotonin 2A receptor activity in women who have recovered from bulimia nervosa. *Am. J. Psychiatry, 158,* 1152-1155.

Kinsey, A. C., Pomeroy, W. B., & Martin, C. E.. (1948). *Sexual behavior in the human male.* Philadelphia: Saunders.

Kinsey, A. C., Pomeroy, W. B., Martin, C. E., & Gebhard, P. H. (1953). *Sexual behavior in the human female.* Philadelphia: Saunders.

Koelsch, S. (2009). Music-syntactic processing and auditory memory – similarities and differences between ERAN and MMN. *Psychophysiology, 46*(1), 179-190.

Koelsch, S., Kilches, S., Steinbeis, N., & Schelinski, S. (2008). Effects of unexpected chords and of performer's expression on brain responses and electrodermal activity. *PLoS One,* 3(7), e2631 DOI: 10.1371/journal.pone.0002631.

Kosfeld, M., Heinrichs, M., Zak, P. J., Fischbacher, U., & Fehr, E. (2005). Oxytocin increases trust in humans. *Nature, 435,* 673-676.

Kraemer, D. J. M., Macrae, C. N., Green, A. E., & Kelley, W. M. (2005). Musical imagery: Sound of silence activates auditory cortex. *Nature, 434,* 158.

Krafft-Ebbing, R. (1886). *Psychopathia sexualis.* Reprinted by Bloat Books, 1999.

Krolak-Salmon, P., Henaff, M. A., Isnard, J. et al. (2003). An attention modulated response to disgust in human ventral anterior insula. *Annals of Neurology, 53,* 446-453.

Kuukasjarvi, S., Eriksson, C. J. P., et al. (2004). Attractiveness of women's body odors over the menstrual cycle: The role of oral contraceptives and receiver sex. *Behavioral Ecology, 15,* 579-584.

Lane, R. D., Ahern, G. L., Schwartz, G. E., & Kasedniak, A. W. (1997). Is alexithymia the emotional equivalent of blindsight? *Biol. Psychiatry* 42 (9), 834-844.

Lane, R. D., & Nadel, L., Eds. (2000). *Cognitive neuroscience of emotion.* New York: Oxford University Press.

Laviolette, S. R., Gallegos, R. A., Henriksen, S. J., & van der Kooy, D. (2004). Opiate state controls bi-directional reward signaling via GABA receptors in the ventral tegmental area. *Nature Neuroscience, 7,* 160-169.

LeDoux, J.E. (1996). *The emotional brain: The mysterious underpinnings of emotional life.* New York: Simon & Schuster.

LeVay, S. (1991). A difference in hypothalamic structure between heterosexual and homosexual men. *Science, 253,* 1034-1037.

LeVay, S. (2011). *Gay, straight, and the reason why: The science of sexual orientation.* New York: Oxford University Press.

Levine, S. B. (2003). The nature of sexual desire: A clinician perspective. *Arch. Sex. Behav., 32,* 3, 279-85.

Levitin, D. J. (2006). *This is your brain on music: The science of a human obsession.* New York: Penguin.

Levitin, D. J. (2008). *The world in six songs: How the musical brain created human nature.* New York: Penguin.

Levitin, D. J., & Menon, V. (2003). Musical structure is processed in "language" areas of the brain: A possible role for Brodmann Area 47 in temporal coherence. *Neuroimage, 18,* 74-82.

Lieberman, D., Pillsworth, E. G., & Haselton, M. G. (2010). Kin affiliation across the ovulatory cycle: Females avoid fathers when fertile. *Psychological Science, 20* (10), 1-6.

Linas, R. (1999). The squid giant synapse: A model for chemical transmission. New York: Oxford University Press.

Linden, M. G., Bender, B. G., & Robinson, A. (2002). Genetic counseling for sex chromosome abnormalities. *American Journal of Medical Genetics, 110* (1), 3-10.

Lindenberger, U., Li, S-C., Gruber, W., & Muller, V. (2009). Brains swinging in concert: Cortical phase synchronization while playing guitar. *BMC Neuroscience, 10* (22).

Liu, C. (2003). Does quality of marital sex decline with duration. *Arch. Sex. Behav., 32,* 1, 55-60.

Logeswaran, N., & Bhattacharya, J. (2009). Crossmodal transfer of emotion by music. *Neuroscience Letters, 455* (2).

Lopez-Larson, M. P., Bogorodzki, P., et al. (2011). Altered prefrontal and insular cortical thickness in adolescent marijuana users. *Beharioural Brain Research, 220,* (1), 164-172.

Loos, R. J., Lindgren, C. M., Li, S., Wheeler, E., et al. (2008). Common variants near MC4R are associated with fat mass, weight and risk of obesity. *Nat. Genet., 40* (6), 768–75.

Lorenzetti, V., Lubman, D. I., Whittle, S., Solowij, N., Yucel, M. (2010). Structural MRI findings in long-term cannabis users: What do we know? *Substance Use & Misuse, 45* (11), 1787-1808.

Loui, P., Aslop, D., & Schlaug, G. (2009). Tone deafness: A new disconnection syndrome? *The Journal of Neuroscience, 29* (33), 10215-10220.

Luria, A., Tsvetkova, L., & Futer, J. (1965). Aphasia in a composer. *Journal of Neurological Science, 2,* 288–92.

Lynch, M. P., & Eilers, R. E. (1992). A study of perceptual development for musical tuning. *Perception and Psychophysics, 52,* 599-608.

Lynch, M. P., Eilers, R. E., Oller, D. & Urbano, R. C. (1990). Innatesness, experience, and music perception. *Psychological Science, 1,* 272-276.

Maes, H. H. M, Neale, M. C., & Eaves, I. J. (1997). Genetic and environmental factors in relative body weight and human adiposity. *Behavior Genetics, 27,* 325-351.

Maess, B., Koelsch, S., Gunter, T. C., & Friederici, A. D. (2001). Musical syntax is processed in Broca's area: An MEG study. *Nature Neuroscience, 4,* 540-545.

Maguire, E. A., Burgess, N., Donnett, J., Frackowiak, S. J., Frith, C., & O'Keefe, J. (1998). Knowing where and getting there: A human navigation network. *Science, 280,* 5365, 921-925.

Maguire, E. A., et al. (2000). Navigation-related structural change in the hippocampi of taxi drivers. *Proceedings of the National Academy of Sciences of the United States, 97(8),* 4398-4403.

Maletzky, B. M. (1998). The paraphilias: Research and treatment. In *A guide to treatments that work,* edited by Peter Nathan and Jack Gorman, Oxford University Press.

Markel, H., Lee, A., Holmes, R. D., & Domino, E. F. (1994). LSD flashback syndrome exacerbated by selective serotonin reuptake inhibitor antidepressants in adolescents. *Journal of Pediatrics, 125* (1), 817-819.

Masters, W., & Johnson, V. (1966). *The human sexual response.* Boston: Little, Brown.

Mather, M., Lighthall, N. R., Nga, L. & Gorlick, M. (2010). Sex differences in how stress affects brain activity during face viewing. *NeuroReport: For Rapid Communication of Neuroscience Research, 21*(14), 933-937.

Mauk, B. (2009). Brain scientists identify close links between arts, learning. *Arts Education in the News,* Dana Foundation.

Mayberg, H. S., Lozano, A. M., Voon, V., et al. (2005). Deep brain stimulation for treatment-resistant depression. *Neuron, 45* (5), 651-660.

Maze, I., Covington, H. E., Dietz, LaPlant, Z., Nestler, E. J., et al. (2010). Essential role of the histone methyltransferease G9a in cocaine-induced plasticity. *Science, 327* (5962), 213-216.

McCoy, N. L., & Pitino, L. (2002). Pheromonal influences on sociosexual behavior in young women. *Physiology and Behavior, 75,* 367-375.

McDermott, J. H. (2009). What can experiments reveal about the origins of music? *Current Directions in Psychological Science, 18* (3), 164-168/

McDermott, J. H., Lehr, A. J., & Oxenham, A. J. (2010). Individual differences reveal the basis of consonance. *Current Biology, 20,* 1035-1041.

McDermott, J. H., & Hauser, M. (2005). The origins of music: Innateness, uniqueness, and evolution. *Music Perception, 23* (1), 29-59.

Menon, V. & Levitin, D. J. (2005). The rewards of music listening: Response and physiological connectivity of themesolimbic system. *NeuroImage 28(1),* 175-184.

Mercader, J. M., Fernandez-Aranda, F., Gratacos, M., et al. (2010). Correlation of BDNF blood levels with interoceptive awareness and maturity fears in anorexia and bulimia nervosa patients. *Journal of Neural Transmission, 117* (4), 502-512.

Merzenich, M. (1998). Long-term change of mind. *Science, 282,* 5391, 1062.

Mesquita, B., & Frijda, N. H. (1992). Cultural variations in emotions: A review. *Psychological Bulletin, 112,* 179-204.

Meston, C. M. & Frolich, P. F. (2000). The neurobiology of sexual function. *Arch. Gen. Psychiatry, 57,* 1012-30.

Miller, B. L., Boone, K., Cummings, J. L., Read, S. L., & Mishkin, F. (2000). Functional correlates of musical and visual ability in frontotemporal dementia. *British Journal of Psychiatry, 176,* 458-463.

Miller, L. K. (1989). *Musical savants: Exceptional skill in the mentally retarded.* New York: Psychology Press.

Miller, S. L., & Maner, J. K. (2010). Scent of a woman: Men's testosterone responses to olfactory ovulation cues. *Psychological Science, 21* (2), 276-283.

Mithen, S. (2006). *The singing Neanderthals: The origins of music, language, mind, and body.* Cambridge, MA: Harvard University Press.

Miyake, Y., Okamoto, Y., Onoda, K., Shirao, N., Okamoto, Y., Otagaki, Y., & Yamawaki, S. (2010). Neural processing of negative word stimuli concerning body image in patients with eating disorders: An fMRI study. *NeuroImage, 50* (3), 1333-1339.

Money, J. (1988). *Lovemaps: Clinical concepts of sexual/erotic health and pathology, paraphilia, and gender transposition in childhood, adolescence, and maturity.* Prometheus books.

Money, J. (1994). The concept of gender identity disorder in childhood and adolescence after 39 years. *Journal of Sex and Marital Therapy, 20* (3), 163–77.

Morewedge, C. K., Huh, Y. E., & Vosgerau, J. (2010). Thought for food: Imagined consumption reduces actual consumption. *Science, 330,* 1530-1533.

Morris, B. J. (1989). Neuronal localisation of neuropeptide Y gene expression in the rat brain. *J. Comp. Neurol., 290* (3): 358–368.

Musacchia, G., Sams, M., Skoe, E., & Kraus, N. (2007). Musicians have enhanced subcortical auditory and audiovisual processing of speech and music. *Proceedings of the National Academy of Sciences, 104* (40), 15894-15898.

Naqvi, N. H., Rudrauf, D. Damasio, H., Bechara, A. (2007). Damage to the insula disrupts addiction to cigarette smoking. *Science, 315,* (5811), 531-534.

Narayan, V.M., Narr, K. L., Kamuri, V., Woods, R. P. et al. (2007). Regional cortical thinning in subjects with violent antisocial personality disorder or schizophrenia. *The American Journal of Psychiatry, 164,* 9.

Navarro, J. (2008). *What everybody is saying: An ex-FBI agent's guide to speed-reading people.* New York: Collins Living.

Nisbett, R. E. (1972). Hunger, obesity, and the ventromedial hypothalamus. *Psychological Review, 79,* 433-453.

Nolley, E. P., & Kelley, B. M. (2007). Adolescent reward system perseveration due to nicotine: Studies with methylphenidate. *Neurotoxicology Teratology, 29* (1), 47–56.

Ohl, R. W., Scheich, H., & Freeman, W. J. (2001). Change in the pattern of ongoing cortical activity with auditory category learning. *Nature, 412,* 733-736.

Okamoto, H., et al. (2010). Listening to tailor-made notched music reduces tinnitus loudness and tinnitus-related auditory cortex activity. *Proceedings of the National Academy of Sciences, 107,* 1207-1210

O'Keefe, J. & Nadel, L. (1978). *The hippocampus as a cognitive map.* Oxford University Press.

Olds, J. & Milner, P. (1954). Positive reinforcement produced by electrical stimulation of septal area and other regions of rat brain. *J. Comp. Physiol. Psychol.,6,* 419-27.

Olds, J. M., & Milner, P. M. (1954). Positive reinforcement produced by electrical stimulation of septal area and other regions of rat brain. *Journal of Comparative and Physiological Psychology, 47,* 419- 427.

Orton, S. (Ed.) (1934). *Localization of function in the cerebral cortex.* Baltimore: Williams & Wilkins.

Padoa-Schioppa, C., & Assad, J. A. (2008). The representation of economic value in the orbitofrontal cortex is invariant for changes of menu. *Nature Neurosciene, 11* (1), 95-102.

Paredes, R. G., Tzschentke, T., & Nakach, N. (1998). Lesions of the medial preoptic area/anterior hypothalamus (MPOA/AH) modify partner preference in male rats. *Brain Research, 813*(1), 1-8.

Parsons, L. M. (2003). Music of the spheres. *BBC Music Magazine,* (November), 34-39.

Patel, A. D. (2008). *Music, language, and the brain.* New York: Oxford University Press.

Pelletier, M., et al. (2003). Separate neural circuits for primary emotions? *Neuroreport, 14* (8), 1111-1116.

Penfield, W., & Perot P. (1963). The brain's record of auditory and visual experience. A final summary and discussion. *Brain, 86,* 595–696.

Perani, Daniela, et al. (2011). Functional specializations for music processing in the human newborn brain. *Proceedings of the National Academy of Sciences of the United States, 107* (10), 4758-4763.

Peretz, I. (1993). Auditory agnosia: A functional analysis. In: McAdams, S. & Bigand, E. (Eds.). *Thinking in sound: The cognitive psychology of human audition.* New York: Oxford Universtiy Press.

Peretz, I. (2001). Brain specialization for music. New evidence from congenital amusia. *New York Academy of Sciences, 8,*243-246.

Peretz, I., & Coltheart, M. (2003). Modularity of music processing. *Nature Neuroscience, 6* (7), 688-691.

Perlman, M. (2004). *Unplayed Melodies: Javanese Gamelan and the Genesis of Music Theory.* Berkeley: University of California Press.

Peterson, C. B., Mitchell, J. E., Crow, S. J., Crosby, R. D., & Wonderlich, S. A. (2009). The efficacy of self-help group treatment and therapist-led group treatment for binge eating disorder. *Am. J. Psychiatry, 166,* 1347-1354.

Philibert, R. A., Beach, S. R. H., Gunter, T. D., et al. (2009). The effect of smoking on MAOA promoter methylation in DNA prepared from lymphoblasts and whole blood. *Amer. J. of Medical Genetics, 153B (2),* 619-628.

Philibert, R. A., Sandhu, H., Hollenbeck, N., Gunter, t., Adams, W., & Madan, A. (2008). The relationship of 5HTT methylation and genotype on mRNA expression and liability to major depression and alcohol dependence in subjects from the Iowa Adoption Studies. *Amer. J. of Medical Genetics, 147B, (5)* 543-549.

Pinker, S. (1997). *How the mind works.* New York: Norton.

Pinker, S. (2007). Toward a consilient study of literature. *Philosophy and Literature, 31,* 161-177.

Pitkow, L. J., Sharer, C. A., Ren, X., Insel, T. R., Terwilliger, E. F., & Young, L. J. (2001). Facilitation of affiliation and pair-bond formation by vasopressin receptor gene transfer into the ventral forebrain of a monogamous vole. *Neuroscience, 21* (18), 7392-7396.

Plantinga, J., & Trainor, L.J. (2005). Memory for melody: Infants use a relative pitch code. Cognition, 98, 1-11.

Posner, M. I., & DiGirolamo, G. J. (1998). Executive attention: Conflict, target detection, and cognitive control. In Parasuraman R. *The attentive brain.* Cambridge, Mass: MIT Press.

Posner, M. I., & Raichle, M. (1994). *Images of mind.* New York: Freeman.

Powell, J. (2010). *How music works: The science and psychology of beautiful sounds, from Beethoven to the Beatles and beyond.* New York: Little, Brown, and Company.

Raine A. et al. (2000). Reduced prefrontal gray matter volume and reduced autonomic activity in antisocial personality disorder. *Arch Gen Psychiatry, 57.*

Raine A., Venables P., & Williams M. (1990). Autonomic orienting responses in 15-year-old male subjects and criminal behavior at age 24. *Am. J. Psychiatry, 147.*

Ray, O. & Ksir, C. (2002). *Drugs, society, and human behavior.* Boston: McGraw-Hill.

Rentfrow, P. J., & Gosling, S. D. (2006). Message in a ballad: The role of music preferences in interpersonal perception. *Psychological Science, 17,* 236-242.

Rimmele, U.m, Hediger, K., Heinrichs, M. & Klaver, P. (2009). Oxytocin makes a face in memory familiar. *J. of Neuro., 29,* 38-42.

Roberts, G., & Garavan, H. (2010). Evidence of increased activation underlying cognitive control in ecstasy and cannabis users. *NeuroImage, 52* (2), 429-435.

Roberts, G., Nestor, L., & Garavan, H. (2009). Learning and memory deficits in ecstasy users and their neural correlates during a face-learning task. *Brain Research, 1292,* 71-81.

Rodriques, A-J., Leao, P., Carvelho, M., Almeida, O. F. X., & Sousa, N. (2011). Potential programming of dopaminergic circuits by early life stress. *Psychopharmacology, 214* (1), 107-120.

Roether, C. L., Omlor, L., & Giese, M. A. (2007). Not just the face: Asymmetry of emotional body expression. *Journal of Vision, 7* (9), 554.

Roselli, C. E., Larkin, K., et al. (2004). The volume of sexually dimorphic nucleus in the ovine medial preoptic area/anterior hypothalamus varies with sexual partner preference. *Endocrinology, 145,* 478-483.

Rule, N. O., Rosen, K. S., Slepian, M. L., & Ambady, N. (2011). Mating interest improves women's accuracy in judging male sexual orientation. Psychological Science, 22 (6), 1-6.

Rump, T. J., Muneer, P. M., et al. (2010). Acetyl-l-carnitine protects neuronal function from alcohol-induced oxidative damage in the brain. *Free Radical Biology & Medicine, 49* (10), 1494-1504.

Ruytjens, L., Georgiadis, J. R., et al. (2007). Functional sex differences in human primary auditory cortex. *European Journal of Nuclear Medicine and Molecular Imaging, 34* (12).

Sabatinelli, D., Fortune, E. E., Li, Q., Siddiqui, A., Krafft, C., Oliver, W., Beck, S., & Jeffries, J. (2011). Emotional perception: Meta-analyses of face and natural scene processing. *NeuroImage, 54,* (3), 2524-2533.

Sacks, O. (2007). *Musicophilia: Tales of music and the brain.* New York, Knopf.

Sakurai, T., Amemiya, A., Ishii, M., et al. (1998). Orexins and orexin receptors: A family of hypothalamic neuropeptides and G protein-coupled receptors that regulate feeding behavior. *Cell, 92* (4), 573-85.

Sambataro, F., Dimalta, S., et al. (2006). Preferential responses in amygdala and insula during presentation of facial contempt and disgust. *European Journal of Neuroscience, 24* (8), 2355-2362.

Santarelli, L., Saxe, M., Gross, C., Surget, A., Battaglia, F., Dulawa, S., Weisstaub, N., Lee, J., Duman, R., Arancio, O., Belzung, C., & Hen, R. (2003). Requirement of hippocampal neurogenesis for the behavioral effects of antidepressants. *Science, 301,* 805-809.

Satoh M. (2007). A case of auditory agnosia with impairment of perception and expression of music: Cognitive processing of tonality. *European Neurology, 58*(2), 70-77.

Savic, I., Berglund, H., & Lindstrom, P. (2005). Brain response to putative pheromones in homosexual men. *PNAS, 102* (20), 7356-7361.

Savic-Berglund, I., & Lindström, P. (2008). PET and MRI show differences in cerebral asymmetry and functional connectivity between homo- and heterosexual subjects. *PNAS Online Early Edition,* 16-20.

Savin-Williams, R. C. (2006). Who's gay? Does it matter? *Current Directions in Psychological Science, 15* (1), 40-44.

Schafer, A., Vaitl, D., & Schienle, A. (2010). Regional grey matter volume abnormalities in bulimia nervosa and binge-eating disorder. *NeuroImage, 50* (2), 639-643.

Schelling, T. C. (1992). Addictive drugs: The cigarette experience. *Science, 255,* 430-433.

Schlaug, G., Jancke, L., Huang, Y., & Steinmetz, H. (1995). In vivo evidence of structural brain asymmetry in musicians. *Science* 267, 699–701.

Schlaug, G., Jancke, L., Huang, Y., & Steinmetz, H. (2009). In vivo evidence of structural brain asymmetry in musicians. *Science, 3,* 699-701.

Schmahmann, J. D., & Caplan, D. (2006). Cognition, emotion and the cerebellum. *Brain, 129* (2), 290-292.

Sears, B., & Ricordi, C. (2011). Anti-inflammatory nutrition as a pharmacological approach to treat obesity. *Journal of Obesity, 2011,* Article ID 431985, 14 pages, doi:10.1155/2011/431985.

Selye, H. (1976). *The stress of life.* New York: McGraw-Hill.

Shapira et al. (2003). Brain activation by disgust-inducing pictures in obsessive-compulsive disorder. *Biological Psychiatry, 54* (7), 751-756.

Silveri, M. M., Jensen, J. E., Rosso, I. M., Sneider, J. T., & Yurgelun-Todd, D. A. (2011). Preliminary evidence for white matter metabolite differences in marijuana-dependent young men using 2D J-resolved magnetic resonance specroscopic imaging at 4 Tesla. *Neuroimaging Section, 191* (3), 201-211.

Simons, G., Ellgring, J. H., Beck-Dossler, K., Gaebel, W., Wölwer, W. (2010). Facial expression in male and female schizophrenia patients. *European Archives of Psychiatry & Clinical Neuroscience, 260* (3), 267-276.

Slimp, J. C., Hart, B. L., & Goy, R. W. (1978). Heterosexual, autosexual and social behavior of adult male rhesus monkeys with medial preoptic anterior hypothalamic lesions. *Brain Research, 142,* 105-122.

Snyder, A. (2009). Explaining and inducing savant skills: Privileged access to lower level, less-processed information. *Philosophical Transactions of the Royal Society, 364* (1522), 1399-1405.

Soto, D., et al. (2009). Pleasant music overcomes the loss of awareness in patients with visual neglect. *Proceedings of the National Academy of Sciences of the United States, 106* (14), 6011-6012.

Spelke, E. S. (2008). Effects of music instruction on developing cognitive systems at the foundations of mathematics and science. *Learning, Arts and the Brain: The Dana Consortium Report on Arts and Cognition.* NY/Washington D.C.: Dana Press.

Sperry, R. W. (1968). Hemisphere disconnection and unity of conscious experience. *American Psychologist, 29,* 723-733.

Spezio, M. L., Huang, P-Y. S., Castelli, F., & Adolphs, R. (2007). Amygdala damage impairs eye contact during conversations with real people. *The Journal of Neuroscience, 27,* (15), 3994-3997.

Springer, S. P., & Deutsch, G. (1998). *Left brain, right brain: Perspectives from cognitive neuroscience,* 5th ed. New York: Freeman.

Stark, R., Zimmermann, M., Kagerer, S., Schienle, A., & Walter, B. (2007). Hemodynamic brain correlates of disgust and fear ratings. *NeuroImage, 37 (2),* 663-673.

Steele, K. M. (2006). Unconvincing evidence that rats show a Mozart effect. *Music Perception, 23,* 455-458.

Stephan, K. E., Marshall, J. C., Friston, K. J., Rowe, J. B., Ritzl, A., Zilles, K., & Fink, G. R. (2003). Lateralized cognitive processes and lateralized task control in the human brain. *Science, 301,* 384-386.

Strait, D. L., Kraus, N., Skoe, E., & Ashley, R. (2009). Musical experience and neural efficiency – effects of training on subcortical processing of vocal expressions of emotion. *European Journal of Neuroscience, 29* (3), 661-668.

Sturm, V., Sollberger, M., Seeley, W., Rankin, K., Rosen, H., Miller, B., & Levenson, R. (2011). Right pregenual anterior cingulate cortex volume predicts self-conscious emotional reactivity in neurodegenerative disease. Paper presentation at National Academy of Neurology meeting, April 14, 2011.

Sudai, E., Croitoru, O., et al. (2011). High cocaine dosage decreases neurogenesis in the hippocampus and impairs working memory. *Addiction Biology, 16* (2), 251-260.

Susskind, J. M., Lee, D. H., Cusi, A., Feiman, R., Grabski, W., & Anderson, A. K. (2008). Expressing fear enhances sensory acquisition. *Nature Neuroscience, 11,* 843-850.

Suzuki, A., Hoshino, T., Shigemasu, K., & Kawamura, M. (2006). Disgust-specific impairment of facial expression recognition in Parkinson's disease. *Brain, 129* (3), 707-717.

Swaab, D. F. (2008). Sexual orientation and its basis in brain structure and function. *PNAS, 105* (30), 10273-10274.

Swaab, D. F., & Hofman, M. A. (1990). An enlarged suprachiasmatic nucleus in homosexual men. *Brain Research, 537* (1-2), 141–148.

Swaab, D. F., & Hofman, M. A. (1990). An enlarged suprachiasmatic nucleus in homosexual men. *Brain Research, 537*(1-2), 141-8.

Swaab, D. F., Slobb, A. K., Houtsmullerb, E. J., Brand, T., & Zhoua, J. N. (1995). Increased number of vasopressin neurons in the suprachiasmatic nucleus (SCN) of 'bisexual' adult male rats following perinatal treatment with the aromatase blocker ATD. *Developmental Brain Research, 85*(2), 273-279.

Swanson, L. W. (1987). *The hypothalamus.* Amsterdam: Elsevier Science.

Taylor, S. E., Saphire-Bernstein, S., & Seeman, T. E. (2010). Are plasma oxytocin in women and plasma vasopressin in men biomarkers of distressed pair-bond relationship? *Psychological Science, 21* (1), 3-7.

Terrizzi, J. A., Shook, N. J., & Ventis, W. L. (2010). Disgust: A predictor of social conservatism and prejudicial attitudes toward homosexuals. *Personality and Individual Differences, 49* (6), 587-592.

Theusch, E., Basu, A., & Gitschier, J. (2009). Genome-wide study of families with absolute pitch reveals linkage to 8q24.21 and locus heterogeneity. *The American Journal of Human Genetics, 85,* 112-119.

Thomas, M. S. C. & Johnson, M. H. (2008). New advances in understanding sensitive periods in brain development. *Psychological Science, 17,* 1.

Thompson, W. F., Schellenberg, E. G., Husain, G. (2001). Arousal, mood, and the Mozart effect. *Psychological Science, 12* (3), 248–251.

Thorleifsson, G., Walters, G. B., Gudbjartsson, D. F., et al. (2009). Genome-wide association yields new sequence variants at seven loci that associate with measures of obesity. *Nat. Genet, 41* (1), 18–24.

Trachtenberg, J.T., Trepel, C., Stryker, M.P. (2000). Rapid extragranular in the absence of thalamocortical plasticity in the developing primary visual cortex. *Science, 287,* 2029-2032.

Trehub, S. (2000). Human processing predispositions and musical universals. In B. Merker and N. L. Wallin (Eds.), *The origins of music* (427-448), Cambridge, Mass: MIT Press.

Trehub, S.E., & Hannon, E.E. (2006). Infant music perception: Domain-general or domain-specific mechanisms? *Cognition, 100,* 73–99.

Treffert, D. (2010). *Islands of genius: The bountiful mind of the autistic, acquired, and sudden savant.* New York: Jessica Kingsley.

Uher, R., & Treasure, J. (2005). Brain lesions and eating disorders. *J. Neurol. Neurosurg. Psychiatry, 76*(6), 852-857.

Ungerleider, L.G., & Haxby, J.V. (1994). What and where in the human brain. *Current Opinion in Neurology, 4,* 157-165.

University of Pittsburgh Medical Center (2006, June 21). Why men are more aggressive: What a mother should know. *ScienceDaily.* Retrieved November 30, 2010, from www.sciencedaily.com/releases/2006/06/060621162228.html

Van Kuyck, K., Gerard, N., Van Laere, K., Casteels, C., Pieters, G., Gabriels, L, & Nuttin, B. (2009). Towards a neurocircuitry in anorexia nervosa: Evidence from functional neuroimaging studies. *Journal of Psychiatric Research, 43* (14), 1133-1145.

Vocks, S., Busch, M., Gronemeyer, D., Schulte, D., Herpertz, S., & Suchan, B. (2010). Neural correlates of viewing photographs of one's own body and another woman's body in anorexia and bulimia nervosa: An fMRI study. *Journal of Psychiatry & Neuroscience, 35* (3), 163-176.

Volkow, N. D., Wang, G-J., & Baler, R. D. (2010). Reward, dopamine and the control of food intake: Implications for obesity. *Trends in Cognitive Sciences, 15* (1), 37-46.

Volkow, N. D., & Wise, R. A. (2005). How can drug addiction help us understand obesity? *Nat. Neurosci., 8,* 555-560.

Voyer, D., Voyer, S., & Bryden, M. P. (2010). Magnitude of sex differences in spatial abilities: A meta-analysis and consideration of critical variables. *Psychological Bulletin, 117* (2), 250-270.

Vuoksimaa, E., Kaprio, J., et al. (2010). Having a male co-twin masculinizes mental rotation performance in females. *Psychological Science, 21* (8), 1069-1071.

Wager, T. D., Luan Phan, K., Liberzon, I., & Taylor, S. F. (2003). Valence, gender, and lateralization of functional brain anatomy in emotion: A meta-analysis of findings from neuroimaging. *NeuroImage, 19,* 513-531.

Wagner, A., Aizenstein, H., Venkatraman, V. K., Kaye, W. H., et al. (2010). Altered striatal response to reward in bulimia nervosa after recovery. *International Journal of Eating Disorders, 43* (4), 289-294.

Walum, H., Westberg, L, et al. (2008). Genetic variation in the vasopressin receptor 1a gene (AVPR1A) associates with pair-bonding behavior in humans. *Proc. of the Nat. Acad. of Sci., 105,* 14153-14156.

Wang, B. D. (2005). The neuronal representation of pitch in primate auditory cortex. *Nature, 436* (7054), 1161-1165.

Wang, G., Volkow, N., Logan, J., Pappas, N. et al. (2001). Brain dopamine and obesity. *The Lancet, 357* (9253), 354-357.

Wedekind, C., Seebeck, T., Bettens, F., & Paepke, A. J., (1995). MHC-dependent mate preferences in humans. *Proceedings of the Royal Society of London, B, 260,* 245-249.

Weis, S., & Hausmann, M. (2010). Sex hormones: Modulators of interhemispheric inhibition in the human brain. *Neuroscientist, 16* (2), 132-138.

Wesley, M. J., Hanlon, C. A., & Porrino, L. J. (2011). Poor decision-making by chronic marijuana users is associated with decreased functional responsiveness to negative consequences. *Neuroimaging, 191* (1), 51-59.

Weston, E. M., Friday, A. E., & Lio, P. (2007). Biometric evidence that sexual selection has shaped the hominin face. *PLos ONE, 2* (8), c710.

Wicker, B., Keysers, C., Plailly, J., Royet, J. P., Gallese, V., & Rizzolatti, G. (2003). Both of us disgusted in my insula: The common neural basis of seeing and feeling disgust. *Neuron, 40,* 655–64.

Williams, C., & Wood, R. L. (2010). Impairment in the recognition of emotion across different media following traumatic brain injury. *Journal of Clinical & Experimental Neuropsychology, 32* (2), 113-122.

Williams, M. A., & Mattingley, J. B. (2006). Do angry men get noticed? *Current Biology, 16,* 402-404.

Winkler, I., et al. (2009). Newborn infants detect the beat in music. *Proceedings of the National Academy of Sciences of the United States, 106* (7), 2468-2470.

Wray, A. (2008). *Formulaic language: Pushing the boundaries.* Oxford University Press.

Wright, A. A., Revera, J. J., Hulse, S. H., Shyan, M., & Neiworth, J. J., (2000). Music perception and octave generalization in rhesus monkeys. *Journal of Experimental Psychology: General, 129,* 291-307.

Yang, J., Brown, M. S., Lian, G., Grishin, N. V., & Goldstein, J. L. (2008). Identification of the acyltransferase that octanoylates ghrelin, an appetite-stimulating peptide hormone. *Cell, 132* (3), 387-396.

Yoshino, A., et al. (2010). Sadness enhances the experience of pain via neural activation in the anterior cingulate cortex and amygdala. *NeuroImage, 50* (3), 1194-1201.

Young, L. J. (2009). The neuroendocrinology of the social brain.. *Frontiers of Neuroendocrinology, 30* (4), 425-428.

Young, L. J., & Wang, Z. (2004). The neurobiology of pair bonding. *Nat. Neurosci., 7*(10), 1048-1054.

Youngentob, S. L., Molina, J. C., Spear, N. E., & Youngentob, L. M. (2007). The effect of gestational ethanol exposure on voluntary ethanol intake in early postnatal and adult rats. *Behavioral Neuroscience, 121* (6), 1306-1315.

Yucel, M., Solowij, N., et al. (2008). Regional brain abnormalities associated with long-term heavy cannabis use. *Archives of General Psychiatry, 65* (6), 694-701.

Yucel, M., Zalesky, A., Takagi, M. J. et al. (2010). White-matter abnormalities in adolescents with long-term inhalant and cannabis use: A diffusion magnetic resonance imaging study. *Journal of Psychiatry & Neuroscience, 35* (6), 409-412.

Yurgelun-Todd, D. (2007) Emotional and cognitive changes during adolescence. *Current Opinions in Neurobiology, 17* (2), 251-257.

Zatorre, R. J. (1985). Discrimination and recognition of tonal melodies after unilateral cerebral excisions. *Neuropsychologia, 23,* 31-41.

Zatorre, R. J. (1988). Pitch perception of complex tones and human temporal lobe function. *Journal of the Acoustical Society of America, 84,* 566-572.

Zatorre, R. J. (2003). Absolute pitch: A model for understanding the influence of genes and development on neural and cognitive function. *Nature Neuroscience, 6,* 692-695.

Zatorre, R. J., Belin, P., & Penhune, V. B. (2002). Structure and function of auditory cortex: Music and speech. *Trends in Cognitive Sciences, 6,* 37-46.

Zatorre, R., & McGill, J. (2005). Music, the food of neuroscience. *Nature, 434* (7031), 312-315.

Zatorre, R. J., Perry, D. W., Beckett, C. A., Westbury, C. F., & Evans, A. C. (1998). Functional anatomy of musical processing in listeners with absolute pitch and relative pitch. *Proceedings of the National Academy of Sciences of the United States of America, 95,* 3172-3177.

Zeki, S., & Romaya, J. P. (2008). Neural correlates of hate. *PLoS One, 3* (10);e3556.Epub2008 Oct. 29.

Zentner, M. R., & Kagan, J. (1998). Infants' perception of consonance and dissonance in muic. *Infant Behavior and Development, 21,* 483-492.

Zheng, H., & Berthoud, H., R. (2007). Eating for pleasure or calories. *Curr. Opin. Pharmacol., 7,* 607-612

Zhou, J., Hofman, M., Gooren, L., & Swaab, D. (1995). A sex difference in the human brain and its relation to transsexuality. *Nature, 378* (6552), 68-70.

Index

E
eardrum 108
earworm 123
eating disorders 47
echolalia 125
Ecstasy (MDMA) 78, 81, 90, 97
ectothermic 35
Ekman, Paul 140, 142
electroencephalogram (EEG) 10, 143
elements of music 114, 115
Elliot 145
Ellis, Havelock 61
embarrassment 154
empathy 154
endocannabinoids 51, 79-80, 91
endocrine system 27, 37
endogenous opioids 26, 74, 80
endomusia 123
endorphins 74, 80
endothermic 35
enjoyment arousal 128
enkephalins 80
envy 156
enzyme 14, 40, 76
epilepsy 17, 150
erectile dysfunction 70
ergot 95
error detection 154
estradiol 58
estrogen 42, 58, 67
ethanol (see alcohol)
ethnomusicology 104
ethology 59
event related potential (ERP) 143
evolution 7, 8, 12, 20, 21, 31, 32, 42, 43, 45, 69, 80,
103-107, 109-115, 131-142, 146, 150-152, 158
evolutionary psychology 31, 45, 106, 138
excitatory 75
excitement phase 62
exhibitionism 71
expressive aphasia 23
extrinsic motivation 33
F
face 20, 22
Facial Action Coding System (FACS) 142
facial expression 134, 141
facial feedback hypothesis 135, 139
fake marijuana 93
fatty acids 40
fear 141, 142, 144, 147, 153
feelings 132, 133
fetal alcohol syndrome (FAS) 77, 86
fetish 71

fight or flight response 25, 26, 135, 148
flashback 95
flashbulb memory 136
flats 110
flavor 37, 43
forget me pill 97
freebase 88
frequencies 110
frontal lobe 8, 9, 21, 48, 92, 97, 116, 119, 144, 149-
150
frontotemporal dementia 117, 118
FTO gene 45
functional magnetic resonance imaging (fMRI) 11
fundamental 111
fusiform face area (FFA) 22
G
GABA 15, 79, 86
galvanic skin response (GSR) 143
gamelan music 104
gamete 54
Gandhi 32
ganglia 8
gap 75
Garcia effect 43
gastric bypass surgery 46
gender 47, 67, 70
gender identity 53, 67, 71
gender identity disorder 67, 71
gender neutrality 68
gender role 67
gene 45, 47, 113
genomic imprinting 44
genotype 56
gestalt 21
GHB 97
ghrelin 40
glial cells 12
glucoprivic hunger 40
glucose 40
glue sniffing 94
glutamate 15, 79, 86, 92
GOAT 40
Golden Crescent 83
Golden Triangle 83
gray matter 14, 65, 84
guilty knowledge 142
gyrus (gyri) 10, 16, 109
H
habituation 28, 43
hallucinogens 93, 94-96
happiness 139, 141, 155
hard wired 32
Hare Psychopathy Checklist 144

harmonic 111
harmony 112
hashish 91
hate 153
hearing 19, 22
hedonic highway 74
hemisphere 16, 68, 116, 117, 150
henbane 78
herbivore 43
hereditary susceptibility 45, 47, 85
hermaphrodite 57
heroin 74, 83
hertz (Hz) 110
Hertz, Heinrich 110
Heschl's gyrus 109
high road 148
hippocampus 27, 41, 86, 92, 100, 120
Hoffman, Albert 95
holistic processing 20, 116
homeostasis 26, 33
Hominids 8
Homo erectus 8
homosexuality 67-70
hormones 27, 57, 59, 69
hotspots 51
human sexual response cycle 62-63
hunger 36
hunger hormone 40
Huntington's disease 153
Huxley, Aldous 96
hyperphagia 38
hyperthermia 90
hypocretin 41, 97
hypothalamus 26, 34, 37, 38, 40, 48, 51, 63, 74, 146
hypovolemic thirst 36

I
incentive 33
infants 105, 115, 118, 121, 135
inferior colliculus 111
inhalants 94
inhibitory 75, 80
insanity herb 79
instinct 23, 31
insula 93 100, 152-153
insulin 39, 41
intelligence 128, 137
intensity 114
International Olympics Committee 56
interpreter, the 20
intersex 57
interval 112, 116, 119
intrinsic motivation 32
ion 13

ion channel 13
ipsilateral 109
isopropyl 85
Izard, Carroll 134, 141
J
James, William 135
James-Lange theory 135
Janata, Petr 111, 119
joy (see happiness)
K
K2 93
karyotype 54
kava 87
ketamine 97
khat 90
K-hole 97
Kinsey, Alfred 60-61
Klinefelter syndrome 55
knowledge emotions 134
kola tree 89
L
Lange, Carl 135
language 9, 23, 32, 105, 116
Lashley, Karl 37
lateral fissure 16, 21, 109
lateral hypothalamus 38
lateralization 17, 117, 150, 151
Law of Initial Value 76
L-dopa 15, 77
learned taste preference 44
Leary, Dr. Timothy 95
LeDoux, Joseph 133, 147-148
leitmotif 115
Lemke, Leslie 125
Lennon, John 129
leptin 39, 41, 45, 91
leptin treatment 41, 46
LeVay, Simon 68, 69
Levitin, Daniel 104, 107, 121
libido 57, 58, 64
lie detector 143
Lie to Me 142
life span 139
life satisfaction 139
life stress 139
liking vs. wanting 50
limbic system 25, 27, 46, 63, 74, 98
lipoprivic hunger 40
lobes 21
lobotomy 149
localization of function 22, 122
longitudinal fissure 16
loudness 114

love 155
love circuit 155
low road 148
LSD 95
lullabies 105
lying 142
M
magic mushrooms96
magnetic resonance imaging (MRI) 11
MAO 14
map 113
marijuana 41, 79, 91-93
marshmallow test 49
Marvin, Elizabeth 113
masculinize 56, 58
Masters and Johnson 62
Mathieu 124
Maudsley method 49
MC4R gene 45
MDMA (see Ecstasy)
medial amygdala 64
medial forebrain bundle (MFB) 74
medial prefrontal cortex 112
medial preoptic area (MPOA) 63, 64, 69
median preoptic nucleus 36
medulla 28
meiosis 54
melanocortin 39
Melodic Intonation Therapy (MIT) 127
melody 105, 110, 115, 117, 119
melody contour 115, 116, 117, 119
memory 92
mental rotation 65
mephedrone 97
mescaline 76, 96
mesencephalon 73
mesolimbic pathway 26, 46, 51, 73, 121
meter 114
methadone 99
methamphetamine 90, 101
methanol 85
methylation 88
Mexican Wolf Recovery Program 43
microexpressions 142
midbrain 73
middle age 10
Miller, Leon 125
Mischel, Walter 49
Mithen, Steven 103, 106
mitosis 55
Moebius syndrome 141
Money, John 53
moral judgment 152

morphine 51, 74, 83
Morrison, Jim 23, 94, 96
mosaic 55
motif 115
motivation 31
motor cortex 22
movement 22-23, 120
Mozart effect 128
multiple sclerosis 13
munchies 80
mu-opioid 80
muscarine 78
mushrooms 96
music agnosia 124
Music Genome Project 122
music perception 103, 107-108
music savant 125
music therapy 126-127
music training 127-128
musical complexity 122
musical hallucinations 123
musical preferences 103, 122
musical syntax 119
musicians 9, 18, 108, 109, 117, 121
musicologists 107
musilanguage 106
myelin 12
N
naloxone 99
naltrexone 99
narcolepsy 41
narcotic 83
Narcotics Anonymous 100
natural selection 32
Neanderthal 103
nerve gas 78
nerve growth factor 48
nerves 16
neural network 12, 14
neurogenesis 27, 100
neuroleptics 76
neuromodulators 77
neurons 8, 12
neuropeptide Y (NPY) 39, 41
neurotransmitter 12, 14, 75, 77, 86, 126
nicotine 76, 78, 81, 83
nicotinic receptors 84
NMDA receptor 15, 79
non-Western societies 104
norepinephrine 15, 79
notes 110, 113
novocaine 87
NST 40, 43